MW00845439

Energy Efficient Cities of Today and Tomorrow

Energy Efficient Cities of Today and Tomorrow

Editors

Jukka Heinonen
Sanna Ala-Mantila
Ortzi Akizu-Gardoki

MDPI • Basel • Beijing • Wuhan • Barcelona • Belgrade • Manchester • Tokyo • Cluj • Tianjin

Editors

Jukka Heinonen
University of Iceland
Iceland

Sanna Ala-Mantila
University of Helsinki
Finland

Ortzi Akizu-Gardoki
University of the Basque Country
Spain

Editorial Office
MDPI
St. Alban-Anlage 66
4052 Basel, Switzerland

This is a reprint of articles from the Special Issue published online in the open access journal *Energies* (ISSN 1996-1073) (available at: https://www.mdpi.com/journal/energies/special_issues/Energy_Efficient_Cities_2019).

For citation purposes, cite each article independently as indicated on the article page online and as indicated below:

LastName, A.A.; LastName, B.B.; LastName, C.C. Article Title. *Journal Name* **Year**, *Volume Number*, Page Range.

ISBN 978-3-0365-0362-2 (Hbk)
ISBN 978-3-0365-0363-9 (PDF)

© 2021 by the authors. Articles in this book are Open Access and distributed under the Creative Commons Attribution (CC BY) license, which allows users to download, copy and build upon published articles, as long as the author and publisher are properly credited, which ensures maximum dissemination and a wider impact of our publications.

The book as a whole is distributed by MDPI under the terms and conditions of the Creative Commons license CC BY-NC-ND.

Contents

About the Editors

Jukka Heinonen works as a Professor at the University of Iceland, Faculty of Civil and Environmental Engineering. His focus area is sustainability in the built environment. He also holds an Adjunct Professor position at Aalto University in the field of built environment life cycle economics. His main fields of research are urban carbon mitigation and low-carbon human settlements. He has published over 50 peer-reviewed research articles and sits on the editorial boards of several highly rated academic journals in these fields. He was recently named among the global top 10 researchers in the field of carbon footprinting.

Sanna Ala-Mantila is an assistant professor and leader of the sustainable urban systems research group at the University of Helsinki. She is part of Helsinki Institute of Sustainability Science (HELSUS), and Faculty of Biological and Environmental Sciences. Her main interest is urban sustainability, from angles of both ecological and social sustainability, and the possible intersections and discrepancies between the two. She is currently running two academy of Finland projects, called "Sustainable urban development emerging from the merger of cutting-edge Climate, Social and Computer Sciences" and "Smart land use policy for sustainable urbanization".

Ortzi Akizu-Gardoki has been lecturing since 2011 and he has been an Associate Professor since 2019 at the Faculty of Engineering of Bilbao of the University of the Basque Country (UPV/EHU). He currently lectures "Graphics in Engineering" to first-year bachelor's degree students of and "Life Cycle Assessment II" and "Tools for Projects Management" at master's degree level. He is a member of the "Ekopol: transition pathways" research team, where he is developing research about footprint analysis using Life Cycle Assessment (LCA) and Multiregional Input–Output (MRIO) methodologies. His main body of research is focused on the analysis of the ongoing energy transitions, particularly calculating the energy footprint created by goods and services. Currently he is collaborating with the University of New South Wales (UNSW), the Basque Centre for Climate Change (BC3), Tecnalia Reseach Centre, and Ecologists in the Action social movement.

Preface to "Energy Efficient Cities of Today and Tomorrow"

The world needs to undergo a rapid transformation to a sustainable low-carbon consumption system. With the ongoing urbanization and ever-growing harmful environmental impacts from urban areas, the focus of this required sustainability transformation is on cities. However, cities are centers of wealth creation and economic growth, also known as two of the main drivers of environmental degradation. Cities also provide their citizens with evermore diverse consumption opportunities, making the lifestyles of city dwellers more and more consumption-oriented. This inevitably leads to increased energy demands and emissions in cities due to needed infrastructure and real estate development, the increased energy demands of users, and the increased energy embodied in the goods and services consumed within cities. Concurrently, we are facing imminent pressure to significantly reduce our energy consumption and greenhouse gas emissions at all levels of society. This pressure urges cities to re-establish themselves as low-energy/low-carbon urban ecosystems, but the transformation is difficult and complex in many ways, and time is running out rapidly. A lively academic discourse on the issue has been ongoing for several years, but so far without widely accepted or unanimous solutions. This Special Issue, "Energy Efficient Cities of Today and Tomorrow", seeks to enhance this conversation and provide a more profound understanding of the future energy requirements of urban areas and low-energy and low-carbon cities. The nine published papers range from macro-level assessments of cities manifesting themselves as forerunners in their environmental work to micro-level studies of pro-environmental attitudes and their impacts on individual emissions, as well as impacts on the carbon footprint from sharing goods and services. They present potential solutions and introduce new discussion points to find potential pathways to a truly sustainable future.

Jukka Heinonen, Sanna Ala-Mantila, Ortzi Akizu-Gardoki
Editors

Article

Passenger Transport Energy Use in Ten Swedish Cities: Understanding the Differences through a Comparative Review

Jeffrey R. Kenworthy [1,2]

[1]   Fachbereich 1, Architektur, Bauingenieurwesen and Geomatik, Frankfurt University of Applied Sciences, Nibelungenplatz 1, 60318 Frankfurt am Main, Germany; jeffrey.kenworthy@fb1.fra-uas.de
[2]   Curtin University Sustainability Policy Institute, Curtin University, Kent Street, Bentley, WA 6102, Australia

Received: 26 June 2020; Accepted: 14 July 2020; Published: 20 July 2020

Abstract: Energy conservation in the passenger transport sector of cities is an important policy matter. There is a long history of transport energy conservation, dating back to the first global oil crisis in 1973–1974, the importance and significance of which is explained briefly in this paper. Detailed empirical data on private and public passenger transport energy use are provided for Sweden's ten largest cities in 2015 (Stockholm, Göteborg, Malmö, Linköping, Helsingborg, Uppsala, Jönköping, Örebro, Västerås and Umeå), as well as Freiburg im Breisgau, Germany, which is a benchmark small city, well-known globally for its sustainability credentials, including mobility. These data on per capita energy use in private and public transport, as well as consumption rates per vehicle kilometer and passenger kilometer for every mode in each Swedish city and Freiburg, are compared with each other and with comprehensive earlier data on a large sample of US, Australian, Canadian, European and Asian cities. Swedish cities are found to have similar levels of per capita car use and energy use in private transport as those found in other European cities, but in the context of significantly lower densities. Possible reasons for the observed Swedish patterns are explored through detailed data on their land use, public and private transport infrastructure, and service and mobility characteristics. Relative to their comparatively low densities, Swedish cities are found to have healthy levels of public transport provision, relatively good public transport usage and very healthy levels of walking and cycling, all of which help to contribute to their moderate car use and energy use.

Keywords: Swedish cities; passenger transport energy use; urban form; transport infrastructure; mobility patterns; public transport; non-motorized modes

---

1. Introduction

Until the 1973–1974 Arab oil embargo from October 1973 to March 1974, (the first global oil crisis) the use of energy in transport was not seriously on any academic or policy agendas. When OPEC (the Organization of Arab Petroleum Exporting Countries) declared an embargo on oil exports to countries deemed supportive of Israel during the 1973 Yom Kippur war with Egypt, the global price of oil essentially quadrupled 'overnight', from about $US3 per barrel to $12 per barrel [1,2]. Suddenly the world realized how vulnerable it is to events in the Middle East which affect the production and export of oil and its price. This stirred a spate of interest in this topic e.g., [3,4] and led to a growing concern about how to reduce dependence on oil in transport, particularly imported oil, and especially in cities [5,6]. The 1973–1974 oil crisis played out very differently in different cities. Dutch cities (The Netherlands was included in the embargo) adapted well to the crisis, since they were compact places which relied heavily on walking and cycling anyway, while the automobile cities in the USA experienced significant societal disruption as people scrambled to fill their very gas guzzling cars [7].

The world was again rudely awakened to this issue in the subsequent Iranian oil crisis in 1979 [8] caused by the Iranian Revolution. Iran's daily oil production of 6.05 million barrels per day, of which about five million barrels were exported to supply about 10% of the non-communist world's daily needs, was thrown into chaos. This event again brought into focus the dire situation of the world in regard to its political vulnerability to oil supply and its sometimes-volatile pricing. The need to reduce petroleum consumption and its dependence on Middle Eastern sources was firmly on the table. Unlike stationary uses of oil, such as for heating homes and in industry, which can be relatively quickly swapped to other energy sources, the petrol and diesel derived from oil and used in transport is a difficult issue because these liquid fossil fuels as a source of energy are particularly suited to mobile uses due to their high-energy density and thus long range of vehicular travel on one fill, ease of distribution, and convenient, compact and safe storage inside a vehicle. Conventional oil cannot be easily substituted, as exemplified over the last years with efforts to produce oil from non-conventional sources and electric cars on a larger scale. Oil from oil shale, tar sands and coal, as well as from other fuels such as ethanol and methanol, have all proved to be difficult. They have been too expensive relative to conventional oil, have had a poor net energy return and have had large environmental impacts from mining and other problems [9].

Despite the above history and the current urgency of CO_2 reduction from carbon-based fuels, liquid fossil fuel consumption in passenger transport throughout the world has continued to rise in the relatively wealthy cities in the West and in currently less wealthy, but rapidly industrializing and motorizing cities elsewhere, such as in China, India and Brazil [10]. The sheer size of the population in such countries and others, as well as the growing environmental problems in cities from, for example, air pollution, has made it even more critical today to try to reduce transport energy use and especially dependence on oil as the major source of transport fuels. Rising living standards and incomes and increasing car ownership and use, especially in such populous countries mentioned above and the continued profligate use of transport energy in North American and Australian cities, for example, make it difficult to reduce global oil demand in the transport sector. This is especially so when there are, for the most part, still few disincentives to car ownership and use in cities and insufficient investment in alternatives to motorized private transport, such as quality public transport and good walking and cycling conditions [10].

Of course, over time there are numerous fluctuations in this general upward trend of transport demand and energy use in transport as economies fluctuate along with the demand for and price of oil. The West Texas Intermediate (WTI) or New York Mercantile Exchange (NYMEX) oil price per barrel (in US dollars) between April 2008 and August 2008 was above $US135, peaking in June 2008 at $164, but by September 2008 and the major onset of the Global Financial Crisis, the oil price dropped to $118 per barrel and proceeded rapidly downward to $50 per barrel by January 2009, as demand fell away. Oil prices did recover to some extent after this as the global economy and demand again picked up, and in December 2019, oil was $61 per barrel [11]. The global COVID-19 pandemic, however, saw passenger transport demand in cities basically collapse, and the price of oil in April 2020 had plummeted to just $19 per barrel.

Regardless of these perturbations, the issue of transport energy use in cities is still of major concern. A focus of discussion since the mid-1990s has been the geopolitical implications of oil reserves concentrated in the Middle East and the issue of "peak oil" when half the world's known oil reserves have been used and the production curve heads downward [12,13]. Although "peak oil" is disputed e.g., [14], the realities of war in the Middle East mostly focused on maintaining oil security for the United States (Gulf War in 1990–1991 and the Iraq War from 2003 to 2011) remain, as does the critical need to engage with the idea of a post-petroleum future.

Since the mid-1970s, much has been published about transport energy use in cities, and the author's own work has had a focus on growing the evidence about the best ways to reduce energy use in urban passenger transport systems through reducing automobile dependence and taking advantage of the different energy consumption rates of urban transport modes [15–17].

This paper continues in this tradition with a special focus on ten Swedish cities, plus Freiburg im Breisgau in Germany, as a benchmark small city known for its sustainable transport performance [18,19]. Sweden established a national research and education think tank on public transport called K2 (The Swedish National Centre for Research and Education on Public Transport), with the express aim of improving public transport's role throughout Sweden and shifting modal share toward public transport. As part of the author's research in K2, this paper reports on detailed comparisons of many aspects of land use, transport and other transport-related factors in ten Swedish cities, including the energy consumption of each passenger transport mode and attempts to answer the following three research questions about private passenger transport energy use in Swedish cities:

(1) How does energy use per capita in private and public transport modes compare within Sweden and with other cities in the USA, Australia, Canada, Europe and Asia?
(2) How do the modal energy-consumption rates per vehicle kilometer and passenger kilometer in Swedish cities differ from each other and other cities worldwide?
(3) Can differences in transport energy use per capita be explained through reference to a range of other important transport indicators in Swedish cities?

2. Methodology

A detailed account of the research methodologies used to obtain all the data contained in the tables in this paper can be found in [17,20,21], along with the geographies defining each city. Table 1 provides a summary of the American, Australian, Canadian, European and Asian cities used to calculate the averages for these groups of cities shown in this paper, as well as the ten Swedish cities and Freiburg. It presents their population and the year of that population, their metropolitan GDP per capita at that year (in US$1995) and the per capita annual boardings for their whole public transport systems (all modes in use in each city are included, which cover buses, minibuses, trams, light rail, metro, suburban rail and ferries). This last item gives a comparative perspective on a key transport-sustainability factor for each city. "Cities" is used here as a shorter term for metropolitan regions because the data mostly represent wider metropolitan areas, not just the "cities" lying at the heart of these areas.

Table 1. List of cities used for the international comparisons with their population, GDP per capita and annual public transport use per capita.

City	Population	Metropolitan GDP Per Capita (US$1995)	Total Annual Public Transport Use Per Capita (Boardings)
American Cities			
Atlanta 2005	3,826,866	$41,641	39
Chicago 2005	8,217,201	$40,666	73
Denver 2005	2,256,442	$45,762	38
Houston 2005	4,853,225	$44,124	19
Los Angeles 2005	9,758,886	$40,899	68
New York 2005	20,580,795	$47,206	168
Phoenix 2005	3,590,804	$32,589	17
San Diego 2005	2,824,259	$42,324	32
San Francisco 2005	4,071,751	$54,266	103
Washington 2005	4,273,361	$55,070	109
Australian Cities			
Brisbane 2006	1,819,800	$29,365	74
Melbourne 2006	3,743,000	$30,411	104
Perth 2006	1,518,700	$37,416	68
Sydney 2006	4,282,000	$31,583	136

Table 1. *Cont.*

City	Population	Metropolitan GDP Per Capita (US$1995)	Total Annual Public Transport Use Per Capita (Boardings)
Canadian Cities			
Calgary 2005	988,193	$36,713	131
Montreal 2005	3,487,520	$26,815	206
Ottawa 2005	1,130,761	$29,956	129
Toronto 2005	5,555,912	$33,103	154
Vancouver 2005	2,116,581	$29,726	134
European Cities			
Graz 2005	247,248	$33,889	411
Copenhagen 2005	1,827,239	$43,108	191
Helsinki 2005	988,347	$47,548	309
Düsseldorf 2005	577,416	$40,270	266
Oslo 2005	1,039,536	$53,941	214
Madrid 2005	5,964,143	$26,964	337
Stockholm 2005	1,889,945	$43,527	332
Bern 2005	303,202	$54,145	543
Geneva 2005	440,982	$50,918	320
London 2005	7,512,000	$33,368	483
Vienna 2005	1,651,437	$36,131	511
Manchester 2005	2,543,800	$26,611	102
Stuttgart 2005	592,028	$33,294	285
Brussels 2005	1,006,749	$39,758	328
Prague 2005	1,181,610	$20,179	1051
Berlin 2005	3,395,189	$21,027	410
Frankfurt 2005	651,583	$38,356	327
Hamburg 2005	1,743,627	$36,733	266
Munich 2005	1,288,307	$45,133	505
Zurich 2005	832,159	$48,756	536
Asian Cities			
Hong Kong 2006	6,857,100	$18,823	548
Singapore 2005	4,341,800	$23,578	353
Swedish Cities			
Stockholm 2015	2,231,439	$49,271	359
Malmö 2015	695,430	$32,709	111
Goteborg 2015	982,360	$40,808	285
Linköping 2015	152,966	$30,260	64
Helsingborg 2015	137,909	$28,917	158
Uppsala 2015	210,126	$31,998	108
Västerås 2015	145,218	$29,594	53
Örebro 2015	144,200	$29,045	39
Jönköping 2015	133,310	$29,952	60
Umeå 2015	120,777	$29,415	45
Freiburg (benchmark small city)			
Freiburg 2015	222,082	$25,782	192

In this paper, Swedish cities have been divided into five larger and five smaller cities so that differences on this basis can be seen. Averages are presented for the larger cities, smaller cities and all ten Swedish cities. The larger cities are Stockholm, Göteborg, Malmö, Linköping and Helsingborg, while the smaller cities are Uppsala, Jönköping, Örebro, Västerås and Umeå.

The value of this research on the Swedish cities, as well as the global sample, is that it uses empirical energy data from cities for private and public transport, as opposed to theoretical modeled data for different vehicular technologies e.g., [22,23]. All data are collected directly for each city from the primary sources of those data, mostly through a variety of government departments in each city or through national datasets that are available for the specific geographies used to define the metropolitan areas in this study. For example, public-transport energy use is obtained directly from every operator and mode in every city. The collection of these data is conducted by consulting published online sources in the first instance and then many emails and phone calls between many people in a plethora of transport, planning, energy, environmental and other departments in every city. Most data require this in-depth work and are not routinely published. Only primary data are collected, never the standardized indicators shown in the tables. These standardized indicators are calculated by the author by combining the relevant primary data (e.g., population and urbanized land area to get urban density). All Swedish city data and Freiburg are for 2015, while the American, Australian, Canadian, European and Asian city data are for 2005–2006, from an earlier study of these other cities e.g., see [15,19,24].

While it would be ideal to have all the comparative data for the same year, it must be pointed out that the collection of these comparative cities' data, which are much more than shown in the tables in this paper, takes many years to complete (the 2005–2006 data commenced in 2007 and was not complete until 2014). Providing 2015 data for the other cities could not have even been commenced until 2017, due to delays in data release. The comparisons, however, are still valid in relative terms, and experience over 40 years of such data collection has shown at each point that the relative differences between cities remain. This is supported by the author's publications in the reference list, including representing these other cities with 2005–2006 data at a much later date and where the 2005–2006 data have been compared to later data [25], including a paper comparing many urban indicators for the five larger Swedish cities in 2015 with the 2005–2006 data on the American, Australian, Canadian, European and Asian cities [21]. Where some variables can change quite rapidly, the discussion provides caveats on the results and cautions readers accordingly.

The point of making comparisons between the Swedish cities in 2015 with a global sample ten years earlier is to gain an insight into the general magnitude of differences, not to be absolutely precise. Over a decade, European cities are, for example, not going to become very like American cities, nor are even Canadian cities, in virtually any of the parameters. There is a basic and relatively stable difference in these fundamental metropolitan-scale indicators across such a global range of cities, which is quite resilient to change over time. The author has 1960, 1970, 1980 and 1990 data that show similar basic patterns. The exact numbers have changed, but the general relativities have not [26].

To demonstrate this, Table 2 provides the ten-year change in an earlier decade from 1995–1996 to 2005–2006 in the value for every variable that has been used in this paper for the US, Australian, Canadian, European and Asian cities. From this, it can be seen, for example, that although private transport energy use per capita has changed, European cities are still very much lower than American cities, and Asian cities are very much lower again than European cities. Australian and Canadian cities maintain their medium position in the sample. Car passenger kilometers per person did not change much in the ten years in any group of cities, so the general magnitude of differences were again stable. With respect to seat kilometers of public transport service per person, this was still worst in the American cities by a large margin, fair to middling in the Australian and Canadian cities, very much better in the European cities and better again in the Asian cities. By 2015, though values will have changed, it is highly unlikely that American cities will have reached even Australian levels of public transport service, let alone European or Asian levels. Likewise, public transport use follows the same pattern and is very similar in its relative differences, even over a decade of change. If we consider the use of non-motorized modes, American cities are the worst, Canadian cities are next and then Australian cities, and the Asian cities, while the European cities are the best. This general perspective has not changed over ten years, even though the value for each group has changed to some degree. Rather than eliminating this global perspective for the sake of 2015 data, which are not possible yet on the global sample, the 2005–2006 perspective still has utility.

Table 2. Changes in energy, land use and transport-related variables in US, Australian, Canadian, European and Asian cities from 1995–1996 to 2005–2006.

Variable	Units	USA 1995	USA 2005	AUS 1996	AUS 2006	CAN 1996	CAN 2006	EUR 1995	EUR 2005	ASIA 1995	ASIA 2005
Private passenger transport energy use per capita	MJ/person	60,034	53,441	31,044	35,972	32,519	30,804	15,324	15,795	6447	6076
Public transport energy use per capita	MJ/person	811	963	876	1036	1044	1190	1243	1532	1905	2691
Total passenger transport energy use (private plus public)	MJ/person	60,845	54,404	31,920	37,008	33,563	31,994	16,567	17,326	8352	8768
Energy use per private passenger vehicle kilometre	MJ/km	4.6	4.1	4.0	4.1	5.1	4.9	3.3	3.1	5.4	4.8
Energy use per public transport vehicle kilometre	MJ/km	26.3	24.6	15.8	17.3	22.0	23.0	13.7	14.7	15.9	19.6
* Energy use per bus vehicle kilometre	MJ/km	28.8	31.3	18.0	21.9	24.1	24.9	15.7	18.8	19.2	23.5
* Energy use per minibus vehicle kilometre	MJ/km	8.5	13.2	-	-	8.1	-	-	-	6.9	9.5
* Energy use per tram wagon kilometre	MJ/km	19.1	19.9	10.1	11.2	12.1	14.2	12.9	14.9	5.5	5.4
* Energy use per light rail wagon kilometre	MJ/km	17.5	15.3	-	10.5	13.1	18.2	14.6	11.7	16.1	14.3
* Energy use per metro wagon kilometre	MJ/km	25.3	16.1	-	22.6	10.6	13.5	11.0	9.3	7.8	18.7
* Energy use per suburban rail wagon kilometre	MJ/km	51.8	50.4	12.7	11.9	48.8	43.0	14.3	15.6	8.9	14.8
* Energy use per ferry vessel kilometre	MJ/km	846.5	1073.3	144.0	140.7	290.8	283.5	151.5	141.0	601.7	641.4
Energy use per private passenger kilometre	MJ/p.km	3.26	2.85	2.55	2.87	3.82	3.79	2.46	2.30	3.46	3.31
Energy use per public transport passenger kilometre	MJ/p.km	2.13	2.09	0.99	0.97	1.14	1.18	0.74	0.76	0.59	0.70
* Energy use per bus passenger kilometre	MJ/p.km	2.85	2.97	1.77	1.87	1.50	1.57	1.10	1.31	0.77	0.95
* Energy use per minibus passenger kilometre	MJ/p.km	1.02	7.68	-	-	2.34	-	-	-	2.66	1.96
* Energy use per tram passenger kilometre	MJ/p.km	0.99	1.02	0.36	0.48	0.31	0.27	0.70	0.73	0.23	0.24
* Energy use per light rail passenger kilometre	MJ/p.km	0.67	0.64	-	0.58	0.25	1.07	0.65	0.53	0.34	0.55
* Energy use per metro passenger kilometre	MJ/p.km	1.65	0.69	-	0.75	0.49	0.64	0.45	0.42	0.12	0.34
* Energy use per suburban rail passenger kilometre	MJ/p.km	1.38	1.29	0.55	0.49	1.31	1.17	0.69	0.60	0.16	0.27
* Energy use per ferry passenger kilometre	MJ/p.km	5.41	6.80	2.97	2.53	3.62	1.23	4.01	4.88	3.64	4.26
Urban density	persons/ha	14.9	15.4	13.3	14.0	26.2	25.8	49.3	47.9	215.4	217.3
Proportion of jobs in CBD	%	9.2%	8.2%	13.3%	12.7%	15.7%	15.0%	22.2%	18.3%	11.4%	9.1%
Metropolitan gross domestic product per capita	USD 1995	$31,386	$44,455	$20,226	$32,194	$20,825	$31,263	$34,673	$38,683	$23,593	$21,201
Length of freeway per person	m/ person	0.156	0.156	0.086	0.083	0.122	0.157	0.080	0.094	0.025	0.026
Parking spaces per 1000 CBD jobs	spaces/1000 jobs units/1000	555	487	367	298	390	319	212	248	135	121
Passenger cars per 1000 persons	persons	587	640	591	647	530	522	412	463	73	78
Average speed of the road network (24/7)	km/h	49.3	50.4	43.6	42.8	44.5	45.4	34.2	34.3	31.8	30.6
Total length of public transport lines per 1000 persons	m/1000 persons	1420	1382	2814	2609	1929	2496	2420	3183	1582	2614
Total length of reserved public transport routes per 1000 persons	m/1000 persons	49	72	170	160	56	67	231	298	18	34
Total public transport seat kilometres of service per capita	seat km/person	1566	1874	3997	4077	2290	2368	5245	6126	6882	7267
Overall average speed of public transport	km/h	27.3	27.3	32.5	33.0	25.1	25.7	28.0	29.8	24.0	26.3
* Average speed of buses	km/h	21.7	19.9	23.8	23.4	22.0	22.4	21.6	21.9	19.3	19.4
* Average speed of suburban rail	km/h	54.7	57.3	46.2	47.6	49.5	44.7	49.4	52.1	40.0	50.8
Total public transport boardings per capita	boardings/person	60.1	66.7	90.4	95.6	140.2	150.7	357.1	386.3	476.6	450.4
Total public transport passenger kilometres per capita	p.km/person	492	571	966	1075	917	1031	1830	2234	3169	3786

Table 2. *Cont.*

Variable	Units	USA 1995	USA 2005	AUS 1996	AUS 2006	CAN 1996	CAN 2006	EUR 1995	EUR 2005	ASIA 1995	ASIA 2005
Overall public transport vehicle occupancy	persons/unit	13.9	13.1	16.9	18.1	19.2	19.8	19.8	21.0	26.9	28.1
Overall public transport seat occupancy	%	29%	29%	25%	27%	40%	44%	38%	39%	46%	52%
Passenger car passenger kilometres per capita	p.km/person	18,155	18,703	12,114	12,447	8645	8495	6319	6817	1978	1975
Percentage of total daily trips by non motorised modes	%	8.1%	9.5%	14.9%	14.2%	10.4%	11.6%	31.7%	34.5%	25.0%	26.1%
Percentage of total daily trips by motorised public modes	%	3.4%	5.5%	5.4%	7.5%	9.1%	13.1%	21.3%	22.4%	39.3%	46.0%
Proportion of total motorised passenger kilometres on public transport	%	2.9%	3.2%	7.5%	8.0%	9.9%	11.3%	22.3%	24.5%	62.0%	62.9%
Ratio of public versus private transport speeds	ratio	0.57	0.55	0.75	0.78	0.57	0.57	0.83	0.88	0.76	0.86
Ratio of segregated public transport infrastructure versus expressways	ratio	0.41	0.56	2.18	1.98	0.55	0.56	4.17	5.51	0.93	1.42

All energy data are end-use data and do not include the energy expended for drilling, extracting, refining or distributing oil to obtain the petrol, diesel and other liquid or gaseous fossil fuels before dispensing them into vehicle fuel tanks. Renewable fuels, such as ethanol, do not include the planting, growing, harvesting and processing of crops or other energy use expended in delivering that fuel to a vehicle's fuel tank. Electrical energy does not include the power station and transmission losses or other energy expended in the production and delivery of electrical energy to its end user.

All other standardized data or indicators on cities such as urban density, which are used to help explain the observed per capita energy use and modal energy use per kilometer, were obtained by using the same methodology as for energy. All the primary data used to calculate the indicators (e.g., freeway length and population for freeway length per capita) were collected directly from the sources of those data (e.g., population data from the relevant official sources of such data, such as local or national censuses and freeway length from road inventories or other sources). All public transport operating and infrastructure data were collected from the same operators and agencies as the energy data. A little more detail is provided about methodology in the results section, when dealing with specific indicators.

3. Transport Energy Use per Capita and Modal Energy Consumption

Table 3 contains all the data on per capita levels of energy use in private and public transport in the ten Swedish cities, along with the modal energy consumption of cars and all public transport modes in each city. Also included are similar data for Freiburg, Germany, and a group of American, Australian, Canadian, European and Asian cities. These patterns are now explained.

3.1. Private Passenger Transport Energy Use per Person

Sections 3.1 and 3.2 address the first research question in the introduction. The biggest user of passenger transport energy in cities is private transport modes, mainly cars. Table 3 shows the data for the ten Swedish cities, as well as averages for the larger five cities and the smaller five cities and Freiburg as something of a benchmark by which to assess the performance of the Swedish cities, especially the smaller ones.

The annual energy use in private motorized passenger transport in Swedish cities was calculated backward from the comprehensive emissions inventories that exist in Sweden for each municipality [27]. Transport is one of the sectors in these emissions inventories, which is further broken down into its component parts and provides CO_2 equivalent emissions (as well as all other transport emissions for each municipality). CO_2 emissions were converted to energy use by using relevant conversion factors. The energy use figures here for private passenger transport are thus dependent on the integrity of CO_2 emissions accounting by the Swedish government. There was no other direct source of fuel consumption for private transport available in Swedish cities.

Figure 1 shows that the ten Swedish cities in 2015 averaged 15,601 MJ/person, which is virtually the same as the average for the other European cities in 2005 (15,795 MJ). It is close to half the global sample average of 28,301 MJ and dramatically below the American, Australian and Canadian cities (Table 3). In addition, there is hardly any difference here between the averages for the larger and smaller Swedish cities (15,886 MJ cf. 15,317 MJ, respectively). Freiburg consumes 16,488 MJ/person or 8% more than in the smaller Swedish cities (one factor could be the significantly slower average speed of traffic in the denser urban fabric of Freiburg—see later). Only the Asian cities, as a group, have lower energy use per person for private passenger transport (6076 MJ), but they are radically denser than Swedish cities (see later).

Table 3. Private and public transport energy use per capita and modal energy use in ten Swedish cities (2015), plus Freiburg im Breisgau (2015), compared to American, Australian, Canadian, European and Asian cities (2005–2006).

Variable	Units	Stockholm	Malmö	Göteborg	Linköping	Helsingborg	SWE LARGE	Uppsala	Västerås	Örebro	Jönköping
Private passenger transport energy use per capita	MJ/person	12,051	15,670	15,905	18,124	17,681	**15,886**	12,157	14,030	17,095	21,678
Public transport energy use per capita	MJ/person	1949	1310	2680	1179	1819	**1787**	1423	939	862	2050
Total passenger transport energy use (private plus public)	MJ/person	14,000	16,980	18,585	19,304	19,500	**17,674**	13,580	14,969	17,957	23,728
Energy use per private passenger vehicle kilometre	MJ/km	2.4	2.9	3.1	3.5	3.3	**3.1**	2.5	2.6	3.3	3.6
Energy use per public transport vehicle kilometre	MJ/km	17.1	19.9	17.8	19.3	18.4	**18.2**	12.2	17.2	16.8	25.0
* Energy use per bus vehicle kilometre	MJ/km	20.0	17.2	15.4	17.5	17.2	**17.4**	13.3	17.0	17.9	32.1
* Energy use per minibus vehicle kilometre	MJ/km	-	-	-	-	-	-	-	-	-	-
* Energy use per tram wagon kilometre	MJ/km	10.5	-	14.0	11.1	-	**11.9**	-	-	-	-
* Energy use per light rail wagon kilometre	MJ/km	7.8	-	-	-	-	**7.8**	-	-	-	-
* Energy use per metro wagon kilometre	MJ/km	-	-	-	-	-	-	-	-	-	-
* Energy use per suburban rail wagon kilometre	MJ/km	38.3	28.7	33.2	30.1	28.7	**31.8**	9.3	18.0	5.0	12.7
* Energy use per ferry vessel kilometre	MJ/km	230.4	-	243.4	-	-	**236.9**	-	-	-	-
Energy use per private passenger kilometre	MJ/p.km	1.82	2.29	2.38	2.69	2.58	**2.35**	1.98	1.99	2.32	2.74
Energy use per public transport passenger kilometre	MJ/p.km	0.76	0.90	1.09	1.34	1.14	**1.00**	0.81	1.06	2.35	2.53
* Energy use per bus passenger kilometre	MJ/p.km	1.37	1.67	1.45	1.65	1.57	**1.54**	1.33	1.40	2.64	3.43
* Energy use per minibus passenger kilometre	MJ/p.km	-	-	-	-	-	-	-	-	-	-
* Energy use per tram passenger kilometre	MJ/p.km	0.52	-	0.47	0.80	-	**0.60**	-	-	-	-
* Energy use per light rail passenger kilometre	MJ/p.km	0.39	-	-	-	-	**0.39**	-	-	-	-
* Energy use per metro passenger kilometre	MJ/p.km	0.39	-	-	-	-	**0.55**	-	-	-	-
* Energy use per suburban rail passenger kilometre	MJ/p.km	0.39	0.47	0.66	0.74	0.48	**0.55**	0.32	0.52	0.46	1.18
* Energy use per ferry passenger kilometre	MJ/p.km	6.88	-	8.66	-	-	**7.77**	-	-	-	-

Table 3. Cont.

Variable	Units	Umeå	Freiburg	SWE SMALL	SWE ALL	USA	AUS	CAN	EUR	ASIA	ALL
Private passenger transport energy use per capita	MJ/person	11,622	16,488	15,317	**15,601**	53,441	35,972	30,804	15,795	6076	28,301
Public transport energy use per capita	MJ/person	1132	1081	**1281**	**1534**	963	1036	1190	1532	2691	1360
Total passenger transport energy use (private plus public)	MJ/person	12,754	17,569	16,598	17,136	54,403	37,008	31,994	17,326	8768	29,661
Energy use per private passenger vehicle kilometre	MJ/km	2.3	3.1	**2.9**	**3.0**	4.1	4.1	4.9	3.1	4.8	3.8
Energy use per public transport vehicle kilometre	MJ/km	12.5	17.8	**16.2**	**17.3**	24.6	17.3	23.0	14.7	19.6	18.6
* Energy use per bus vehicle kilometre	MJ/km	12.0	17.9	**18.5**	**18.0**	31.3	21.9	24.9	18.8	23.5	23.1
* Energy use per minibus vehicle kilometre	MJ/km	-	-	-	-	13.2	-	-	-	9.5	12.9
* Energy use per tram wagon kilometre	MJ/km	-	-	-	-	19.9	11.2	14.2	14.9	5.4	14.4
* Energy use per light rail wagon kilometre	MJ/km	-	13.0	-	**11.9**	15.3	10.5	18.2	11.7	14.3	13.3
* Energy use per metro wagon kilometre	MJ/km	-	-	-	**7.8**	16.1	22.6	13.5	9.3	18.7	12.7
* Energy use per suburban rail wagon kilometre	MJ/km	22.4	19.0	**13.5**	**22.6**	50.4	11.9	43.0	15.6	14.8	23.9
* Energy use per ferry vessel kilometre	MJ/km	-	-	-	**236.9**	1073.3	140.7	283.5	141.0	641.4	358.8
Energy use per private passenger kilometre	MJ/p.km	1.74	2.39	**2.18**	**2.27**	2.85	2.87	3.79	2.30	3.31	2.72
Energy use per public transport passenger kilometre	MJ/p.km	1.01	0.79	**1.30**	**1.10**	2.09	0.97	1.18	0.76	0.70	1.16
* Energy use per bus passenger kilometre	MJ/p.km	1.06	1.66	**1.97**	**1.76**	2.97	1.87	1.57	1.31	0.95	1.78
* Energy use per minibus passenger kilometre	MJ/p.km	-	-	-	-	7.68	-	-	-	1.96	7.16
* Energy use per tram passenger kilometre	MJ/p.km	-	-	-	-	1.02	0.48	0.27	0.73	0.24	0.65
* Energy use per light rail passenger kilometre	MJ/p.km	-	0.33	-	**0.60**	0.64	0.58	1.07	0.53	0.55	0.63
* Energy use per metro passenger kilometre	MJ/p.km	-	-	-	**0.39**	0.69	0.75	0.64	0.42	0.34	0.52
* Energy use per suburban rail passenger kilometre	MJ/p.km	0.68	0.65	**0.64**	**0.59**	1.29	0.49	1.17	0.60	0.27	0.76
* Energy use per ferry passenger kilometre	MJ/p.km	-	-	-	**7.77**	6.80	2.53	1.23	4.88	4.26	4.60

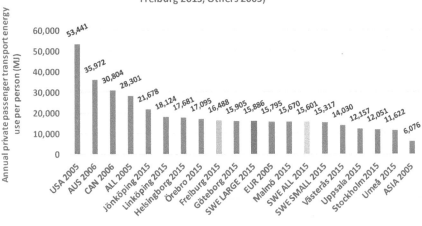

Figure 1. Annual private passenger transport energy use per person in ten Swedish cities (2015), and in American, Australian, Canadian, European and Asian cities (2005–2006).

Uppsala, Stockholm and, interestingly, Umeå consume the least energy, with 12,157, 12,051 and 11,622 MJ/person, respectively. Jönköping and Linköping, which are amongst the least-dense of the Swedish cities, consume the most private transport energy use (21,678 and 18,124 MJ, respectively), which might be expected. However, transport energy use per capita does not relate well, overall, to urban density in Swedish cities, probably due to the very small range in urban densities and other factors in these mostly small cities with short travel distances and high use of non-motorised modes (see Section 4 for these other data on Swedish cities). Overall, Swedish cities in 2015 performed comparatively well against other cities in the world, consuming only moderate quantities of energy in private passenger transport in this very energy-hungry sector. Improvements are, however, always possible through less driving and better technology.

3.2. Public Transport Energy Use per Person

The use of energy in public transport systems is important to understand and to compare with its private passenger transport equivalent. As already indicated, public-transport energy-use data were obtained from each of the public transport operators by mode (Figure 2). Public transport here considers every mode that exists in the city, whether it is just buses or whether it includes multiple modes (buses, trams, trams and light rail (LRT), metro, suburban rail and ferries). Even cable cars and small funiculars are included if they exist. Taxis are considered private transport. All public transport modes and operators must be included to properly and accurately represent the public transport system.

The data reported here are the average for all modes in each city. Swedish cities are identical to the other European cities in their per capita energy use by public transport, but significantly more than in the three auto-oriented groups of cities, with their lesser public transport systems. Freiburg consumes a modest 1081 MJ/person. The larger Swedish cities on average consume 1787 MJ/person, while the smaller cities consume a significantly lower 1281 MJ. Göteborg is the biggest per capita energy consumer in public transport (2680 MJ), which is surprisingly almost the same as the Asian cities. This is followed quite a bit behind by Jönköping and Stockholm, both of which are, however, still relatively high. The range of public transport energy use per person in Swedish cities is large (2680 MJ in Göteborg and 862 MJ in Örebro—Göteborg provides a vastly higher magnitude of public transport service, including a large LRT system, compared to Örebro—see Section 4).

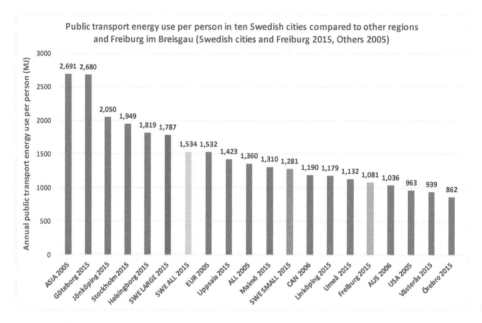

Figure 2. Annual public transport energy use per person in ten Swedish cities (2015); Freiburg (2015); and American, Australian, Canadian, European and Asian cities (2005–2006).

Figures 1 and 2 highlight the huge difference between the energy consumption by public transport systems, compared to private transport. In the case of the Swedish cities (and European cities generally), private transport consumes over ten times more per capita than that used by public transport. In the case of US cities, it is over 55 times more, while Australian and Canadian cities show less dramatic differences (35 and 26 times more, respectively). It is only in the Asian cities, with their very heavy dependence on public transport and their low levels of car use, that private and public transport energy use per capita are more equitable (private transport is a little more than twice as high). The data also suggest that there is considerable untapped energy conservation potential in public transport systems, particularly given the frequent similarity in energy use per capita in public transport in different cities, but the vast differences in levels of usage (see Section 4).

3.3. Modal Energy Consumption in Private Transport

This section addresses the second research question in the introduction. Energy consumption by mode can be examined in two ways—energy use per vehicle kilometer traveled (VKT), which is common for cars and something that consumers consider when purchasing a vehicle, or energy use per passenger kilometer traveled (PKT). The latter is more common for public transport, since vehicular energy consumption for higher capacity public transport vehicles is not useful to compare with cars because of the greatly different vehicle sizes and occupancy levels. Therefore, when comparing the relative energy use between modes, energy use per passenger kilometers is used.

3.3.1. Energy Use per Private Passenger Vehicle Kilometer

Table 3 shows that energy use per private passenger vehicle kilometer varies from a high of 4.9 mega-joules per km (MJ/km) in Canadian cities (4.8 MJ/km in Asian cities and 4.1 MJ/km in the American and Australian cities), down to 2.3 MJ/km in Umeå and 2.4 MJ/km in Stockholm. It must be borne in mind, however, that the data for the Swedish cities and Freiburg are from 2015, ten years later than the data for US, Australian, Canadian, European and Asian cities, over which time, technological advances and changes in the size and weight of vehicles may have yielded increases in the fuel efficiency of vehicles. It might be that 2015 data for the other cities could show lower rates of energy use per vehicle kilometer than they did in 2005, though the relativities between cities are likely to remain similar. Figure 3 summarizes these results.

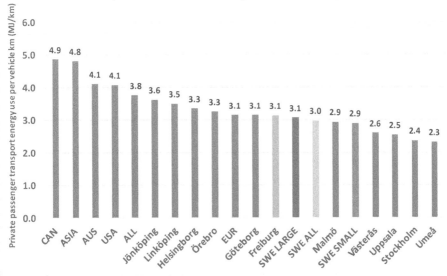

Figure 3. Energy use per vehicle kilometer in private passenger transport in ten Swedish cities (2015); Freiburg (2015); and American, Australian, Canadian, European and Asian cities (2005–2006).

The larger Swedish cities consume, on average, 3.1 MJ/km in private passenger modes, which is the same as the European cities, while the small cities consume 2.9 MJ/km (less congestion and higher vehicle operating speeds may partly explain this—see Section 4). Freiburg has the same rate of energy use as the larger Swedish cities (3.1 MJ/km). The range in energy use per VKT in private passenger transport in Swedish cities is from 2.3 MJ/km (Umeå) to 3.5 and 3.6 MJ/km in Linköping and Jönköping, respectively.

3.3.2. Energy Use per Public Transport Vehicle Kilometer

Whilst it has been explained that energy use per VKT for public transport modes is of no real use in comparing to private transport, it is interesting to compare the differences in Table 3 across cities for the same mode.

Buses: Examining buses first, we see that Jönköping and American city buses consume 32.1 and 31.3 MJ/km, respectively. At the lower end, we find Umeå and Uppsala have only 12.0 and 13.3 MJ/km, respectively, while Freiburg consumes 17.9 MJ/km, and European cities, overall, show 18.8 MJ/km, quite like the average for all Swedish cities of 18.0 MJ/km. The larger cities in Sweden consume 17.4 MJ/km, while buses in the smaller cities consume 18.5 MJ/km or quite close to the European average. In 2005–2006, the "world average" for buses, based on this large sample of global cities, was 23.1 MJ/km.

Trams and light rail (LRT): These rail modes represent very similar technologies, and their differentiation is somewhat artificial. In the Swedish cities and Freiburg, all such modes have been classed as LRT, and they only exist in Stockholm, Göteborg, Linköping and Freiburg. In the global sample from 2005, trams and LRT exist in at least some of the cities in all regional groupings. For the purposes of comparison with the Swedish cities and Freiburg, the average for the other regional groupings of tram and LRT were used (i.e., American, 17.3 MJ/km; Australian, 10.8 MJ/km; Canadian, 16.2 MJ/km; European, 13.3 MJ/km; Asian, 9.8 MJ/km; and with a global average of 13.8 MJ/km).

The data reveal the Swedish cities to be well within the normal range of energy use by these modes (11.9 MJ/km) and closest to the Australian cities, while Freiburg (13.0 MJ/km) is very close to the European average (13.3 MJ/km) and the global average from 2005–2006 (13.8 MJ/km). Swedish cities are within a relatively tight range in the three cities where LRT exists (10.5 to 14.0 MJ/km). Overall, tram/LRT systems have a range of about 10.0 to 17.0 MJ/km, depending on the age and type of system.

Metros: Metro systems are mostly underground systems and tend to operate in the denser inner parts of metro regions (e.g., the Paris metro in the Ville de Paris at the center of the Paris region known as the Île de France). In Sweden, a metro only exists in Stockholm (tunnelbana), while in the global sample, metros exist in at least some cities in all regional groupings. Stockholm's energy use per vehicle kilometer (wagon kilometer not train kilometer) is 7.8 MJ/km, which is reasonably close to the European average of 9.3 MJ/km, but significantly less than in all other groups of cities (a range of 13.5 MJ/km in Canadian cities to 22.6 MJ/km in Australian cities and a global average of 12.7 MJ/km).

Suburban rail: This rail mode covers the rail systems that operate over longer distances and include both underground sections in denser parts of cities and a lot of aboveground operations in lower-density suburban-type environments. These include the S-Bahn and regional rail systems in Germany, the RER suburban rail services throughout the Île de France and the regional rail operations that exist in all ten Swedish cities in this paper, as well as in Freiburg. Rolling stock is mostly bigger and heavier, including double-decker wagons, and train speeds are much higher than those of metro systems (see Section 4). In this mode, there is a very wide range of vehicular energy use per kilometer, depending on the type of trains, their fuel (diesel services are much higher in energy use than electric services), their age, number of wagons, their size, weight, passenger loadings and operating speeds.

All Swedish suburban train services are longer-distance regional rail lines which operate at high average speeds. Their energy use is, on average, 22.6 MJ/km, which is like the global average of 23.9 MJ/km, but with a big difference between the larger cities (31.8 MJ/km) and the smaller cities (13.5 MJ/km). Freiburg averages 19.0 MJ/km. Globally, there are also huge differences with a range of 11.9 MJ/km in the all-electric Australian cities, up to 50.4 MJ/km in the USA with a mixture of diesel and electric, mostly commuter rail style services. Canadian systems are similar, averaging a relatively high 43.0 MJ/km, whereas the European and Asian systems are virtually all electric and average only 15.6 and 14.8 MJ/km, respectively. The range in energy use per vehicle kilometer in the ten Swedish cities is from 5.0 MJ/km in Örebro up to 38.3 MJ/km in Stockholm.

Ferries: These modes only exist in Stockholm and Göteborg in the Swedish sample, but all the other regional groupings of cities have at least some ferry services. Ferries are very high in their vehicular energy use, a main factor being the very large frictional forces that must be overcome to ply through water and the speeds at which operate. Naturally, the size of vessels, which varies hugely around the world, is also a key determinant of energy use. Swedish cities average 236.9 MJ/km, with not much difference between the two cities (230.4 and 243.4 MJ/km). The global average was 358.8 MJ/km, with a massive range from 140.7 MJ/km for the ferries in Perth, Brisbane and Sydney (European cities were virtually identical at 141 MJ/km), up to 1073.3 MJ/km for ferries in US cities (only New York and San Francisco). The Asian cities (Hong Kong only) are also very high, with many large and heavily loaded double-decker ferries in operation.

3.3.3. Energy Use per Private Passenger Kilometer (PKT)

Energy use per PKT is a more meaningful measure of energy consumption in public transport, which enables genuine comparisons to be made with private passenger transport energy use. Table 3 provides the energy consumption per PKT for private transport, and Figure 4 depicts the data for the Swedish and global sample. The European cities, including Freiburg, and especially the Swedish cities, are amongst the lowest energy consumers in cars, though there is a range in Sweden from 2.74 MJ/PKT in Jönköping down to 1.74 MJ/PKT in Umeå. The larger Swedish cities (2.35 MJ/PKT) are about the same as Freiburg (2.39) and the average for the European cities (2.30), while the smaller cities are little lower at 2.18 MJ/PKT. Compared to the Canadian (3.79 MJ/PKT), Asian (3.31), Australian (2.87) and American (2.85) cities, the Swedish cities are significantly less energy hungry in cars (2.27 MJ/PKT). Of course, this sets a greater challenge for public transport to compete in energy terms, especially where loadings in public transport vehicles are low.

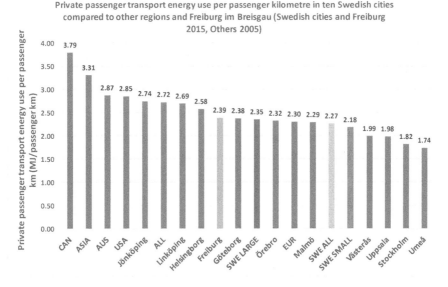

Figure 4. Energy use per passenger kilometer (PKT) in private passenger transport in ten Swedish cities (2015); Freiburg (2015); and American, Australian, Canadian, European and Asian cities (2005–2006).

3.3.4. Energy Use per Public Transport Passenger Kilometer (PKT)

Table 3 also provides the energy use per public transport PKT, and Figure 5 graphs the results. It reveals that Swedish cities have over a threefold difference in energy use per PKT, from a low in Stockholm of 0.76 MJ/PKT (identical to the European sample and almost the same as Freiburg with 0.79), up to 2.53 MJ/PKT in Jönköping, which is only 8% lower than for cars in that city. Overall, Swedish cities consume 1.10 MJ/PKT in public transport or some 45% higher than in European cities, but lower than in the American and Canadian cities. The smaller cities are more consumptive (1.30 MJ/PKT) than the larger Swedish cities (1.00 MJ/PKT). Generally, it could be said that the energy result for public transport in Swedish cities is a little disappointing, with, for example, Jönköping and Örebro exceeding US consumption levels per PKT. This is indicative of a larger public transport problem in Swedish cities related to usage levels, as discussed in Section 4.

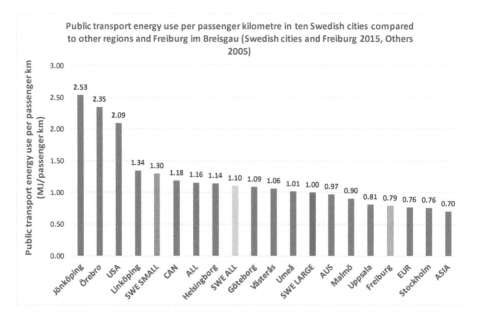

Figure 5. Energy use per PKT in public transport in ten Swedish cities (2015); Freiburg (2015); and American, Australian, Canadian, European and Asian cities (2005–2006).

3.3.5. Ratio of Private to Public Transport Energy Use per PKT

A useful way of considering the last two sets of data is to examine the ratio between private and public transport energy use per PKT. Figure 6 provides these data and shows that the Asian cities have, by far, the greatest advantage in energy consumption for public transport (cars are 4.74 times more consumptive), while in Freiburg and the other European cities, cars are three times higher in energy use per PKT. In Swedish cities, the energy advantage of public transport is significantly reduced, with cars being only a little more than twice as energy demanding per PKT, but in the larger cities, the figure is 2.36, while in the smaller cities, cars are only 1.68 times higher in energy use. Of even larger concern is that, in Örebro, public transport energy use per PKT is basically identical to that of cars and does not appear to offer any energy advantage at current levels of occupancy for cars and public transport.

3.3.6. Bus Energy Use per PKT

It is important to consider the relative energy use of the different public transport modes. Table 3 shows that buses are the second highest public transport mode for energy use after ferries. They have considerably more energy consumption than rail modes in every case, but in most cases, they are still less energy consumptive than cars (except in Örebro, where buses consume 14% more energy/PKT than cars, and in US cities, where buses are 4% higher than in cars). In the Swedish cities, buses overall consume 1.76 MJ/PKT or almost identical to the global sample at 1.78. Buses in the larger Swedish cities are a little more economical in energy (1.54 MJ/PKT) than in the smaller cities (1.97). However, clearly, the Swedish urban buses do not perform as well in energy terms as other European cities (1.31 MJ/PKT), which is likely related to their lower levels of usage (Section 4).

3.3.7. Tram/LRT Energy Use per PKT

As mentioned before, for simplicity, tram and LRT in the global sample are combined here to provide an overview perspective. These rail modes are generally the second-lowest energy-demanding modes in cities after metros (see below) and average around 0.60 MJ/PKT (e.g., the global average is 0.64 MJ/PKT, Swedish cities 0.60 and European cities 0.63). Freiburg is exceptionally good, with 0.33 MJ/PKT, and the two Asian cities quite close to this (0.40). In every case, trams and LRT are also much less energy consumptive than buses, due to their generally higher loadings, electric propulsion and the fact that they tend to operate in generally denser, more public-transport-supportive urban fabrics, especially inner areas of cities.

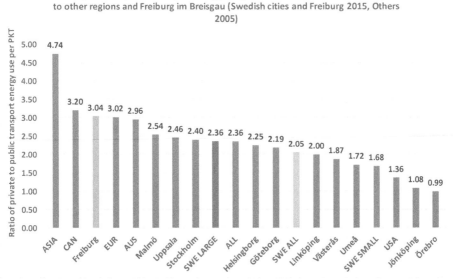

Ratio of private to public transport energy use per PKT in ten Swedish cities compared to other regions and Freiburg im Breisgau (Swedish cities and Freiburg 2015, Others 2005)

Figure 6. Ratio of private to public transport energy use per PKT in ten Swedish cities (2015); Freiburg (2015); and American, Australian, Canadian, European and Asian cities (2005–2006).

3.3.8. Metro Energy Use per PKT

Metros are very often the least-energy-consuming mode in cities. Stockholm, the only Swedish city with a metro, consumes only 0.39 MJ/PKT, even a little lower than the European average of 0.42 and only a little higher than the Asian average of 0.34 MJ/PKT. Globally, metros average 0.52 MJ/PKT, but in the auto-dependent cities in the US, Australia and Canada, they average higher energy use (0.69, 0.75 and 0.64 MJ/PKT, respectively).

3.3.9. Suburban Rail Energy Use per PKT

Suburban rail is generally the third least-energy-consumptive public-transport mode in cities, after metros and LRT. In Asian cities, however, suburban rail averages only 0.27 MJ/PKT. Swedish cities acquit themselves well here, by averaging 0.59 MJ/PKT (0.55 and 0.64 MJ/PKT in the larger and smaller cities, respectively). This is very like the other European cities (0.60) and Freiburg (0.65) and significantly better than the US and Canadian cities (1.29 and 1.17 MJ/PKT, respectively), due in no small part to the use of diesel fuel in some of their systems. In no case is suburban rail energy use more than that used in buses and is sometimes less than metros (e.g., in Linköping, Australian and Asian cities).

3.3.10. Ferry Energy Use per PKT

Ferries are the most-energy-consuming modes in cities, though they are not so common. In Swedish cities, they consume, on average, 7.77 MJ/PKT versus a global figure of 4.60 MJ/PKT. In other European cities, they consume 4.88 MJ/PKT. Although ferry systems are not generally energy-efficient anywhere, they often form critical links across water bodies where bridges for traffic are not very practicable or desirable. Therefore, their energy conservation quality is realized more in substituting for long car trips that would otherwise be needed to circumvent water obstacles in cities.

It is important to note here that Table 3 shows minibuses to also be high energy consumers per PKT (7.16 MJ/PKT), but they are a category found only in the American cities and in Hong Kong in this study. However, this is due to the high-energy-consuming-demand-responsive bus systems in American cities that drive many millions of kilometers in low-density areas, picking up very few passengers.

4. Understanding Differences in Patterns of Energy Use in Swedish Cities

This section addresses the third research question in the introduction which seeks to explain patterns of passenger transport energy use per capita in Swedish cities by reference to a set of standardized transport and land-use indicators developed for each city and compared to other global cities and Freiburg. Table 4 contains these data.

The preceding data have shown that Swedish cities have almost identical average per capita use of energy in both private and public transport systems, despite, as Table 4 shows, having densities which are significantly below those in other European cities (16.9 cf. 47.9 persons/ha) and notwithstanding that density has been shown to be the most strongly correlated variable in explaining urban energy use in private passenger transport [26,28]. This low energy use is, of course, linked to the fact that Swedish cities also have nearly identical car passenger kilometers (PKT) per capita as other European cities (6888 car PKT/person cf. 6817, respectively), which is at least partly explained by the Swedish cities' lower car occupancy of 1.31 compared to 1.38 in other European cities in 2005. Car passenger kilometers is the result of car vehicle kilometers multiplied by the average 24 h/7 days per week car occupancy, and of course includes the driver. Such low car occupancy and underutilized capacity in public transport due to low vehicle and seat occupancy (explained later) are naturally also sources of potential energy conservation if occupancies can be increased.

So, how might the relatively low car use per person and low private transport energy use per person, despite comparatively low urban densities in Swedish cities, be explained? A review of the data in Table 4 highlights some significant findings regarding Swedish cities which serve as mitigating factors in understanding the above issue. However, it is first important to highlight the metropolitan Gross Domestic Product (GDP) per capita factor in Table 4. It is common to hear that greater wealth generates more car use, but Table 4 shows that Swedish cities had a similar average GDP per capita ($30,001) in 2015 to the Australian ($32,194) and Canadian cities ($31,263) in 2006, whose car and energy use per capita are much higher than in Swedish cities (around double or more in private transport energy use). Similarly, European cities had an average GDP of $38,683/person in 2005, which was very much higher than the Australian and Canadian cities at that time, and yet all of their mobility factors are strongly oriented to public transport, walking and cycling, and they have much lower transport energy use per capita. These inconsistent relationships between wealth and transport energy use mean that wealth is generally a weak factor in predicting per capita transport energy use data at an aggregate level in cities across the globe. In the 2005–2006 data for the cities in Table 1, GDP per capita had the strongest positive relationship with private passenger transport energy use per capita, using a power function with an r^2 value of only 0.172. By contrast, urban density (persons per ha) showed a very strong negative relationship, with an r^2 value of 0.827.

Table 4. Key transport and land use indicators in ten Swedish cities (2015), plus Freiburg im Breisgau (2015), as compared to American, Australian, Canadian, European and Asian cities (2005–2006).

Variable	Units	Stockholm	Malmö	Göteborg	Linköping	Helsingborg	SWE LARGE	Uppsala	Västerås	Örebro	Jönköping
Urban density	persons/ha	23.5	20.0	19.7	13.8	21.9	**19.8**	15.3	17.1	13.7	12.6
Proportion of jobs in CBD	%	28.2%	7.8%	7.0%	18.9%	19.7%	**16.3%**	19.2%	23.3%	14.6%	20.6%
Metropolitan gross domestic product per capita	USD 1995	$49,271	$32,709	$40,808	$30,260	$28,917	**$36,393**	$31,998	$29,594	$29,045	$29,952
Length of freeway per person	m/person	0.138	0.232	0.225	0.269	0.287	**0.230**	0.180	0.224	0.366	0.496
Parking spaces per 1000 CBD jobs	spaces/1000 jobs	125	237	160	225	483	**246**	169	501	461	287
Passenger cars per 1000 persons	units/1000 persons	398	442	405	432	435	**423**	387	461	435	481
Average speed of the road network (24/7)	km/h	37.1	41.0	39.0	30.5	39.1	**37.3**	51.3	48.5	47.4	45.0
Total length of public transport lines per 1000 persons	m/1000 persons	4867	3109	6098	11,055	3031	**5632**	11,176	6894	9876	9024
Total length of reserved public transport routes per 1000 persons	m/1000 persons	234	222	283	378	432	**310**	584	1275	422	1457
Total public transport seat kilometres of service per capita	seat km/person	8,294	5,837	9,376	4,647	6,321	**6895**	7115	2677	3642	4,330
Overall average speed of public transport	km/h	33.6	46.8	30.9	38.6	31.5	**36.3**	64.4	38.4	33.4	40.7
* Average speed of buses	km/h	24.8	27.8	28.0	31.3	23.6	**27.1**	46.0	28.0	30.5	31.5
* Average speed of suburban rail	km/h	56.3	75.6	66.0	93.8	65.8	**71.5**	102.0	93.9	89.0	72.5
Total public transport boardings per capita	boardings/person	359	111	285	64	158	**195**	108	53	39	60
Total public transport passenger kilometres per capita	p.km/person	2579	1451	2463	877	1590	**1792**	1765	884	367	809
Overall public transport vehicle occupancy	persons/unit	22.6	22.0	16.3	14.4	16.1	**18.3**	15.2	16.2	7.2	9.9
Overall public transport seat occupancy	%	31%	25%	26%	19%	25%	**25%**	25%	33%	10%	19%
Passenger car passenger kilometres per capita	p.km/person	6630	6839	6689	6734	6862	**6751**	6131	7048	7361	7902
Percentage of total daily trips by non motorised modes	%	22.1%	31.2%	26.3%	33.0%	23.0%	**27.1%**	46.8%	32.7%	34.0%	21.2%
Percentage of total daily trips by motorised public modes	%	31.6%	17.6%	20.0%	9.7%	18.0%	**19.4%**	14.1%	6.7%	9.0%	9.6%
Proportion of total motorised passenger kilometres on public transport	%	27.8%	17.4%	26.7%	11.4%	18.7%	**20.4%**	22.2%	11.1%	4.7%	9.2%
Ratio of public versus private transport speeds	ratio	0.91	1.14	0.79	1.27	0.81	**0.98**	1.25	0.79	0.71	0.90
Ratio of segregated public transport infrastructure versus expressways	ratio	1.69	0.96	1.26	1.41	1.51	**1.36**	5.48	10.34	2.32	7.67

Table 4. *Cont.*

Variable	Units	Umeå	Freiburg	SWE SMALL	SWE ALL	USA	AUS	CAN	EUR	ASIA	ALL
Urban density	persons/ha	11.5	46.0	14.0	16.9	15.4	14.0	25.8	47.9	217.3	42.2
Proportion of jobs in CBD	%	13.7%	16.3%	18.3%	17.3%	8.2%	12.7%	15.0%	18.3%	9.1%	14.5%
Metropolitan gross domestic product per capita	USD 1995	$29,415	$25,782	$30,001	$33,197	$44,455	$32,194	$31,263	$38,683	$21,201	$37,700
Length of freeway per person	m/person	0.000	0.063	0.253	0.242	0.156	0.083	0.157	0.094	0.026	0.112
Parking spaces per 1000 CBD jobs	spaces/1000 jobs	240	271	332	289	487	298	319	248	121	314
Passenger cars per 1000 persons	units/1000 persons	435	393	440	431	640	647	522	463	78	512
Average speed of the road network (24/7)	km/h	46.7	29.9	47.8	42.6	50.4	42.8	45.4	34.3	30.6	40.2
Total length of public transport lines per 1000 persons	m/1000 persons	18,969	5131	11,188	8410	1382	2609	2496	3,183	2,614	2,576
Total length of reserved public transport routes per 1000 persons	m/1000 persons	1878	411	1123	716	72	160	67	298	34	188
Total public transport seat kilometres of service per capita	seat km/person	4963	3957	4546	5720	1874	4077	2368	6126	7267	4486
Overall average speed of public transport	km/h	34.0	32.1	42.2	39.2	27.3	33.0	25.7	29.8	26.3	28.8
* Average speed of buses	km/h	31.2	26.1	33.4	30.3	19.9	23.4	22.4	21.9	19.4	21.5
* Average speed of suburban rail	km/h	90.4	50.6	89.6	80.5	57.3	47.6	44.7	52.1	50.8	51.7
Total public transport boardings per capita	boardings/person	45	192	61	128	67	96	151	386	450	254
Total public transport passenger kilometres per capita	p-km/person	1117	1375	988	1390	571	1,075	1031	2234	3786	1644
Overall public transport vehicle occupancy	persons/unit	12.3	22.6	12.1	15.2	13.1	18.1	19.8	21.0	28.1	19.0
Overall public transport seat occupancy	%	23%	35%	22%	24%	29%	27%	44%	39%	52%	37%
Passenger car passenger kilometres per capita	p-km/person	6680	6899	7024	6888	18,703	12,447	8495	6817	1975	10,234
Percentage of total daily trips by non motorised modes	%	29.3%	63.0%	32.8%	30.0%	9.5%	14.2%	11.6%	34.5%	26.1%	23.2%
Percentage of total daily trips by motorised public modes	%	6.9%	16.0%	9.3%	14.3%	5.5%	7.5%	13.1%	22.4%	46.0%	16.8%
Proportion of total motorised passenger kilometres on public transport	%	14.2%	16.4%	12.3%	16.3%	3.2%	8.0%	11.3%	24.5%	62.9%	18.0%
Ratio of public versus private transport speeds	ratio	0.73	1.07	0.88	0.93	0.55	0.78	0.57	0.88	0.86	0.75
Ratio of segregated public transport infrastructure versus expressways	ratio	-	19.10	6.45	3.26	0.56	1.98	0.56	5.51	1.42	3.16

4.1. Differences and Similarities in Car-Related Factors

Firstly, Swedish cities had lower car ownership in 2015 (431/1000 people) than the European cities had in 2005 (463/1000), and the difference would have widened, since car ownership in European cities would have grown over the intervening ten years. This lower car ownership in Swedish cities will tend to reduce their energy use. However, they also have 2.5 times more linear length of freeway provision than European cities (0.242 cf. 0.094 m/person), which generally tends to increase per capita transport energy use in cities [29] because it encourages more driving over longer distances.

However, the average speed of individual vehicles is also known to be the most important single variable in explaining the fuel consumption of vehicles in traffic streams [30–32], with higher average speeds up to about 60 km/h being shown to reduce the consumption of fuel per kilometer in a vehicle. The ten Swedish cities have an average traffic speed of 42.6 km/h, compared to only 34.3 km/h in other denser European cities. Swedish average traffic speed is almost identical to the much more auto-oriented Australian cities (42.8 km/h).

While this result would tend to mitigate fuel use somewhat by reducing the fuel consumption per kilometer of vehicles in Swedish cities, it has also been shown that there is a trade-off between fuel-efficient traffic and fuel-efficient cities. Policies that try to minimize transport energy consumption by building more roads and speeding up traffic will, overall, tend to increase the amount of energy use per person through greater car-orientation of the city and more driving, and therefore should never be pursued [33].

Swedish cities also have quite similar parking spaces per 1000 Central Business District (CBD) jobs to their European cousins. European cities average 248 spaces/1000 jobs while Swedish cities average 289, though the larger Swedish cities have only 246 spaces/1000 jobs with the smaller ones being more generously supplied with parking (332/1000 jobs). Reduced parking in the CBD will greatly favor non-car modes, especially for the journey to work [34]. Overall, the similarity in Swedish cities with other European cities on this factor, and especially when compared to the very high CBD parking in US cities, will tend to reduce transport energy use. When this is combined with the relatively high centralization of jobs in their CBDs (17.3% in the Swedish cities overall and 18.3% in their smaller cities), the possibility of using public transport, walking and cycling to work is enhanced.

Table 4 shows that private transport modes constitute 55.7% of all daily trips in the ten Swedish cities, with a slightly better result in the five larger cities (53.5%). Other lower-density, auto-oriented cities in the USA, Australia and Canada have between 75% and 85% of daily trips by private modes. This is a very big factor in keeping Swedish car use and private passenger transport energy use per capita very much lower than it is in the USA, Australia and Canada.

When the fuel consumption rate in MJ/km and MJ/passenger km (PKT) is considered, as detailed earlier in the paper, it can also be seen that Sweden follows the European phenomenon of more fuel-efficient vehicles. For example, cars in the ten Swedish cities average 3.0 MJ/km, while the European cities average 3.1 MJ/km. In all other groups of cities, cars are consuming between 4.1 and 4.9 MJ/km. Likewise, considering passenger loadings, Swedish cities average 2.27 MJ/PKT, while European cities average 2.30 and the other cities average between 2.85 and 3.79 MJ/PKT. Thus smaller, more fuel-efficient cars in Swedish cities also help to suppress their transport energy use.

4.2. Public Transport and Non-Motorized Mode Factors

There are a series of other important factors that make Swedish cities a somewhat unique cohort in the global system of cities. Firstly, relative to other lower-density cities, Sweden provides a lot of public transport infrastructure. The length of all public transport lines in the ten cities averages 8410 m/1000 persons, while in other European cities, it is 3183. In American cities, it is only 1382 meters, and in Australia, in the best of the auto cities, it is 2609 m/1000 persons. The reserved route length per 1000 persons is also high in Swedish cities with 716 m/1000 persons and only 298 in other European cities (reserved routes are those that are reserved only for public transport such as bus lanes and rail lines, including segregated LRT/tram routes), so that congestion from other vehicles does not interfere with their operation. Other lower-density cities typically average only around 100 m/1000 persons. Additionally, the ratio of reserved public transport route to freeways (the two premium measures of private and public transport infrastructure) is 3.26 in the Swedish cities, only exceeded by other European cities with 5.51 times more premium public transport route than freeways.

This means that public transport systems in Swedish cities offer quite competitive average speeds. The ratio of overall public transport system speed (all modes) is 0.93 (so approaching parity with average road traffic speed), while in other European cities, it is 0.88. American and Canadian cities have public transport systems that operate at little more than half the average speed of general road traffic. The Swedish suburban rail services are especially competitive with road traffic, averaging 80.5 km/h cf. 42.6 km/h. Even Swedish urban bus systems have the best average speed of all buses in the world (30.3 km/h compared to a range in other cities from 19.4 to 23.4 km/h, with a global average of 21.5 km/h).

Furthermore, Swedish cities are blessed with relatively high levels of public transport service as measured by the annual seat kilometers of service per person. They provide on average 5720 seat km/person, with the five larger cities at 6895 km/person, which is more than other European cities (6126 seat km/person).

It could be concluded that Swedish cities do a great deal for public transport, to help compensate for what are atypically low densities for European cities and therefore quite dramatically reduced catchment densities around public transport stops. Stockholm is an exception here and has had a strong policy of transit-oriented development around stations on its tunnelbana (metro) system [35,36], thereby achieving the highest public transport use in Sweden (359 annual boardings/person), comparable to other European cities with 386/person. This suggests that even where densities are relatively modest overall (23.5 persons/ha in Stockholm), if significantly focused and denser, mixed-use urban fabrics can be developed and integrated with good public transport services, high levels of use can still be achieved.

Because of overall good infrastructure and service for public transport, the ten Swedish cities achieve what is a respectable performance in public transport use despite their lower densities. They average 128 annual boardings per capita and 195 in the larger five cities, compared to 67, 96 and 151 per capita in US, Australian and Canadian cities, respectively (and Canadian cities average 58% higher urban density than the average for the Swedish cities). Swedish cities are, however, 67% less in per capita boardings than in other European cities. Their public transport passenger kilometers are better, due most likely to longer travel distances, averaging 1390 PKT/person, compared to 571, 1075 and 1031 in US, Australian and Canadian cities, though they are still 38% below the European cities (2234/person). Swedish cities also have 16.3% of total motorized travel by public transport (20.4% in the larger cities), compared to only 3.2%, 8.0% and 11.3% in US, Australian and Canadian cities respectively. Not surprisingly, though, they lag the other European cities in this factor (24.5%).

The major public transport problem for Swedish cities is their low density. This can be seen in the vehicle and seat occupancy data. These data show how many people on average are in a public transport vehicle (for rail, a vehicle is one wagon of a train) and what percentage of the seats supplied are on average occupied. Table 4 shows that there are on average only 15 persons per public transport vehicle (23 in Stockholm), which is lower than all other groups of cities, apart from the American cities (13). In seat occupancy (24% for all Swedish cities), there are no groups of cities with lower occupancy, and the range is from 31% in Stockholm down to 10% in Örebro. Thus, there is a lot of unutilized public transport capacity in Swedish cities and therefore high energy conservation potential if occupancy of the generous services provided can be increased.

Finally, Table 4 also suggests that the strong orientation to non-motorized modes in Swedish cities, despite a cold climate for much of the year, is also contributing significantly to their moderate private passenger transport energy use per capita. Swedish cities average 30% of all daily trips by walking and cycling (and a further 14.3% by public transport), with 32.8% walking and cycling in the five smaller cities, not far behind the other European cities with 34.5%. This is in stark contrast to 9.5%

in American, 14.2% in Australian and 11.6% non-motorized-mode use in Canadian cities. Despite low overall densities, Swedish cities do have significant areas of higher density, mixed use walking city fabric which facilitates greater use of both walking and cycling [21,37].

A simple way of summarizing the collective importance of all these factors in understanding transport energy use is to look at a pair of contrasting examples from Sweden with quite different per capita energy use in private passenger transport. Table 5 contrasts these key differences and shows that Jönköping has 80% higher private transport energy use per capita than Stockholm (21,678 MJ/person cf. 12,051 MJ/person). Furthermore, despite public transport use being dramatically less than in Stockholm (60 boardings/person cf. 359 in Stockholm), even public transport energy use per capita is a fraction higher (2050 in Jönköping cf. 1949 MJ/person in Stockholm). This highlights the energy conservation potential of public transport in a simple way—despite very similar public transport energy use per capita, Stockholm carries six times more boardings. The efficiency of energy use is also very different between the two cities. Jönköping's private and public transport energy use per passenger km are very similar (2.74 versus 2.53 MJ/PKT respectively) so that public transport has only a slight advantage in energy consumption. By contrast, private transport uses 2.4 times more energy per passenger km than public transport in Stockholm.

Table 5. Key differences between Stockholm and Jönköping with low compared to high per capita energy use in private passenger transport.

Variable	Units	Stockholm	Jönköping
Private passenger transport energy use per capita	MJ/person	12,051	21,678
Public transport energy use per capita	MJ/person	1949	2050
Energy use per private passenger kilometre	MJ/p.km	1.82	2.74
Energy use per public transport passenger kilometre	MJ/p.km	0.76	2.53
Urban density	persons/ha	23.5	12.6
Proportion of jobs in CBD	%	28.2%	20.6%
Metropolitan gross domestic product per capita	USD 1995	$49,271	$29,952
Length of freeway per person	m/ person	0.138	0.496
Parking spaces per 1000 CBD jobs	spaces/1000 jobs	125	287
Passenger cars per 1000 persons	units/1000 pers.	398	481
Average speed of the road network (24/7)	km/h	37.1	45.0
Total length of public transport lines per 1000 persons	m/1000 persons	4867	9024
Total length of reserved public transport routes per 1000 persons	m/1000 persons	234	1457
Total public transport seat kilometres of service per capita	seat km/person	8294	4330
Overall average speed of public transport	km/h	33.6	40.7
* Average speed of buses	km/h	24.8	31.5
* Average speed of suburban rail	km/h	56.3	72.5
Total public transport boardings per capita	boardings/person	359	60
Total public transport passenger kilometres per capita	p.km/person	2579	809
Overall public transport vehicle occupancy	persons/unit	22.6	9.9
Overall public transport seat occupancy	%	31%	19%
Passenger car passenger kilometres per capita	p.km/person	6630	7902
Percentage of total daily trips by non motorised modes	%	22.1%	21.2%
Percentage of total daily trips by motorised public modes	%	31.6%	9.6%
Proportion of total motorised PKT on public transport	%	27.8%	9.2%
Ratio of public vs private transport speeds	ratio	0.91	0.90
Ratio of segregated public transport infrastructure vs expressways	ratio	1.69	7.67

It can also be seen how different many of the other factors are between the two cities. Urban density is 87% higher in Stockholm, the proportion of jobs in the CBD is 1.4 times more, parking spaces per 1000 jobs are 2.3 times higher in Jönköping and GDP per capita in Stockholm is 1.6 times higher than Jönköping, despite Stockholm having significantly lower car use per capita than in Jönköping (6630 PKT/person cf. 7902 PKT/person). Freeway provision per person is 3.6 times greater in Jönköping, and car ownership is 21% higher, reflecting a higher commitment to the car than in Stockholm. Average road traffic speed is 45 km/h in Jönköping versus 37.1 km/h in Stockholm, thus encouraging more car use, although the ratio between public transport system speed and road traffic speed is virtually identical in both cities due to Jönköping's average public transport speed also being higher (40.7 km/h cf. 33.6 km/h).

Although Jönköping has more public transport lines and greater reserved public transport route per person than Stockholm, this infrastructure is not as well serviced as in Stockholm (only 4330 seat km/person cf. 8294 in Stockholm). This is reflected in all the public transport usage variables in Table 5 being so much higher in Stockholm, including vehicle and seat occupancy levels. Such differences are, to a degree, expected, given the difference in density and therefore the reduced public transport catchment populations around stops/stations in Jönköping. Interestingly, in non-motorized mode use as a percentage of total daily trips, Stockholm only has a slight edge over Jönköping, and both cities are the two lowest of the ten Swedish cities in this factor.

When taken collectively, it is likely that there is a strong multiplicative effect at work in determining the differences in energy use between the two cities.

5. Conclusions

This paper has provided a detailed insight into the private and public transport energy consumption patterns in ten Swedish cities and some broad urban planning, infrastructure and mobility patterns data that help to explain that consumption, both within Sweden and in relation to other world cities. The introduction posed three research questions, and the summary answers to those questions are provided in this section.

5.1. How Does Energy Use per Capita in Private and Public Transport Modes Compare within Sweden and with Other Cities in the USA, Australia, Canada, Europe and Asia?

Swedish cities are typical European cities in both their average private and public transport energy use per capita (15,601 MJ and 1534 MJ/person, respectively), with the smaller Swedish cities being a little less than the larger cities in both. However, there is considerable variation from 11,622 to 21,678 MJ/person in Umeå and Jönköping, respectively. On average, Swedish cities have about one-half the per capita private transport energy use of Australian and Canadian cities and less than one-third that of US cities. Their public transport energy use per capita is higher than the automobile cities in the USA, Australia and Canada, about the same as in other European cities, but much lower than in the Asian cities. This public transport energy use reflects much higher levels of public transport service and therefore greater commitment to public transport in Swedish cities than in the auto-oriented cities with a similar density.

5.2. How Do the Modal Energy Consumption Rates per Vehicle Kilometer and Passenger Kilometer in Swedish Cities Differ from Each Other and Other Cities Worldwide?

5.2.1. Energy Use per Vehicle Kilometer

Private transport energy use per vehicle km in Swedish cities is on average similar in the smaller and larger cities (2.9 and 3.1 MJ/km, respectively, with an average of 3.0) and very like Freiburg (3.1), as well as the other European cities in 2005 (3.1 MJ/km). This factor is, however, much less than in all the other groups of cities, which ranged in 2005 from 4.1 to 4.9 MJ/km.

Public transport energy use per kilometer (17.3 MJ/km all modes) is lower than in the global sample (18.6 MJ/km). Swedish buses consume less energy per kilometer than all groups of cities, apart from the European cities and Freiburg, with which they are very alike. LRT energy use per wagon km is also very like European cities, but lower than the other groups of cities. Metro energy use per wagon km (Stockholm's tunnelbana) is again akin to European cities, but very much lower than metros everywhere else. Suburban rail energy use varies a lot and is higher than in European, Australian and Asian cities, but very much lower than in American and Canadian cities (which have numerous less energy-efficient diesel operations).

5.2.2. Energy Use per Passenger Kilometer

Private transport energy use per passenger km follows the same patterns as outlined above, with Swedish cities on average being almost identical to European cities, but significantly below all the other cities. On the other hand, the lower use of public transport services sees Swedish cities consuming more energy per passenger kilometer (1.10 MJ/PKT) than all groups of cities, except those in the US and Canada. This includes Freiburg and the European cities which consume 0.79 and 0.76 MJ/PKT, respectively. This pattern is mainly due to the buses, because for the rail modes (LRT, metro and suburban rail), Swedish cities are much more alike, or sometimes better than, the other groups of cities.

5.3. Can Differences in Transport Energy Use per Capita Be Explained through Reference to a Range of Other Important Transport Indicators in Swedish Cities?

An examination of a wide range of other transport-related indicators has revealed insights into why Swedish cities differ between one another in passenger transport energy use and between other cities in the world. The key point to note here is that Swedish cities have similar levels of car use to other European cities and therefore similar per capita private transport energy use. This is despite Swedish cities being significantly lower in density than other European cities. However, unlike cities of similar density in North America and Australia, Swedish cities are still more centralized in work than their more auto-oriented cousins, thus favoring walking, cycling and public transport; they have significantly lower car ownership and they provide very good levels of public transport infrastructure and service, including competitive speeds with the car. They also have respectable levels of public transport use and very healthy levels of walking and cycling, especially considering their density.

Unlike most lower-density cities in North America and Australia, Swedish cities, being much older, do retain much more significant areas of "walking city" and "transit city" urban fabric and are therefore not uniformly low in density but rather have substantially higher density mixed-land-use areas, which are very supportive of public transport, walking and cycling [37]. For a more detailed explanation of how Swedish cities distinguish themselves from other cities in these matters, readers can refer to Kenworthy [21], which also contains photographic evidence of this urban fabrics' argument.

The variation in per capita private transport energy use between Swedish cities can generally be explained by the lower energy-consuming Swedish cities having a combination of (a) more energy-efficient cars, (b) higher density, or at least more extensive areas of walking and transit city fabric, (c) more centralized jobs in the CBD, (d) less parking in their CBDs, (e) less freeway availability, (f) lower car ownership, (g) lower car use, (h) lower car speed (which makes cars somewhat less attractive), (i) higher public transport service levels and (j) better public transport use. Higher public transport energy use per capita in Swedish cities generally relates to a combination of higher service levels and how much of that service is provided by buses compared to rail—rail modes have much lower energy use per passenger kilometer.

The data in this paper can be used to explore the transport energy conservation potential of a variety of different scenarios in Swedish cities.

Funding: The research reported in this paper was funded by two small research grants from K2: Sweden's National Centre for Research and Education on Public Transport.

Acknowledgments: The author is very grateful to K2 for providing the funding to support this research and the countless individuals in each of the cities who provided the requested data. I am especially grateful to Monika Brunetti, my research assistant, and Helena Svensson in K2 for her support in locating some key data.

Conflicts of Interest: The author declares no conflict of interest.

References

1. Amadeo, K. OPEC Oil Embargo, Its Causes, and the Effects of the Crisis: The Truth about the 1973 Arab Oil Crisis. 2020. Available online: https://www.thebalance.com/opec-oil-embargo-causes-and-effects-of-the-crisis-3305806 (accessed on 8 May 2020). The Balance.
2. Kettel, S. Oil Crisis. Encyclopedia Britannica. 2014. Available online: https://www.britannica.com/topic/oil-crisis (accessed on 8 May 2020).
3. United States Office of International Energy Affairs. *U.S. Oil Companies and the Arab Oil Embargo*; University of Michigan Library: Ann Arbor, MI, USA, 1975.
4. Vernon, R. *Oil Crisis. US Department of Energy*; Office of Scientific and Technical Information: Washington, DC, USA, 1976. Available online: https://www.osti.gov/biblio/7186106 (accessed on 12 May 2020).
5. Pisarski, A.; de Terra, N. American and European transportation responses to the 1973–74 oil embargo. *Transportation* **1975**, *4*, 291–312. [CrossRef]
6. Hirst, E.; Hylander, W. Transportation Energy Conservation Policies. *Science* **1976**, *192*, 15–20. [CrossRef] [PubMed]
7. Hamilton, J.D. *Historical Oil Shocks*; Working Paper 16790; National Bureau of Economic Research: Cambridge, MA, USA, 2011.
8. Phillips, J. *The Iranian Oil Crisis*; Backgrounder No. 76; The Heritage Foundation: Washington, DC, USA, 1979; Available online: http://s3.amazonaws.com/thf_media/1979/pdf/bg76.pdf (accessed on 8 May 2020).
9. Kaden, D.; Rose, T. *Environmental and Health Issues in Unconventional Oil and Gas Development*; Elsevier: Amsterdam, The Netherlands, 2016.
10. Pojani, D.; Stead, D. *The Urban Transport Crisis in Emerging Economies*; Springer Nature: Cham, Switzerland, 2017.
11. Macrotrends. Crude Oil Prices—70 Year Historical Chart. 2020. Available online: https://www.macrotrends.net/1369/crude-oil-price-history-chart (accessed on 3 July 2020).
12. Campbell, C.J.; Leherrere, J.H. *The World's Oil Supply 1930–2050: Report*; Petroconsultants: Geneva, Switzerland, 1995.
13. Ruppert, M.C.; Campbell, C. *Confronting Collapse: The Crisis of Energy and Money in a Post Peak Oil World*; Chelsea Green Publishing: White River Junction, VT, USA, 2009.
14. Lynch, M. *The "Peak Oil" Scare and the Coming Oil Flood*; Praeger: Westport, CT, USA, 2016.
15. Newman, P.; Kenworthy, J. *Urban Passenger Transport Energy Consumption and Carbon Dioxide Emissions: A Global Review and Assessment of Some Reduction Strategies*; Hickman, R., Givoni, M., Bonilla, D., Banister, D., Eds.; Handbook on Transport and Development; Edward Elgar Publishing: Cheltenham, UK, 2015; Chapter 3; pp. 36–58.
16. Kenworthy, J.; Laube, F. *The Millennium Cities Database for Sustainable Transport*; (CDROM Database); International Union (Association) of Public Transport (UITP): Brussels, Belgium; Institute for Sustainability and Technology Policy (ISTP): Perth, Australia, 2001.
17. Kenworthy, J.R. Reducing Passenger Transport Energy Use in Cities: A Comparative Perspective on Private and Public Transport Energy Use in American, Canadian, Australian, European and Asian Cities. In *Urban Energy Transition: Renewable Strategies for Cities and Regions*, 2nd ed.; Droege, P., Ed.; Elsevier: Amsterdam, The Netherlands, 2018; Chapter 2.1; pp. 169–204.
18. Pucher, J.; Clorer, S. Taming the automobile in Germany. *Transp. Q.* **1992**, *46*, 383–395.
19. Schiller, P.; Kenworthy, J.R. *An Introduction to Sustainable Transportation: Policy, Planning and Implementation*, 2nd ed.; Earthscan: London, UK, 2018; 420p.
20. Kenworthy, J.R. *The Good, the Bad and the Ugly in Urban Transport: Comparing Global Cities for Dependence on the Automobile*; Hartz-Karp, J., Marinova, D., Eds.; Methods for Sustainability Research; Edward Elgar Publishing: Cheltenham, UK, 2017; Chapter 3; pp. 46–62.
21. Kenworthy, J. Urban Transport and Eco-Urbanism: A Global Comparative Study of Cities with a Special Focus on Five Larger Swedish Urban Regions. *Urban Sci.* **2019**, *3*, 25. [CrossRef]
22. An, F.; Rousseau, A. Integration of a Modal Energy and Emissions Model into a PNGV Vehicle Simulation Model, PSAT. *J. Engines* **2001**, *110*, 781–793.
23. Faris, W.F.; Rakha, H.A.; Kafafy, R.I.; Idres, M.; Elmoselhy, S. Vehicle fuel consumption and emission modelling: An in-depth literature review. *Int. J. Veh. Syst. Model. Test.* **2011**, *6*, 318. [CrossRef]

24. Kenworthy, J. *Trends in Transport and Urban Development in Thirty-Three International Cities, 1995-6 to 2005-6: Some Prospects for Lower Carbon Transport*; Lehmann, S., Ed.; Low Carbon Cities: Transforming Urban Systems; Routledge: London, UK, 2014; Chapter 5; pp. 113–130.
25. Kenworthy, J. Is Automobile Dependence in Emerging Cities an Irresistible Force? Perspectives from São Paulo, Taipei, Prague, Mumbai, Shanghai, Beijing, and Guangzhou. *Sustainability* **2017**, *9*, 1953. [CrossRef]
26. Kenworthy, J.R.; Laube, F.B. *An International Sourcebook of Automobile Dependence in Cities, 1960–1990*; University Press of Colorado: Boulder, CO, USA, 1999; 704p.
27. Airviro. *Emissions Inventories for Swedish Counties and Municipalities*; The Swedish Meteorological and Hydrological Institute: Malmo, Sweden, 2019; Available online: http://www.airviro.smhi.se/cgi-bin/RUS/apub.html_rusreport.cgi (accessed on 19 June 2020).
28. Newman, P.W.G.; Kenworthy, J.R. *Sustainability and Cities: Overcoming Automobile Dependence*; Island Press: Washington, DC, USA, 1999; 442p.
29. Watt, K.E.F.; Ayres, C. Urban land use patterns and transportation energy cost. In Proceedings of the Paper Presented at the 140th Annual Meeting of the American Association for the Advancement of Science (AAAS), San Francisco, CA, USA, 25 February 1974.
30. Chang, M.F.; Evans, L.; Herman, R.; Wasielewski, P. Gasoline Consumption in Urban Traffic. *Transp. Res. Rec.* **1976**, *599*, 25–30.
31. Chang, M.-F.; Herman, R. An Attempt to Characterize Traffic in Metropolitan Areas. *Transp. Sci.* **1978**, *12*, 58–79. [CrossRef]
32. Chang, M.F.; Horowitz, A.J. Estimates of fuel savings through improved traffic flow in seven US cities. *Traffic Eng. Control* **1979**, *20*, 62–65.
33. Newman, P.W.G.; Kenworthy, J.R. The transport energy trade-off: Fuel-efficient traffic versus fuel-efficient cities. *Transp. Res.* **1988**, *22A*, 163–174. [CrossRef]
34. Thomson, J.M. *Great Cities and Their Traffic*; Penguin Books: Middlesex, UK, 1977.
35. Cervero, R. Sustainable new towns: Stockholm's rail served satellites. *Cities* **1995**, *12*, 41–51. [CrossRef]
36. Cervero, R. *The Transit Metropolis: A Global Inquiry*; Island Press: Washington, DC, USA, 1998.
37. Newman, P.; Kosonen, L.; Kenworthy, J. Theory of urban fabrics: Planning the walking, transit/public transport and automobile/motor car cities for reduced car dependency. *Town Plan. Rev.* **2016**, *87*, 429–458. [CrossRef]

© 2020 by the author. Licensee MDPI, Basel, Switzerland. This article is an open access article distributed under the terms and conditions of the Creative Commons Attribution (CC BY) license (http://creativecommons.org/licenses/by/4.0/).

Article

The Geographical Distribution and Correlates of Pro-Environmental Attitudes and Behaviors in an Urban Region

Áróra Árnadóttir *, Michał Czepkiewicz and Jukka Heinonen

Faculty of Civil and Environmental Engineering, The University of Iceland, Hjarðarhagi 6, 107 Reykjavík, Iceland; mcz@hi.is (M.C.); heinonen@hi.is (J.H.)
* Correspondence: aroraarnadottir@gmail.com

Received: 13 March 2019; Accepted: 18 April 2019; Published: 24 April 2019

Abstract: A lot of emphasis has been put on the densification of urban form to reduce greenhouse gas emissions from transportation. However, many recent studies have found that central urban dwellers, even though their carbon footprints of daily transportation may be lower, might be responsible for higher total emissions than those that reside in suburban areas. Similarly, as with the urban form, higher environmental concern is often considered as an indicator of lower emissions, but several studies have found that pro-environmental attitude (PEA) does not always correlate with less energy intensive behavior. This study analyzes how urban zones, PEA, and several sociodemographic variables are associated with annual travel emissions and pro-environmental behaviors (PEB), using a dataset collected with a map-based online survey (softGIS) survey, contributed by 841 participants from the Helsinki Metropolitan Area (HMA), Finland. Although PEA can affect PEBs related to household energy consumption ($\beta = 0.282$, $p < 0.001$), clothing ($\beta = 0.447$, $p < 0.001$) and produce purchases ($\beta = 0.449$, $p < 0.0001$), their relationship with emissions from local ($\beta = -0.067$), national ($\beta = -0.019$) and international ($\beta = -0.016$) travel was not significant. Clusters of low emissions from local travel and high international travel emissions were found in pedestrian-oriented urban zones and residents of car-oriented zones were more likely to conserve household energy ($\beta = 0.102$, $p < 0.05$). These results might help broaden the current perspective of city planners, as well as identify opportunities for more effective mitigation policies.

Keywords: pro-environmental attitude; pro-environmental behavior; greenhouse gases; urban zones; local travel; national travel; international travel

---

1. Introduction

Anthropogenic activity contributes to global warming, changes in the water cycle, changes in climate extremes, rising of sea levels, and the melting of ice caps. In fact, it is extremely likely that humans have been the dominant cause since the 1950s by contributing to an increased concentration of greenhouse gas (GHG) emissions in the atmosphere, which is the main cause of climate forcing [1]. The current state of anthropogenic activity is distressing the earth system, in some cases, beyond the planetary boundaries [2].

The production and consumption activities of cities are responsible for the majority of global GHG emissions [3]. While around half of the world's population resides in urban areas, cities have been said to be responsible for 71% to 76% of global energy-related CO_2 emissions [4]. The mitigation of these GHG emissions has been a common focus of researchers and policy-makers.

As cities become more compact, distances between services decrease, resulting in less dependency on cars and shorter trip lengths [5–12]. Many cities have emphasized dense urbanization and the reduction of emissions from the private transport sector in their plans, even though these aspects may constitute only a small part of cities' total baseline emissions [13] and factors other than land use planning may have a more decisive role in shaping the structure of emissions from travel [14].

Emissions from aviation are rarely included in city-level policies and studies, even though they can exceed those from ground transport in wealthy European countries [15–17], especially when short-lived climate forcers are included in calculations. The aviation sector currently produces 2% to 3% of total anthropogenic carbon emissions [18,19] and the emissions from it are expected to grow at a rate of around 8% annually [20]. Emissions related to tourism alone account for 8% of global GHG emissions [21].

Many recent studies have found that urban dwellers, although their carbon footprints of local transportation may be lower, are responsible for higher emissions than those that reside in rural areas, due to higher consumption levels [22–28]. Several studies have also extended this pattern to within city-levels, reporting higher carbon footprints in the densest city centers in comparison to those in the outer urban areas [29–33]. This pattern is also related to the so-called rebound effect; cars are expensive to possess and operate, and a car-free lifestyle provides new consumption opportunities that seem to be taken advantage of, resulting in the overall emission load being higher than when possessing and operating a car [34].

Another popular urban planning and development related mitigation strategy is the creation of more energy efficient housing as 68% of cities plan GHG reductions in the building sector [13]. However, while housing energy related emissions might indeed go down significantly along with new energy efficient buildings, again, the overall carbon footprints of the residents might still show upward curves due to higher consumption levels [30].

One of the most common policy levers for GHG mitigation is the raising of awareness [13,35]. However, although public awareness of the impacts of global warming is growing, studies on reduced emissions or changes in behaviors of concerned citizens vary. This implies that there are awareness–attitude–behavior gaps, where an individual's awareness, values, or beliefs are not reflected in their actions or market behaviors. Some suggest that comfort, convenience, and cost overrule values, and barriers include the lack of relevant information easily available, organizational challenges, and time and money constraints [36], and that pro-environmental self-identity may not translate to pro-environmental behaviors (PEBs) due to a lack of available options [37].

Studies vary on the extent of these gaps, however. The impact of attitudes on purchasing behavior related to produce and products has been found to be weak, while norms are a significant predictor [38]. Another study, which used a value–belief–norm model, found a weak connection [39]. The same value–belief–norm model also explained household energy savings and cost-effective behaviors while other studies suggest little connection between environmental concern and energy consumption [36]. Conserving energy is usually done for reasons other than concern for environmental impacts [40] and change in travel behavior is rarely due to climate concern [36,40,41]. However, other researchers found that environmental concern or knowledge (along with lower income) can lead to more PEB related to food, energy, and travel [42,43].

A dissonance between environmental attitudes and behaviors has also been found regarding air travel [44,45], and when it comes to international travel and tourism, individuals do not take the same measures to limit their environmental damage as they do around the home [46,47]. In addition, it is not uncommon that "green" measures taken at home are used as a justification of long-distance travel [48].

Factors other than climate concern are often found to be more decisive in GHG mitigation. Higher education is associated with lower personal CO_2 emissions [49], and income with higher emissions and other environmental impacts [9,49,50]. Environmental attitudes have been found to have no effect on the income–carbon relationship, except with the most climate concerned of the population [9]. Another obstacle in GHG mitigation is that PEBs related to household energy saving do not necessarily translate to lower emissions due to structural factors [51].

Even though the connection between environmental attitudes and behavior has been extensively studied, so far, few studies have paid attention to the spatial aspect. However, it is likely that environmental attitudes are manifested differently, and that they affect the behavior differently in different types of residential areas and housing types.

The aim of this study is to analyze how pro-environmental attitudes (PEAs) and residential urban zones affect PEBs regarding household energy consumption, purchasing choices of produce and clothing, and GHG emissions from travel, using results from a map-based online survey (softGIS) [52] targeting young adults living in the Helsinki Metropolitan area (HMA).

The research questions, of which the main novelty value lies on the fourth, are:

- How does the PEA affect PEB regarding household energy use, and clothing and produce purchases?
- How does the PEA affect the amount of GHG emissions stemming from local, national, and international travel?
- How do PEA, PEB, and travel-related emissions cluster geographically within the study area?
- How do these relationships differ depending on residential location?

2. Research Design

2.1. Case Area

The data collected were from inhabitants of HMA in Southern Finland. Around a quarter of the country's five million inhabitants live in the area and the fast-growing population has a high proportion of young adults. The predominance of young adults and households without children is especially pronounced in the capital city of Helsinki [53]. High demand for housing has resulted in urban sprawl, but the regional land use plan focuses on densification with development focused in the center and the densely populated corridors around the public transportation network [54]. HMA is the most affluent region in Finland and the location of the biggest and by far most diversely connected airport, thus offering conditions for frequent long-distance travel. At the same time, HMA is also the core of support of the Green Party in Finland with almost a quarter of the votes in the region going for the Green Party [55], which is likely related to a high level of environmental concern among the residents of the region. These features make the region an illustrative case for the purpose of this study.

2.2. Data Collection

The data were collected using a softGIS method, in which conventional survey questions, such as multiple choice and scaled questions, were combined with an interactive map [52,56]. The map allowed respondents to mark visited locations and answer questions pertaining to these locations. Thus, it allowed for an accurate way of measuring travel distances, frequencies, and associated emissions using geographical information systems (GIS). The survey is presented in Appendix A, in Table A1. It was targeted to individuals aged 25 to 40 years residing in the HMA municipalities of Helsinki, Vantaa, Kauniainen, and Espoo. This relatively narrow age range was chosen to minimize the effect of life course variables and generational differences. People in this age group are usually employed, are independent from their parents, and have grown up in a globalized world, with good access to information and communication technologies [15]. A random sample of 5000 individuals from the target group was drawn from the Population Register Center of Finland. Two rounds of personal letter invitations were sent to the sampled individuals in August and September 2016. After deducting incomplete responses, the response rate was 16.82% with 841 responses out of the 5000 individuals invited (see [15] for more details). The geographic distribution of the study participants' residences was similar to that of the target population: Pearson's r calculated in a 1 km hexagon grid equals 0.81, which was deemed satisfactory and close to that in other related studies [57]. The sample over-represented people with higher education (70% compared to 46% in the HMA population aged 25 to 40) and women (58% to 50%). However, as the aim of the analysis was not to estimate descriptive statistics of the population, but to estimate correlations, no weights were used in the analyses [58]. The dataset included socio-demographic variables, locations visited every day, behaviors, attitudes, values, consumption figures and background information, travel distances, estimated GHG emissions from that travel, and residential coordinates categorized into urban zones.

2.3. Data Analysis

The process of data processing and analysis is summarized in Figure 1. Subsequent steps are described in following sections, except for computing variables related to income, household type, education, and gender, which are presented in Appendix B.

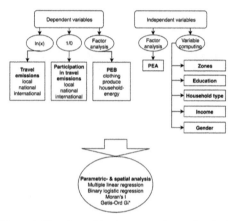

Figure 1. Flowchart of the data processing and analysis.

2.3.1. Factor Analyses

For the behavior variables, principal axis factoring was used to reduce data, with the orthogonal rotation method varimax with Kaiser normalization used to produce independent factors with no multicollinearity. Kaiser-Meyer-Olkin (KMO) and Bartlett's test was used to test the adequacy of the sampling and produced a score of 0.831, which confirmed the sampling was adequate for factor analysis. Each PEB variable had a value of 0 to 4 (a value of 0 is for never and 4 is always), which were answers to how often participants engaged in 11 behaviors (Table 1). Coefficients below 0.4 were suppressed.

Table 1. Results of factor analysis of pro-environmental behavior variables.

	Factor 1	Factor 2	Factor 3
Reduce heating in unoccupied rooms		0.757	
Reduce hot water temperature		0.542	
Switch off lights in unoccupied rooms			
Keep heating low to save energy		0.740	
Use high-efficiency appliances			
Buy organic produce			0.585
Buy local produce			0.707
Purchase items with as little packaging as possible			0.494
Buy second-hand clothes	0.534		
Choose to buy clothes according to environmental impact	0.834		
Choose to buy clothes according to ethical aspects of production	0.786		

Note: Extraction method: principal axis factoring. Rotation method: Varimax with Kaiser normalization.

The PEB factor analysis indicated that the 11 variables of environmentally significant behaviors could be reduced to just 3 factors related to clothing purchases (factor 1), household energy saving (factor 2), and produce purchases (factor 3). All three factors had an eigenvalue above 1.0 and the accumulated percentage of the explained variance was 59.917.

Each PEA variable had a value of 1 to 5 (value of 1 was "strongly disagree" and 5 was "strongly agree"), which were answers to how much participants agreed or disagreed with five statements (Table 2). Principal component analysis was used to reduce data. KMO and Bartlett's test produced a score of 0.850, which confirmed the sampling was adequate for factor analysis.

Table 2. Results of factor analysis of pro-environmental attitude variables.

Pro-Environmental Attitude Variable	Factor 1
I want to live as ecologically as possible	0.853
I am very concerned about environmental issues	0.787
I think about how I can reduce environmental damage when I go on holiday	0.760
I think about the environmental impact of services I use	0.836
When shopping, I rarely think about the environmental impact of the things I buy [reversed]	0.713

Note: Extraction method: principal component analysis.

The factor analysis confirmed that due to a high correlation between all variables, only one factor was needed. It had just over 62% of the explained variance and an eigenvalue of 3.1. The regression factor score was named the pro-environmental attitude (PEA factor score).

2.3.2. Travel-Related Urban Zones

The respondents were allocated into the following six zones depending on the coordinates of their home locations: Central pedestrian zone, the fringe of the pedestrian zone, pedestrian zones of the sub-centers, intensive public transport zone, basic public transport zone, and car zone. The zones were taken from the Travel-Related Urban Zone GIS-based classification of the Finnish Environment Institute, which divides the regions into zones depending on the distance from the center, population characteristics, public transportation infrastructure, building stock, and jobs [59].

For this study, the residential zones were merged into three categories, based on location, density, similarities in the mode of travel to work, and on having approximately the same number of respondents in each group. The central pedestrian zone and the fringe of the pedestrian zone became the pedestrian-oriented zone (33% of respondents), the pedestrian zones of sub-centers and intensive public transport zones became the public transport-oriented zone (31%), and the basic public transport zone and the car zone became the car-oriented zone (36%).

2.3.3. Travel Behavior and GHG Emissions

The variables used in analyzing travel emissions were annual per capita transportation emissions from local, domestic, and international travel. The GHG emissions were taken from the previous study of Czepkiewicz et al. [15]. They used a broad life cycle assessment (LCA) approach, accounting for both direct and indirect emissions, such as those from direct combustion, fuel and electricity production, transport infrastructure construction, and vehicle manufacturing and maintenance [15].

A large number of respondents reported zero emissions from either local, domestic, or international travel. Binary variables signifying participation or non-participation in each type of travel were computed. For those that participated in travel, the natural logarithm of emissions was used to normalize the data.

2.3.4. Spatial Statistical Analyses

The variables that were analyzed with spatial statistics were PEB factor scores related to clothing, produce and household energy, the PEA factor scores, and travel emissions from local, national, and international travel. We used two spatial statistical methods in ArcGIS 10 to identify patterns of spatial association. We used Global Moran's I statistic [60] to check whether the values were clustered in space in the whole region, and Getis-Ord Gi* to identify areas in which high or low values cluster locally [61]. Moran's I is not sensitive to some cases of local spatial association, so we computed the Gi* even in cases when Moran's I did not show a significant pattern of spatial association.

2.3.5. Multivariate Analyses

We used bivariate analysis methods, such as bar charts and Spearman correlations, and multiple regression models to analyze the relationships between explanatory variables, such as household type, gender, education, income, PEA factor scores, urban zone of the residential location, and the outcome variables: PEB factor scores related to clothing (factor 1), heating (factor 2), and produce (factor 3), and travel emissions from local, national, and international travel.

The statistical analyses were run in IBM SPSS Statistics 24. Three models for each of the PEB factor scores were prepared and the first model included the four sociodemographic variables as independent variables. In the second model, PEA factor scores were added as independent variables, and in the third model, the three residential urban zones were added too. Ordinary least squares (OLS) regression was used due to the quantitative character of the dependent variables.

Two models were calculated for each type of travel (local, domestic, and international). Binary logistic regression was used to analyze participation in emissions from travel, due to the dichotomous character of the dependent variable. OLS regression was used to analyze the amount of emissions of those who participated. By also running a binary logistic regression on participation in travel emissions, it was possible to capture which variables impacted whether a respondent had traveled in the past year and see if those same variables affected the amount of emissions. The independent variables in all models were gender, income, education level, household type, PEA factor scores, and urban zones.

3. Results and Discussion

Our results show that PEAs cluster in space and have, on average, higher values in the pedestrian-oriented zones than in the car-oriented zones. We found that PEA influenced environmentally significant behaviors regarding household energy, clothing, and produce, but it did not have an effect on the amount of GHG emissions from local, national, or international travel. Residents of car-oriented zones were more likely to conserve heating at home, but less likely to purchase environmentally-friendly produce than residents of the pedestrian-oriented zones, after controlling for socio-demographic variables and the PEA. Residents of pedestrian-oriented zones generated lower emissions from local travel and were more likely to participate in emissions from international travel than residents of the remaining urban zones. In the following, we present the results of the spatial and multivariate analyses divided into three topical sections: PEAs, PEBs, and emissions from travel. Each section is followed by a short discussion that relates the results to previous studies.

3.1. Pro-Environmental Attitudes

3.1.1. Results

Those with low income tended to have higher PEA factor scores and the same can be said about those with a high level of education (Figure 2a). Although there was a correlation between income and education ($r_s = 0.225$, $p < 0.001$, n = 847), respondents with the highest PEA scores were the most highly educated while the opposite can be said regarding income: Respondents with high income had a lower PEA score. Household size did not have a strong effect on PEA, although single people did have the lowest PEA factor scores. Women had considerably higher factor scores than men. Residents of the pedestrian-oriented zone had the highest PEA score of the three zones.

Pro-environmental attitude factor scores were significantly spatially autocorrelated (Moran's I = 0.23, $p < 0.001$). Areas with values higher than expected were located in pedestrian-oriented parts of Helsinki (Figure 2b). It is of note that the spatial association was not very strong, and residents with high factor scores lived next to residents with low factor scores, and vice-versa.

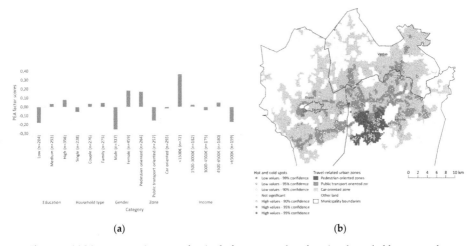

(a)   **(b)**

Figure 2. (a) Mean pro-environmental attitude factor scores by education, household type, gender, zone, and income categories; (b) Hot spot (Getis-Ord Gi*) map of pro-environmental attitude factor scores (n = 814). Areas highlighted in red (hot spots) have a local mean higher than the global mean, and areas highlighted in blue (cold spots) have a local mean lower than the global mean scores.

3.1.2. Discussion

In regards to our bivariate results for education level, similar trends were established [62]. The same study found that being male and having a high income were indicators of high concern, which contradicts our results. However, the high pro-environmental attitude scores of women are in line with other previous research [63,64]. Although we found clusters of high PEAs in central areas, the environmental concern of central and suburban residents has previously been found to not differ [65]. On the urban-rural scale, differences in environmental attitudes and concerns depend largely on specific issues [66], and therefore, the results of various studies might differ depending on the types of questions used. As our PEA variable consisted of quite broad terms (considerations of environmental impacts, concern for environmental issues, and wanting to live ecologically), specific environmental issues were not determined. The spatial and bivariate analysis of PEAs lays the foundation for the next two results sections of PEBs and travel emissions; it shows the distribution of our specific PEA factor scores in space, and within sociodemographic variables.

3.2. Pro-Environmental Behaviors

3.2.1. Results

There were significant differences in the PEBs of different groups, extending to the spatial dimension. Respondents within the low education category had the lowest clothing and produce related PEB factor scores, while the high education category had the highest (Figure 3a). PEB factor scores regarding household energy use did not differ greatly depending on education level. The household type with the highest PEB factor scores in all three categories was families. Women, in general, seemed to have higher PEB scores in all three categories, although the most variance was in the clothing category. The higher the income category of the respondents, the lower their PEB factor score in the clothing category. An opposite trend was found in the produce category, where the wealthiest respondents bought the most organic, local, and package free produce. Regarding household energy, very little variance was found, but in general, the wealthier respondents were less likely to make a conscious decision of reducing household energy consumption.

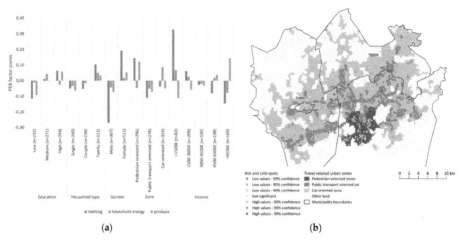

(a)　　　　　　　　　　　　　　　　　**(b)**

Figure 3. (a) Mean pro-environmental behavior (PEB) factor scores by categories; **(b)** Hot spot (Getis-Ord Gi*) map of factor scores of PEB factor 1: clothing (n = 831). Areas highlighted in red have values higher than the regional average, and areas highlighted in blue have values lower than the regional average.

Most notable is that the residents of the pedestrian-oriented zone had relatively high PEB factor scores related to clothing and produce purchases, which is also reflected in the spatial analysis. Local indicators of spatial association show that high values of the factors related to produce and clothing purchases cluster in central parts of the pedestrian-oriented zones of Helsinki (Figures 3b and 4b). We found no significant spatial association of the factor related to household energy and heating saving (Figure 4a and Table 3).

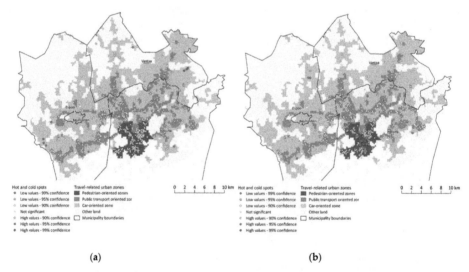

(a)　　　　　　　　　　　　　　　　　**(b)**

Figure 4. (a) Hot spot (Getis-Ord Gi*) map of factor scores of PEB factor 2: household energy (n = 831). Areas highlighted in red have values higher than the regional average, and areas highlighted in blue have values lower than the regional average.; **(b)** hot spot (Getis-Ord Gi*) map of factor scores of PEB factor 3: produce (n = 831). Areas highlighted in red have values higher than the regional average, and areas highlighted in blue have values lower than the regional average.

Table 3. Results of the spatial analyses of PEB factor scores.

PEB Factor	Moran's I	Getis-Ord Gi*
Clothing (F1)	0.099 ($p = 0.124$)	Areas with the local mean higher than the global mean are located in the northern part of the pedestrian-oriented zone of Helsinki.
Household energy (F2)	−0.022 ($p = 0.747$)	No significant patterns of spatial association
Produce (F3)	0.070 ($p = 0.272$)	Areas with the local mean higher than the global mean are located in the central part of the pedestrian-oriented zone of Helsinki.

As can be seen in Table 4, the only independent variable that influenced all three PEB categories was PEA, all of which were positive and had relatively large effect sizes and impacts on R^2 (model 1 improved from $R^2 = 0.100$ to $R^2 = 0.298$ in model 1a; model 3 improved from $R^2 = 0.013$ to $R^2 = 0.203$ in model 3a).

Table 4. Multiple linear regression of clothing, household energy, and produce related pro-environmental behavior factor scores, with education level, household type, income category, gender, pro-environmental attitude, and zones as dependent variables.

PEB Model [1]		1	1a	1b	2	2a	2b	3	3a	3b
			Clothing			Household Energy			Produce	
		β	β	β	β	β	β	β	β	β
Education level	Low	-	-	-	-	-	-	-	-	-
	Medium	0.048	0.007	−0.002	0.017	−0.013	0.001	0.070	0.032	0.019
	High	0.100*	0.047	0.033	−0.023	−0.070	−0.049	0.067	0.015	−0.005
Household type	Single	-	-	-	-	-	-	-	-	-
	Couple	0.078	0.034	0.036	0.029	−0.013	−0.015	−0.007	−0.048	−0.046
	Family	0.158***	0.125**	0.139***	0.068	0.030	0.008	−0.001	−0.049	−0.027
Income category	Very low	-	-	-	-	-	-	-	-	-
	Low	−0.148**	−0.082	−0.084	−0.036	0.007	0.008	0.038	0.112*	0.111*
	Medium	−0.221***	−0.140**	−0.136**	−0.053	0.008	0.004	0.044	0.143*	0.147**
	High	−0.249***	−0.176***	−0.174***	−0.047	0.013	0.007	0.087	0.179**	0.185***
	Very high	−0.318***	−0.209***	−0.207***	−0.080	0.005	0.000	0.137*	0.274***	0.279***
Gender	Male	-	-	-	-	-	-	-	-	-
	Female	0.242***	0.163***	0.161***	0.012	−0.039	−0.037	0.076*	−0.008	−0.010
PEA			0.452***	0.447***		0.277***	0.282***		0.453***	0.449***
Zones	Pedestrian			-			-			-
	Public transport			−0.047			0.040			−0.032
	Car			−0.067			0.102*			−0.100*
R^2		0.100***	0.298***	0.311***	−0.005	0.077***	0.084***	0.013*	0.203***	0.221***
F		10.906***	31.955***	26.937***	0.534	6.036***	5.509***	2.167*	19.569***	16.936***

Notes. *$p < 0.05$. **$p < 0.01$. ***$p < 0.001$. [1] Model 1: PEB regarding clothing as a dependent variable. Education level, household type, income category, and gender as independent variables. 1a: PEA added as an independent variable. 1b: zones added as an independent variable. Model 2: PEB regarding household energy-saving as a dependent variable. Education level, household type, income category, and gender as independent variables. 2a: PEA added as an independent variable. 2b: zones added as an independent variable. Model 3: PEB regarding the purchase of produce as a dependent variable. Education level, household type, income category, and gender as independent variables. 3a: PEA added as an independent variable. 3b: zones added as an independent variable.

The wealthy residents were less likely to buy environmentally-friendly clothing (Table 4), which could be due to the purchasing of second-hand clothing being a part of our clothing measure. Education level had a significant effect on PEBs related to clothing only when attitudes and urban zones were not included (model 1), indicating that it only affects the model through attitudes. Household types affected the PEB clothing model (models 1, 1a, and 1b). Families were more likely to buy environmental, ethical, or second-hand clothing. Women had positive coefficients throughout the models, which suggest that they not only had more environmental concern, but also were more likely to take care of the kind of clothing they did purchase. There was no influence of geographical location on the models, despite spatial clustering of the factor scores, which suggests geographical clustering was due to patterns in PEAs.

Models 2, 2a, and 2b confirmed the small household energy variance found between income groups in the bivariate analysis (Figure 3a); none of the coefficients were statistically significant. A high level of income had a significantly positive effect on PEBs regarding produce and significant negative coefficients in the clothing models; the more affluent population is more likely to take care when purchasing food, but less likely to think about the environmental effects related to clothing. Residents of the car-oriented zones were more likely to save heating energy than the residents of pedestrian-oriented zones (model 2b), despite the lack of a spatial association of this variable (Figure 4a).

Gender lost significance when attitudes were added to the produce model, which suggests that it only affects the produce purchases through attitudes. Residents of the car-oriented zones were less likely to engage in PEBs related to produce purchases than residents of the pedestrian-oriented zones. Spatial autocorrelation and residual analysis was performed on models 1b, 2b, and 3b (see Appendix D, Table A6). No spatial autocorrelation was found, using global Moran's I with a threshold of $p < 0.05$, but the residuals of the clothing model (1b) showed signs of heteroskedasticity, exhibiting more variance with higher predicted values. As a result, the regression was run again using robust standard errors to see if the coefficients held their significance. The p values of these models were very similar and no coefficients lost or gained significance, indicating that our initial models predicted the significance adequately. Although OLS might not provide the best possible fit for the data, it still provided unbiased estimation of which variables influence the dependent variable, which was the primary goal of our analysis.

3.2.2. Discussion

The regression (Table 4) showed that PEA had a significant positive effect on all three PEB categories, which suggests that the attitude-behavior gap related to household energy-saving and the purchase of produce and clothing was small in our results. Value–belief–norm models have been more successful at explaining these low-cost, "good intention" behaviors than ones that have larger behavioral restrictions, such as limiting car-use [67]. Interestingly, PEAs had the least effect on household energy-related PEBs of the three categories. The effect was still quite large and significant, which is in line with other studies [39,42,43]. This could indicate that it is easier and more accessible to install secondary heating or control personal energy use in detached houses in the suburbs than in apartment buildings in the centers, as suggested by Kyrö et al. [64].

The only other variable that had a significant positive relationship with the energy PEB factor score was the residential zone, where the residents of the more sparsely populated areas were more likely to minimize household energy use. However, this is likely due to only the single-family house residents in the car-oriented zones paying directly for their heating, whereas those living in apartment buildings pay it as a part of the housing management fee or rent, having no monetary incentive to reduce usage [68,69]. Furthermore, in HMA, over 80% of households are connected to district heating, covering virtually all apartment buildings, while electricity is used for heating in the low-rise outer fringe areas [23]. Electricity is more expensive than district heating, which in turn could lead to less energy use due to monetary reasons.

The effect of zones on PEBs related to produce might be due to characteristics of the urban surroundings, which differ in availability of organic, package free, and local produce. Suburban residents may find it more difficult to practice sustainable consumption than their urban counterparts [70]. Overall, the higher the income category of respondents, the less likely they were to have high PEB scores related to household energy and clothing (Figure 3a), which is in line with several papers that state a positive correlation between income and carbon footprints related to consumption [27,49,50,71].

Multiple linear regression performed on the data split by zones showed that the relationships between PEB and PEA did not differ notably between residential zones, as the coefficients for PEA in all three zones were similar in size and significance (see Table A2 in Appendix C).

3.3. Emissions from Travel

3.3.1. Results

Participation in and amount of emissions from all travel categories increased with increased income, and the most notable difference in participation in international travel was found between respondents with very low and very high income (Figure 5). Single people had the lowest participation rates and mean annual emissions from all travel categories. Families had the highest participation rates and mean annual local travel emissions, and couples had the highest participation rates and mean annual emissions from national travel. Mean emissions from international and national travel increased with education level while local travel emissions decreased. Very little difference was found in participation in local travel between education levels. Respondents with a medium level of education had the highest participation scores, closely followed by the high education category. Women had slightly higher participation percentages than men throughout all travel categories. They had higher mean annual emissions in the national and international travel categories, while men had slightly higher emissions from local travel.

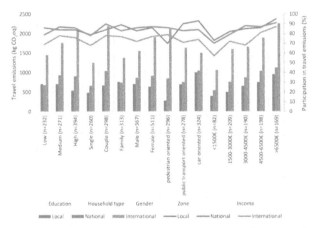

Figure 5. Mean annual local, national, and international per capita travel emissions (kg CO_2 eq) and participation (%) in emissions by gender, household type, income, education, and zone categories.

Respondents from car-oriented zones had the highest participation rates (93%) and mean annual emissions from local travel, while respondents from pedestrian-oriented zones had the lowest participation rates (70%) and mean annual emissions from local travel. On the other hand, residents of pedestrian-oriented zones had the highest participation rates and annual emissions in international travel. Participation rates and annual emissions in national travel were similar throughout the zones. Spatial clustering was the strongest in the case of emissions from local travel (Moran's I = 0.22, $p < 0.001$), and not significant in the case of domestic or international travel (Table 5), although there were significant local clusters of high emissions (Figure 6b, Figure 7).

Table 5. Results of spatial analyses of local, domestic, and international travel emissions.

Variable	Moran's I	Local Indicators of Spatial Association
Local emissions—all	0.22 (p = 0.001)	Areas with the local mean lower than the global mean are located in the pedestrian-oriented zones of Helsinki. Areas with the local mean higher than the global mean are located in the car-oriented zones of Espoo and Vantaa (Figure 6a).
Domestic emissions—all	0.023 (p = 0.775)	Areas with the local mean higher than the global mean are located in areas along the Helsinki-Vantaa border in Helsinki (Figure 6b).
International emissions—all	−0.019 (p = 0.776)	Areas with the local mean higher than the global mean are located in the pedestrian-oriented zones of Helsinki (Figure 7).

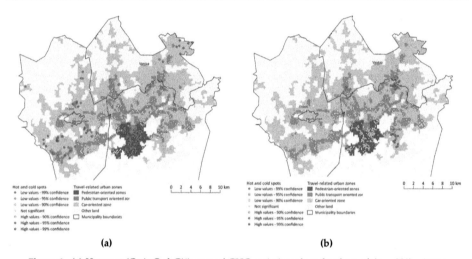

(a)   (b)

Figure 6. (a) Hot spot (Getis-Ord Gi*) map of GHG emissions from local travel (n = 831). Areas highlighted in red have values higher than expected, and areas highlighted in blue have values lower than expected.; (b) hot spot (Getis-Ord Gi*) map of GHG emissions from domestic leisure travel (n = 831). Areas highlighted in red have values higher than expected, and areas highlighted in blue have values lower than expected.

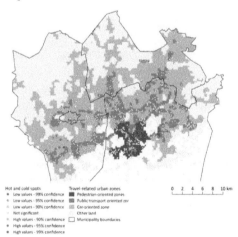

Figure 7. Hot spot (Getis-Ord Gi*) map of GHG emissions from international leisure travel (n = 831). Areas highlighted in red have values higher than the regional average, and areas highlighted in blue have values lower than the regional average.

Education level and household type did not have a statistically significant relationship to local travel, neither on the participation rates nor the amount of emissions (Table 6). High income, being a woman, and living in car-oriented zones were all positively associated with participation in local travel emissions. The largest odds ratio was found with participants of a very high income, who were more likely to participate in local travel emissions than the lowest income group.

Table 6. Binary logistic regression on participation in local travel emissions (1) and multiple linear regression on the amount of local travel emissions (1a) of local per capita annual emissions (CO_2 eq) of those participating.

Travel Model [1]		1		1a	
		B (S.E.)	OR	B (S.E.)	β
Education level	Low	-	-	-	-
	Medium	0.220 (0.343)	1.247	0.102 (0.150)	0.032
	High	−0.039 (0.325)	0.961	0.056 (0.144)	0.019
Household type	Single	-	-	-	-
	Couple	−0.133 (0.304)	0.874	−0.008 (0.159)	−0.003
	Family	0.106 (0.342)	1.112	−0.073 (0.161)	−0.024
Income category	Very low	-	-	-	-
	Low	0.817 (0.379) *	2.263 *	−0.107 (0.226)	−0.031
	Medium	0.471 (0.383)	1.601	0.009 (0.233)	0.003
	High	0.920 (0.426) *	2.509 *	0.250 (0.242)	0.071
	Very high	2.074 (0.560) ***	7.957 ***	0.362 (0.248)	0.103
Gender	Male	-	-	-	-
	Female	0.647 (0.253) **	1.910 **	−0.116 (0.114)	−0.039
Zones	Pedestrian	-	-	-	-
	Public transport	1.284 (0.296) ***	3.612 ***	0.870 (0.144) ***	0.276 ***
	Car	1.746 (0.338) ***	5.732 ***	1.299 (0.142) ***	0.429 ***
PEA		−0.333 (0.125) **	0.717 **	−0.100 (0.057)	−0.067
Constant		−0.050 (0.427)	0.951	5.070 (0.248) ***	
X^2 (Goodness-of-fit)[2]		11.265 (p = 0.187)			
Pseude R^2 (Nagelkerke)		0.196			
R^2					0.155 ***
F					9.545 ***

Notes. *p < 0.05. **p < 0.01. ***p < 0.001. [1] Model 1: Binary logistic regression on participation in emissions from local travel. Education level, household type, income category, gender, zones, and PEAs are independent variables. Model 1a: Multiple linear regression on the natural logarithm of the amount of yearly emissions from local travel. Education level, household type, income category, gender, zone, and PEAs are independent variables. [2] Hosmer-Lemeshow test of goodness-of-fit.

The only significant contributor to the amount of local emissions was residential location. Residents of the car-oriented zones were most likely to participate in local travel and had the highest emissions from local travel. PEAs had a negative effect on participation in emissions from local travel, but did not have a statistically significant effect on the amount of emissions.

Binary logistic regressions performed with the data split by residential zones showed that although residents with high PEA scores of all three zones were less likely to participate in local travel emissions, only the coefficients from the pedestrian-oriented zone data were statistically significant (see Table A3 in Appendix C). This suggests that those with high PEA scores living in the central pedestrian zone are able to adopt sustainable urban mobility. No statistical significance was found between PEA and international or national travel when data was split by zones (see Tables A4 and A5 in Appendix C).

Neither PEA factor scores nor residential zones had a significant relationship to domestic travel emission participation or the amount of emissions (Table 7). Single people generated significantly more emissions from travel within the country than couples and families did. Wealthier respondents were significantly more likely to participate in travel and generated more emissions. Although the amount of emissions generated by women was not significantly different to men, they were more likely to participate in national travel. Education level had no significant effect on emissions from domestic travel.

Table 7. Binary logistic regression on participation in domestic travel emissions (2) and multiple linear regression on the amount of travel emissions (2a) of domestic per capita annual emissions (CO_2 eq) of those participating.

Travel Model [1]		2		2a	
		B (S.E.)	OR	B (S.E.)	β
	Low	-	-	-	-
Education level	Medium	0.436 (0.337)	1.547	0.184 (0.123)	0.074
	High	0.302 (0.326)	1.352	0.128 (0.119)	0.055
	Single	-	-	-	-
Household type	Couple	0.402 (0.373)	1.495	−0.286 (0.124) *	−0.120 *
	Family	−0.045 (0.349)	0.956	−0.312 (0.130) *	−0.130 *
	Very low	-	-	-	-
	Low	0.968 (0.382) *	2.634 *	0.052 (0.183)	0.019
Income category	Medium	1.451 (0.429) ***	4.269 ***	0.334 (0.187)	0.123
	High	1.678 (0.486) ***	5.356 ***	0.586 (0.195) **	0.218 **
	Very high	1.906 (0.523) ***	6.726 ***	0.773 (0.202) ***	0.280 ***
	Male	-	-	-	-
Gender	Female	0.823 (0.277) **	2.277 **	−0.018 (0.093)	−0.008
Zones	Pedestrian	-	-	-	-
	Public transport	−0.590 (0.352)	0.555	−0.104 (0.113)	−0.042
	Car	−0.360 (0.367)	0.697	0.087 (0.112)	0.037
PEA		0.202 (0.134)	1.224	−0.021 (0.046)	−0.019
Constant		0.620 (0.451)	1.859	6.158 (0.201) ***	
X^2 (Goodness-of-fit)[2]		10.410 (p = 0.237)			
Pseude R^2 (Nagelkerke)		0.142			
R^2				0.057 ***	
F				3.276 ***	

Notes. *$p < 0.05$. **$p < 0.01$. ***$p < 0.001$. [1] Model 2: Binary logistic regression on participation in emissions from domestic travel. Education level, household type, income category, gender, zones, and PEAs are independent variables. Model 2a: Multiple linear regression on the natural logarithm of the amount of yearly emissions from domestic travel. Education level, household type, income category, gender, zones, and PEAs are independent variables. [2] Hosmer-Lemeshow test of goodness-of-fit.

Respondents with high income and living in pedestrian-oriented zones were more likely to participate in international travel emissions, but for those participating the amount of emissions were not significantly different from other zones or income categories (Table 8). Families had a significantly negative relationship with international travel emissions and the highly educated had a significantly positive relationship with emissions.

Table 8. Binary logistic regression on participation in international travel emissions (3) and multiple linear regression on the amount of travel emissions (3a) of international per capita annual emissions (CO_2 eq) of those participating.

Travel Model [1]		3		3a	
		B (S.E.)	OR	B (S.E.)	β
	Low	-	-	-	-
Education level	Medium	0.335 (0.267)	1.398	0.184 (0.124)	0.077
	High	0.075 (0.253)	1.078	0.368 (0.121) **	0.164 **
	Single	-	-	-	-
Household type	Couple	0.045 (0.264)	1.046	0.085 (0.128)	0.036
	Family	0.394 (0.281)	1.483	−0.377 (0.133) **	−0.163 **
	Very low	-	-	-	-
	Low	1.020 (0.334) **	2.772 **	0.070 (0.188)	0.027
Income category	Medium	0.503 (0.331)	1.653	0.113 (0.197)	0.041
	High	1.374 (0.384) ***	3.951 ***	0.258 (0.201)	0.099
	Very high	1.821 (0.433) ***	6.175 ***	0.404 (0.207)	0.154
	Male	-	-	-	-
Gender	Female	0.324 (0.207)	1.383	0.098 (0.093)	0.043

Table 8. *Cont.*

Travel Model [1]		3		3a	
		B (S.E.)	OR	B (S.E.)	β
Zones	Pedestrian	-	-	-	-
	Public transport	−0.826 (0.263) **	0.438 **	−0.204 (0.116)	−0.083
	Car	−0.556 (0.276) *	0.573 *	−0.180 (0.113)	−0.078
PEA		0.148 (0.104)	1.159	−0.018 (0.046)	−0.016
Constant		0.579 (0.373)	1.784	6.973 (0.209) ***	
X^2 (Goodness-of-fit)[2]		4.021 ($p = 0.855$)			
Pseude R^2 (Nagelkerke)		0.129			
R^2				0.082 ***	
F				4.298 ***	

Notes. *$p < 0.05$. **$p < 0.01$. ***$p < 0.001$. [1] Model 3: Binary logistic regression on participation in emissions from international travel. Education level, household type, income category, gender, zones, and PEAs are independent variables. Model 3a: Multiple linear regression on the natural logarithm of the amount of yearly emissions from international travel. Education level, household type, income category, gender, zones, and PEAs are independent variables. [2] Hosmer-Lemeshow test of goodness-of-fit.

Spatial autocorrelation and residual analysis was performed on travel models 1a, 2a, and 3a (see Appendix D, Table A6). No spatial autocorrelation was found, using global Moran's I with a threshold of $p < 0.05$, and the residuals showed no signs of heteroskedasticity; they were symmetrically distributed, showed no signs of patterns, and were clustered towards the middle of the plots.

3.3.2. Discussion

The results align with previous studies in that centrally located, pedestrian-friendly areas with mixed land use have lower levels of private car use, travel shorter distances, and thus generate less GHG emissions from local travel [7,12,72,73]. Residential location in travel-related zones was connected both to non-zero emissions and their amount, which suggests that it contributes to multiple aspects of local travel, such as car ownership, travel mode choice, and distances. PEAs, in turn, only contributed to participation in emissions: Respondents with a higher concern for the environment were more likely to rely solely on walking or cycling (Table 6). This is largely in line with previous research that suggests that PEAs are significantly related to car ownership and use [74–76]. Similarly, as in previous studies [14,21] higher incomes were related to higher GHG emissions from local travel, and the likelihood of non-zero emissions, in particular (Table 6). It likely results from differences in car-ownership, which strongly correlated with income in our sample ($r_s = 0.441$, $p < 0.001$, n = 846).

The differences in international travel emissions depending on residential location are also in line with previous studies, with residents of centrally-located dense urban areas generating higher emissions than those living farther away from the centers (Table 8) [15,56,72,77–79]. With regard to PEAs, our results are similar to those presented in a recent paper by Alcock et al. [44], where correlations were found between climate concern and PEBs, but not between environmental concern and actively refraining from air travel. Our results also reinforce the well-known link between income level and international travel [77]. The statistically significant relationship between high education and emissions from international travel, when income is controlled for, has also been previously observed [9,72]. Interestingly, in our results, higher income increased the likelihood of international travel and university education increased the amount of emissions. This suggests that income is an enabling factor, while education level contributes to traveled distances among those who can afford it, for instance, through higher cultural capital and more extensive social networks among the educated [14].

Previous studies suggest that the amount of domestic travel decreases with increasing population density and settlement size [80,81]. These studies, however, primarily compare settlements of different sizes (e.g., large cities with small towns) and not areas within one urban region. Looking at within-city differences in three Nordic cities, a previous study [82] found that distance traveled on weekends increases with distance from the city center, which is in line with the existence of clusters of high emissions from domestic travel in city outskirts in our results (Figure 6b). However, our regression shows no significant influence of urban zones on the emissions from domestic travel (Table 7). Higher income was positively associated with more domestic travel in our results, as well as in previous research [82], but we found no relationship with education level or gender, which is present elsewhere.

4. Limitations of the Study

The generalizability of the study is limited due to the single case study research design. Case studies are said to be objective due to the insights and knowledge of the researcher conducting it [83], but their generalizability is low until enough studies have been conducted [84].

The age range for the target group, 25 to 40 years, was relatively narrow. The reason this range was chosen was to minimize the effect of life course variables and generational differences, as people in this age group are usually employed, are independent from their parents, and have grown up in a globalized world, with good access to information and communication technologies [15]. The accuracy of behavior variables not related to travel might be compromised by their reliance on the respondent's perception of their behavior rather than direct observation (see Appendix A, Table A1 for the survey). An example is that instead of having access to information on the actual household energy used, respondents answered questions on how often they try to limit their use of household energy with various actions. The scope of the study is limited by the omission of business travel. This choice was made on an assumption that business trips are often involuntary and driven by different variables than leisure trips. Additionally, they constituted a very small share of the international travel emissions in our sample [15].

5. Conclusions

Previous research conducted in the study region has suggested that living in the densest urban core areas is associated with higher carbon footprints than living in suburban areas [29–31]. Similar findings have been presented by Chen et al. [32] for Sydney. Minx et al. [27] found for London that it is the spatial accumulation of wealth that is the decisive factor, not the spatial location as such. Furthermore, it is known from previous studies that PEAs do not always correlate with less energy intensive behavior [37,39–41].

Our study included local, domestic, and international travel, which has been called for by other researchers [72]. On the one hand, the results confirmed the well-established connection between compact urban form and local travel and thus suggest that land use planning may be instrumental in reducing carbon emissions by urban dwellers [7,12]. On the other hand, emissions generated from the international travel of urban dwellers are higher than those generated from their daily travel [15,72,78]. This suggests that other processes have a stronger influence on total travel-related emissions than land use planning [14]. Our results showed a correlation between residential location and international travel, but did not explain the reasons behind it. Numerous potential explanations exist, such as compensating for a lack of urban environmental quality, monetary rebounds related to car ownership, prevalence of cosmopolitan attitudes and lifestyles among urban dwellers, or influence of their higher cultural capital and extent of their social networks [34,56,72,79,85,86]. To illuminate these relationships, future studies should supplement quantitative research designs with qualitative methods to reveal motivations behind leisure travel behavior among urban dwellers [56,85].

Several mixed-methods and qualitative studies have already investigated motivations for holiday travel in the context of sustainability. They have highlighted the discrepancies between environmental concern and holiday travel and identified barriers that may hinder behavioral change in this domain [46–48]. These include, among others, high perceived benefits of leisure long-distance travel, such as its importance for social status and personal well-being [87,88]. Some travelers use PEBs in other domains of life to justify their lack of action in leisure travel [48] or may adjust their attitudes to behaviors that are beneficial and well integrated into their lifestyles, despite being aware of climate change and its factors [47]. International leisure travel has not been as often or widely discussed as an important contribution to emissions as private car travel or household energy use. This may have contributed to the awareness–behavior gap in this domain and suggest the need for education about the environmental cost of flying among the public. Future studies should further explore the discrepancy between PEA and flying, using both quantitative and qualitative methods to inform action aimed at behavioral changes. In addition, quantitative studies should use more nuanced models, which include values, beliefs, and norms, as a single PEA index can overly simplify these relationships.

Although changes in travel behavior can directly affect personal emissions, the connection between other PEBs and emissions is less clear and has even been found to be non-existent in the case of heating and energy saving, due to structural factors [51]. Household energy consumption is said to be accountable for over 25% of the personal consumption of GHG emissions in HMA [23] and is thus a key category in lowering the GHG emissions in the area. A shift away from fossil fuels in district heat production would effectively reduce the emissions due to the wide coverage of the district heating network, whereas individual incentives to engage in more energy efficient behavior could be created by installing apartment-based meters and moving from building-level heat contracts to a pay-per-use system. One of our variables for the PEB factor related to produce was organic purchases, which, compared to conventional produce, has been found to have similar global warming potential (GWP) [89].

The effectiveness of policy that relies on "green" consumers as agents of change has been doubted [90,91]. Green consumerism is still a driver of resource depletion and pollution while sustainable consumption is not. In addition, the carbon capability of individuals—that is, how equipped they are to engage in mitigation—has been found to be limited [92] and they might evaluate the environmental impact of the product incorrectly when engaging in "green" purchasing behavior [38]. In this context, it is important to acknowledge that both PEAs and PEBs are varied and complex; an attitude that emphasizes the importance of conserving biodiversity does not necessarily translate to a willingness to mitigate climate change.

More research on the carbon footprints of people with different levels of PEAs is required to fully understand the overall climate change pressure of urban residents. Such research may shed light on how much one can mitigate their climate impacts by different levels of behavioral changes, such as making pro-environmental purchasing choices of goods in the same category, spending on different consumption categories, or reducing the spending budget rather than allocating it differently. It was found that at equal income levels, the carbon footprints of HMA residents are quite similar regardless of how they spend their money as consumption is simply reallocated from one category to another [24]. Moreover, all the carbon footprints assessed for the residents of HMA were far above the remaining global per capita quota estimated for reaching even the 2 degree warming target [93]. Connecting future assessments to the 2 degree or 1.5 degree [94] target would be an important improvement for positioning the findings and making comparisons and mitigation consideration more tangible.

Author Contributions: Conceptualization, Á.Á., M.C. and J.H.; Data curation, M.C. and J.H.; Formal analysis, Á.Á., M.C.; Funding acquisition, M.C. and J.H.; Methodology, M.C.; Project administration, M.C. and J.H.; Supervision, M.C. and J.H.; Visualization, Á.Á., M.C. and J.H.; Writing—original draft, Á.Á.; Writing—review and editing, Á.Á., M.C. and J.H.

Funding: This research was funded by the Icelandic National Planning Agency, the Icelandic Road Administration and the University of Iceland.

Conflicts of Interest: The authors declare no conflict of interest. The funders had no role in the design of the study; in the collection, analyses, or interpretation of data; in the writing of the manuscript, or in the decision to publish the results.

Appendix A

This appendix presents relevant sections of the online softGIS survey used for data collection.

Table A1. Relevant sections of the softGIS survey.

	Gender	Male
		Female
	Age	25-40
	Main occupation at the moment	Employed
		Other
		Retired
		Stay-at-home-parent/Paternity or maternity leave
2/14 Background information		Student/Pupil
		Unemployed
	Education level	Basic education
		Upper secondary education
		Lowest level of tertiary education
		Undergraduate level
		Graduate level
		Postgraduate level
	How many hours per week do you usually spend working and studying combined?	Less than 30
		30 to 35
		35 to 40
		40 to 45
		More than 45
	Type of household	Couple living together
		Couple with child/children
		None
		Several people with separate budgets
		Single parent with child/children
		Single person living on her or his own
		Single person living with parents
4/14 Household	Household monthly income	Less than €1500
		€1500–€3000
		€3000–€4500
		€4500–€6500
		More than €6500
	How many cars are there in your household	None
		1
		2
		3
		More than 3

Table A1. *Cont.*

4/14 Household	Please indicate how much fuel your car consumes per 100 km of combined urban and highway driving	Car no. 1	less than 4
			4 to 6
			6 to 8
			8 to 10
			Above 10
			Does not apply
		Car no. 2	less than 4
			4 to 6
			6 to 8
			8 to 10
			Above 10
			Does not apply
		Car no. 3	less than 4
			4 to 6
			6 to 8
			8 to 10
			Above 10
			Does not apply
	Car no. 1 annual mileage (in kilometers)		
	Car no. 2 annual mileage (in kilometers)		
	Car no. 3 annual mileage (in kilometers)		
5/14 Home and work	How long have you lived in the Helsinki metropolitan area	Less than a year	
		One to three years	
		Three to ten years	
		More than ten years	
	Home	Please mark your main place of residence on a map	
	Work or study place	Please mark main locations	Place type
			How do you usually travel to this place?
			How often do you usually visit this place?
	What reasons were important when making decision on moving to current place of residence?	0—not at all important, 4—very important, N—not sure/not applicable. Please skip this question if it doesn't apply to you	Access to private yard
			Social life in the neighbourhood
			House or apartment size
			Housing price and cost
			Access to green areas
			Neighbourhood reputation
			Proximity to services
			Environmental impact
			House or apartment quality
			Distance from work or study place
			Distance from city centre

Table A1. *Cont.*

6/14 Local trips and services	Please mark locations that you have been frequently visiting within Helsinki metropolitan area	Please mark between 5 and 15 places. Don't worry about location accuracy. It is fine to mark just approximate location	Shopping—Grocery stores, shopping malls, markets etc.
			Daycare, kindergarten or school—Places where you bring your own children to
			Services and errands—Post office, bank, health care, personal care etc.
			Sports and active recreation—Indoor and outdoor physical activities
			Culture and sport events—Theatre, cinema, music, spectator sports etc.
			Leisure and going out—Restaurants, cafes, bars, meeting places etc.
7/14 Regional trips	Please mark locations within Finland but away from Helsinki metropolitan area, which you visited during the last 12 months	Please mark all locations that you can remember. Don't worry about location accuracy. It is fine to mark just approximate locations	Trips by car
			Trips by train
			Trips by bus
			Trips by plane
8/14 International trips	How many international trips did you make during the last 12 months?		
	If you have travelled abroad at least once during the last 12 months, please mark all the trips you can remember	Please don't worry about location accuracy. It is fine to mark just approximate location	International trips by plane
			International by boat
			International by train
			International by bus
			International by car
9/14 Pro-environmental behaviors	How often do you do the things listed below? (0—never, 1—rarely, 2—sometimes, 3—usually, 4—always, N—not sure/not applicable	Reduce heating in unoccupied rooms	
		Keep heating low to save energy	
		Buy organic produce	
		Purchase items with as little packaging as possible	
		Buy local produce	
		Buy second-hand clothes	
		Use high efficiency appliances	
		Switch off lights in unoccupied rooms	
		Choose to buy clothes according to ethical aspects of production	
		Choose to buy clothes according to environmental impact	
		Reduce hot water temperature	

Table A1. *Cont.*

		Every now and then it is good to take a break from urban life
11/14 Personal attitudes	Please state how much you agree or disagree with statements below (where 1 = strongly disagree, 3 = neither agree nor disagree, 5 = strongly agree)	Experience of different cultures is very important to me
		I feel at home wherever in the world I go
		It is easy for me to jump on a plane and go on a trip
		When shopping, I rarely think about the environmental impact of the things I buy
		I prefer spending my free time at home than going out
		There are many other things that are more important to me than housing
		I want to live as ecologically as possible
		I am not willing to limit the amount of my travel due to its environmental footprint
		I think about how I can reduce environmental damage when I go on holiday
		Exploring new places is an important part of my lifestyle
		I am very concerned about environmental issues
		I think about the environmental impact of the services I use
		Taking a holiday is very important for my wellbeing

Appendix B

The income categories of reported household incomes were computed into the following categories: Less than €1500 = very low, €1500–€3000 = low, €3000–€4500 = medium, €4500–€6500 = high, and more than €6500 = very high.

Household type was reported in the following six categories: "Several people with separate budgets", "single person living on her or his own", "single person living with parents", "couple living together", "couple with child/children", and "single parent with child/children". Categories were merged based on these three household types: Being in a childless relationship (couple, n = 298), having a child (family, n = 313), and being single and childless (single, n = 260).

Education was reported in six categories: Basic education, upper secondary, lowest tertiary, under graduate, graduate, and postgraduate. To ensure an adequate number of respondents in each category, the six categories were merged into three—low, medium, and high—based on the real-world background information they represent and the number of respondents in each group. "Under graduate" became the category "medium" (n = 271) so an education level below that became "low" (n = 232) and above became "high" (n = 394).

Gender was reported dichotomously: Men were computed into 0 and women into 1.

Appendix C

This appendix presents regressions performed on the data split by zones to see how the relationships between attitudes and behaviors vary in space. Each urban zone was regressed in a separate model. A multiple linear regression table of clothing, household energy, and produce related PEB factor scores is first presented, followed by three binary logistic regression tables on participation in local, national, and international travel emissions.

Table A2. Multiple linear regression of clothing, household energy, and produce related PEB factor scores, with education level, household type, income category, gender, and PEA as dependent variables, with data split by zones.

Zone		1	2	3	1	2	3	1	2	3
		Clothing			*Household Energy*			*Produce*		
		β	B	β	β	β	β	β	B	B
Education level	Low	-	-	-	-	-	-	-	-	-
	Medium	0.014	−0.007	0.016	−0.183	0.067	0.003	−0.085	0.035	0.014
	High	0.043	0.185*	−0.093	−0.273*	−0.016	−0.002	−0.218*	−0.043	0.156*
Household type	Single	-	-	-	-	-	-	-	-	-
	Couple	0.019	0.040	0.031	−0.074	−0.002	0.080	−0.035	−0.087	0.011
	Family	0.176**	0.106	0.112	−0.034	0.020	0.095	−0.003	−0.064	0.030
Income category	Very low	-	-	-	-	-	-	-	-	-
	Low	−0.105	−0.143	0.028	−0.132	0.254*	−0.129	0.081	−0.045	0.296**
	Medium	−0.197*	−0.219*	0.019	−0.028	0.182	−0.152	0.235**	0.084	0.130
	High	−0.116	−0.276**	−0.096	−0.102	0.167	−0.101	0.197*	0.109	0.272*
	Very high	−0.183*	−0.265**	−0.105	−0.053	0.096	−0.096	0.365***	0.240*	0.238*
Gender	Male	-	-	-	-	-	-	-	-	-
	Female	0.163**	0.187***	0.141*	0.014	−0.068	−0.066	0.085	−0.013	−0.042
Pro-environmental attitude		0.447***	0.410***	0.475***	0.299***	0.264***	0.296***	0.417***	0.484***	0.387***
R^2		0.332***	0.321***	0.290***	0.085***	0.048*	0.066**	0.252***	0.269***	0.228***
F		11.025***	10.397***	11.839***	3.143***	2.163*	2.867**	7.488***	8.089***	7.526***

Notes. *$p < 0.05$. **$p < 0.01$. ***$p < 0.001$.

Table A3. Binary logistic regression on participation in local travel emissions with data split by residential zones. Education level, household type, income category, gender, and PEA are dependent variables.

Zone		1		2		3	
		B (S.E.)	OR	B (S.E.)	OR	B (S.E.)	OR
Education level	Low	-	-	-	-	-	-
	Medium	−0.242 (0.599)	0.786	−0.608 (0.625)	0.544	1.055 (0.706)	2.871
	High	−0.987 (0.568)	0.373	0.070 (0.665)	1.072	1.706 (0.839)*	5.506*
Household type	Single	-	-	-	-	-	-
	Couple	−0.255 (0.410)	0.775	0.616 (0.648)	1.851	−1.182 (0.914)	0.307
	Family	−0.040 (0.474)	0.961	0.235 (0.656)	1.264	−0.691 (0.979)	0.501
Income category	Very low	-	-	-	-	-	-
	Low	0.478 (0.530)	1.612	0.982 (0.699)	2.669	1.210 (0.928)	3.352
	Medium	0.005 (0.550)	1.005	0.847 (0.677)	2.333	1.261 (0.990)	3.530
	High	0.628 (0.600)	1.873	0.737 (0.809)	2.090	2.215 (1.124)*	9.163*
	Very high	1.923 (0.755)*	6.389*	19.659 (5909.168)	344,910,941.4	1.663 (1.180)	5.276
Gender	Male	-	-	-	-	-	-
	Female	0.609 (0.356)	1.839	1.195 (0.535)*	3.303*	0.310 (0.618)	1.364
PEA		−0.422 (0.169)*	0.656*	−0.335 (0.263)	0.716	−0.179 (0.321)	0.836
Constant		1.054 (0.688)	2.868	0.822 (0.640)	2.275	1.347 (0.799)	3.845
X^2 (Goodness-of-fit)[1]		7.204 ($p = 0.515$)		5.511 ($p = 0.702$)		6.172 ($p = 0.628$)	
Pseudo R^2 (Nagelkerke)		0.143		0.196		0.146	

Notes. *$p < 0.05$. **$p < 0.01$. ***$p < 0.001$. [1] Hosmer-Lemeshow test of goodness-of-fit.

Table A4. Binary logistic regression on participation in national travel emissions with data split by residential zones. Education level, household type, income category, gender, and PEA are dependent variables.

Zone		1		2		3	
		B (S.E.)	OR	B (S.E.)	OR	B (S.E.)	OR
Education level	Low	-	-	-	-	-	-
	Medium	19.472 (4308.355)	286,194,371.8	−0.080 (0.504)	0.923	0.314 (0.580)	1.369
	High	0.714 (0.678)	2.043	0.340 (0.527)	1.404	0.307 (0.635)	1.359
Household type	Single	-	-	-	-	-	-
	Couple	1.721 (1.012)	5.589	0.394 (0.548)	1.483	−0.378 (0.760)	0.685
	Family	0.393 (0.847)	1.481	−0.262 (0.518)	0.769	−0.470 (0.687)	0.625
Income category	Very low	-	-	-	-	-	-
	Low	0.676 (0.791)	1.966	0.205 (0.642)	1.227	2.125 (0.733)**	8.374**
	Medium	19.202 (5401.501)	218,445,271.6	0.275 (0.646)	1.316	2.787 (0.870)***	16.225***
	High	1.195 (1.031)	3.302	0.324 (0.734)	1.383	4.072 (1.045)***	58.663
	Very high	0.293 (1.092)	1.341	2.323 (1.175)*	10.211*	3.050 (0.937)***	21.125***
Gender	Male	-	-	-	-	-	-
	Female	0.101 (0.612)	1.106	0.412 (0.412)	1.511	2.167 (0.626)***	8.731***
PEA		0.062 (0.294)	1.064	−0.060 (0.214)	0.941	0.410 (0.257)	1.506
Constant		0.269 (0.861)	1.309	1.126 (0.620)	3.082	−0.816 (0.654)	0.442
X^2 (Goodness-of-fit)[1]		6.586 (p = 0.582)		6.702 (p = 0.569)		6.608 (p = 0.579)	
Pseudo R^2 (Nagelkerke)		0.309		0.090		0.354	

Notes. *p < 0.05. **p < 0.01. ***p < 0.001. [1] Hosmer-Lemeshow test of goodness-of-fit.

Table A5. Binary logistic regression on participation in international travel emissions with data split by residential zones. Education level, household type, income category, gender, and PEA are dependent variables.

Zone		1		2		3	
		B (S.E.)	OR	B (S.E.)	OR	B (S.E.)	OR
Education level	Low	-	-	-	-	-	-
	Medium	0.206 (0.709)	1.229	0.248 (0.415)	1.282	0.558 (0.429)	1.747
	High	0.128 (0.665)	1.137	−0.004 (0.398)	0.996	0.145 (0.400)	1.156
Household type	Single	-	-	-	-	-	-
	Couple	−0.208 (0.553)	0.812	0.169 (0.397)	1.185	0.016 (0.508)	1.017
	Family	−0.274 (0.600)	0.761	0.533 (0.430)	1.704	0.519 (0.504)	1.680
Income category	Very low	-	-	-	-	-	-
	Low	2.128 (0.701)**	8.395	0.364 (0.536)	1.439	0.968 (0.592)	2.633
	Medium	0.618 (0.593)	1.856	0.100 (0.520)	1.105	0.816 (0.635)	2.261
	High	2.320 (0.824)**	10.171**	1.088 (0.647)	2.968	1.138 (0.660)	3.119
	Very high	2.272 (0.848)**	9.701**	1.341 (0.686)	3.822	1.969 (0.769)**	7.161**
Gender	Male	-	-	-	-	-	-
	Female	0.460 (0.462)	1.585	0.164 (0.320)	1.178	0.345 (0.360)	1.412
PEA		0.257 (0.219)	1.293	0.012 (0.168)	1.012	0.183 (0.185)	1.201
Constant		0.251 (0.764)	1.285	0.192 (0.511)	1.212	−0.148 (0.544)	0.863
X^2 (Goodness-of-fit)[1]		5.583 (p = 0.694)		15.270 (p = 0.54)		8.489 (p = 0.387)	
Pseudo R^2 (Nagelkerke)		0.167		0.097		0.122	

Notes. *p < 0.05. **p < 0.01. ***p < 0.001. [1] Hosmer-Lemeshow test of goodness-of-fit.

Appendix D

This appendix presents the results of the residual analysis and spatial autocorrelation of standardized residuals. Standardized predicted values and standardized residuals are plotted and global Moran's I is used to assess spatial autocorrelation, with a 1500 m fixed distance band.

Table A6. Results of residual analysis and spatial autocorrelation of standardized residuals.

Model	Heteroskedasticity [1] (Predicted*Residual)	Spatial Autocorrelation [1] (Moran's I Z-Score, *p*-Value), 1500 m Fixed Distance Band
Local travel (1a)		1.82 (*p* = 0.06)
National travel (2a)		−0.33 (*p* = 0.74)
International travel (3a)		−1.37 (*p* = 0.17)
Clothing (1b)		−0.46 (*p* = 0.64)

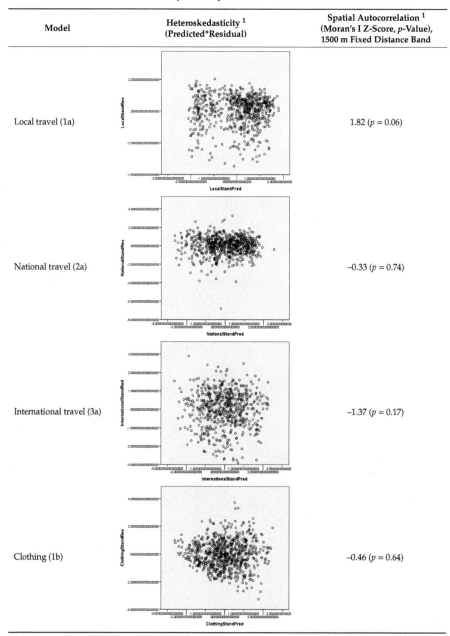

Table A6. *Cont.*

Model	Heteroskedasticity [1] (Predicted*Residual)	Spatial Autocorrelation [1] (Moran's I Z-Score, *p*-Value), 1500 m Fixed Distance Band
Household energy (2b)		−0.44 (*p* = 0.66)
Produce (3b)		−0.46 (*p* = 0.64)

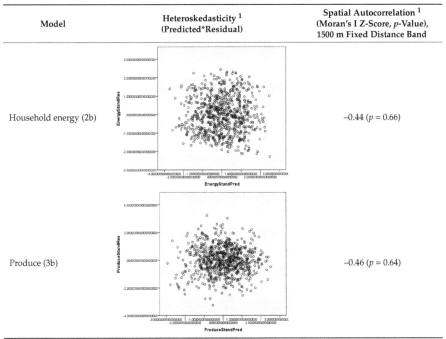

Note: [1] Standardized residuals used.

References

1. IPCC. *Climate Change 2013: The Physical Science Basis. Contribution of Working Group I to the Fifth Assessment Report of the Intergovernmental Panel on Climate Change*; IPCC: Cambridge, UK; New York, NY, USA, 2013; pp. 3–29.
2. Steffen, W.; Richardson, K.; Rockstrom, J.; Cornell, S.E.; Fetzer, I.; Bennett, E.M.; Biggs, R.; Carpenter, S.R.; de Vries, W.; de Wit, C.A.; et al. Planetary boundaries: Guiding human development on a changing planet. *Science* **2015**, *347*, 1259855. [CrossRef]
3. Kennedy, C.; Demoulin, S.; Mohareb, E. Cities reducing their greenhouse gas emissions. *Energy Policy* **2012**, *49*, 774–777. [CrossRef]
4. CCFLA. The Cities Climate Finance Leadership Alliance: Action Statement. In Proceedings of the Climate Summit 2014, New York, NY, USA, 23 September 2014.
5. Churchman, A. Disentangling the Concept of Density. *J. Plan. Lit.* **1999**, *13*, 389–411. [CrossRef]
6. Ewing, R.; Cervero, R. Travel and the Built Environment: A Synthesis. *Transp. Res. Rec.* **2001**, *1780*, 87–114. [CrossRef]
7. Ewing, R.; Cervero, R. Travel and the Built Environment. *J. Am. Plan. Assoc.* **2010**, *76*, 265–294. [CrossRef]
8. Rickwood, P.; Glazebrook, G.; Searle, G. Urban Structure and Energy—A Review. *Urban Policy Res.* **2008**, *26*, 57–81. [CrossRef]
9. Boucher, J.L. Culture, Carbon, and Climate Change: A Class Analysis of Climate Change Belief, Lifestyle Lock-in, and Personal Carbon Footprint. *Soc. Ekol.* **2016**, *25*, 53–80. [CrossRef]
10. Mindali, O.; Raveh, A.; Salomon, I. Urban density and energy consumption: A new look at old statistics. *Transp. Res. Part A Policy Pract.* **2004**, *38*, 143–162. [CrossRef]
11. Norman, J.; MacLean, H.L.; Kennedy, C.A. Comparing High and Low Residential Density: Life-Cycle Analysis of Energy Use and Greenhouse Gas Emissions. *J. Urban Plan. Dev.* **2006**, *132*, 10–21. [CrossRef]

12. Næss, P. Urban form and travel behavior: Experience from a Nordic context. *J. Transp. Land Use* **2012**, *5*. [CrossRef]
13. Croci, E.; Lucchitta, B.; Janssens-Maenhout, G.; Martelli, S.; Molteni, T. Urban CO_2 mitigation strategies under the Covenant of Mayors: An assessment of 124 European cities. *J. Clean. Prod.* **2017**. [CrossRef]
14. Holz-Rau, C.; Scheiner, J. Land-use and transport planning—A field of complex cause-impact relationships. Thoughts on transport growth, greenhouse gas emissions and the built environment. *Transp. Policy* **2019**, *74*, 127–137. [CrossRef]
15. Czepkiewicz, M.; Ottelin, J.; Ala-Mantila, S.; Heinonen, J.; Hasanzadeh, K.; Kyttä, M. Urban structural and socioeconomic effects on local, national and international travel patterns and greenhouse gas emissions of young adults. *J. Transp. Geogr.* **2018**, *68*, 130–141. [CrossRef]
16. Aamaas, B.; Borken-Kleefeld, J.; Peters, G.P. The climate impact of travel behavior: A German case study with illustrative mitigation options. *Environ. Sci. Policy* **2013**, *33*, 273–282. [CrossRef]
17. Aamaas, B.; Peters, G.P. The climate impact of Norwegians' travel behavior. *Travel Behav. Soc.* **2017**, *6*, 10–18. [CrossRef]
18. Kousoulidou, M.; Lonza, L. Biofuels in aviation: Fuel demand and CO_2 emissions evolution in Europe toward 2030. *Transp. Res. Part D Transp. Environ.* **2016**, *46*, 166–181. [CrossRef]
19. Staniland, M. Regulating aircraft emissions: Leadership and market power. *J. Eur. Public Policy* **2012**, *19*, 1006–1025. [CrossRef]
20. Chen, D.; Hu, M.; Han, K.; Zhang, H.; Yin, J. Short/medium-term prediction for the aviation emissions in the en route airspace considering the fluctuation in air traffic demand. *Transp. Res. Part D Transp. Environ.* **2016**, *48*, 46–62. [CrossRef]
21. Lenzen, M.; Sun, Y.-Y.; Faturay, F.; Ting, Y.-P.; Geschke, A.; Malik, A. The carbon footprint of global tourism. *Nat. Clim. Chang.* **2018**, *8*, 522–528. [CrossRef]
22. Heinonen, J. The Impacts of Urban Structure and the Related Consumption Patterns on the Carbon Emissions of an Average Consumer. Ph.D. Thesis, Aalto University, Helsinki, Finland, 2012.
23. Heinonen, J.; Jalas, M.; Juntunen, J.K.; Ala-Mantila, S.; Junnila, S. Situated lifestyles: I. How lifestyles change along with the level of urbanization and what the greenhouse gas implications are—A study of Finland. *Environ. Res. Lett.* **2013**, *8*, 025003. [CrossRef]
24. Heinonen, J.; Jalas, M.; Juntunen, J.K.; Ala-Mantila, S.; Junnila, S. Situated lifestyles: II. The impacts of urban density, housing type and motorization on the greenhouse gas emissions of the middle-income consumers in Finland. *Environ. Res. Lett.* **2013**, *8*, 035050. [CrossRef]
25. Lenzen, M.; Dey, C.; Foran, B. Energy requirements of Sydney households. *Ecol. Econ.* **2004**, *49*, 375–399. [CrossRef]
26. Sovacool, B.K.; Brown, M.A. Twelve metropolitan carbon footprints: A preliminary comparative global assessment. *Energy Policy* **2010**, *38*, 4856–4869. [CrossRef]
27. Minx, J.; Baiocchi, G.; Wiedmann, T.; Barrett, J.; Creutzig, F.; Feng, K.; Förster, M.; Pichler, P.-P.; Weisz, H.; Hubacek, K. Carbon footprints of cities and other human settlements in the UK. *Environ. Res. Lett.* **2013**, *8*, 035039. [CrossRef]
28. Poom, A.; Ahas, R. How Does the Environmental Load of Household Consumption Depend on Residential Location? *Sustainability* **2016**, *8*, 799. [CrossRef]
29. Heinonen, J.; Kyro, R.; Junnila, S. Dense downtown living more carbon intense due to higher consumption: A case study of Helsinki. *Environ. Res. Lett.* **2011**, *6*. [CrossRef]
30. Ottelin, J.; Heinonen, J.; Junnila, S. New Energy Efficient Housing Has Reduced Carbon Footprints in Outer but Not in Inner Urban Areas. *Environ. Sci. Technol.* **2015**, *49*, 9574–9583. [CrossRef]
31. Ottelin, J.; Heinonen, J.; Junnila, S. Carbon footprint trends of metropolitan residents in Finland: How strong mitigation policies affect different urban zones. *J. Clean. Prod.* **2018**, *170*, 1523–1535. [CrossRef]
32. Chen, G.; Hadjikakou, M.; Wiedmann, T.; Shi, L. Global warming impact of suburbanization: The case of Sydney. *J. Clean. Prod.* **2018**, *172*, 287–301. [CrossRef]
33. Rice, J.L.; Cohen, D.A.; Long, J.; Jurjevich, J.R. Contradictions of the Climate-Friendly City: New Perspectives on Eco-Gentrification and Housing Justice. *Int. J. Urban Reg. Res.* **2019**. [CrossRef]
34. Ottelin, J.; Heinonen, J.; Junnila, S. Rebound effects for reduced car ownership and driving. In *Nordic Experiences of Sustainable Planning: Policy and Practice*; Kristjánsdóttir, S., Ed.; Taylor & Francis Group: London, UK, 2017.

35. Gratiela, B. Sustainable consumption in the area of transportation. *Constanta Marit. Univ.* **2013**, *14*, 209–212.
36. Newton, P.; Meyer, D. Exploring the Attitudes-Action Gap in Household Resource Consumption: Does "Environmental Lifestyle" Segmentation Align with Consumer Behaviour? *Sustainability* **2013**, *5*, 1211–1233. [CrossRef]
37. Whitmarsh, L.; O'Neill, S. Green identity, green living? The role of pro-environmental self-identity in determining consistency across diverse pro-environmental behaviours. *J. Environ. Psychol.* **2010**, *30*, 305–314. [CrossRef]
38. Moser, A.K. Thinking green, buying green? Drivers of pro-environmental purchasing behavior. *J. Consum. Mark.* **2015**, *32*, 167–175. [CrossRef]
39. Bronfman, N.; Cisternas, P.; López-Vázquez, E.; Maza, C.; Oyanedel, J. Understanding Attitudes and Pro-Environmental Behaviors in a Chilean Community. *Sustainability* **2015**, *7*, 14133–14152. [CrossRef]
40. Whitmarsh, L. Behavioural responses to climate change: Asymmetry of intentions and impacts. *J. Environ. Psychol.* **2009**, *29*, 13–23. [CrossRef]
41. Poortinga, W.; Steg, L.; Vlek, C. Values, Environmental Concern, and Environmental Behavior. *Environ. Behav.* **2016**, *36*, 70–93. [CrossRef]
42. Bruderer Enzler, H.; Diekmann, A. *Environmental Impact and Pro-Environmental Behavior: Correlations to Income and Environmental Concern*; ETH Zurich Sociology Working Papers: Zurich, Switzerland, 2015.
43. Díaz-Siefer, P.; Neaman, A.; Salgado, E.; Celis-Diez, J.; Otto, S. Human-Environment System Knowledge: A Correlate of Pro-Environmental Behavior. *Sustainability* **2015**, *7*, 15510–15526. [CrossRef]
44. Alcock, I.; White, M.P.; Taylor, T.; Coldwell, D.F.; Gribble, M.O.; Evans, K.L.; Corner, A.; Vardoulakis, S.; Fleming, L.E. 'Green' on the ground but not in the air: Pro-environmental attitudes are related to household behaviours but not discretionary air travel. *Glob. Environ. Chang.* **2017**, *42*, 136–147. [CrossRef] [PubMed]
45. Davison, L.; Littleford, C.; Ryley, T. Air travel attitudes and behaviours: The development of environment-based segments. *J. Air Transp. Manag.* **2014**, *36*, 13–22. [CrossRef]
46. Barr, S.; Shaw, G.; Coles, T.; Prillwitz, J. "A holiday is a holiday": Practicing sustainability, home and away. *J. Transp. Geogr.* **2010**, *18*, 474–481. [CrossRef]
47. Hares, A.; Dickinson, J.; Wilkes, K. Climate change and the air travel decisions of UK tourists. *J. Transp. Geogr.* **2010**, *18*, 466–473. [CrossRef]
48. Dickinson, J.; Robbins, D.; Lumsdon, L. Holiday travel discourses and climate change. *J. Transp. Geogr.* **2010**, *18*, 482–489. [CrossRef]
49. Baiocchi, G.; Minx, J.; Hubacek, K. The Impact of Social Factors and Consumer Behavior on Carbon Dioxide Emissions in the United Kingdom. *J. Ind. Ecol.* **2010**, *14*, 50–72. [CrossRef]
50. Ivanova, D.; Stadler, K.; Steen-Olsen, K.; Wood, R.; Vita, G.; Tukker, A.; Hertwich, E.G. Environmental Impact Assessment of Household Consumption. *J. Ind. Ecol.* **2016**, *20*, 526–536. [CrossRef]
51. Tabi, A. Does pro-environmental behaviour affect carbon emissions? *Energy Policy* **2013**, *63*, 972–981. [CrossRef]
52. Kahila, M.; Kyttä, M. SoftGIS as a Bridge-Builder in Collaborative Urban Planning. In *Planning Support Systems Best Practice and New Methods*; Springer: Dordrecht, The Netherlands, 2009; Volume 95, pp. 389–411. [CrossRef]
53. Jaakola, A.; Vilkama, K. *Helsinki's Present State and Development 2016: Summary of Key Findings*; Helsinki Quarterly: Helsiki, Finland, 2017; pp. 9–25.
54. Jenks, M.; Kozak, D.; Takkanon, P. *World Cities and Urban Form: Fragmented, Polycentric, Sustainable?* Routledge: London, UK, 2013.
55. Official Statistics of Finland. *Municipal Elections*; 2323-1114; Statistics Finland: Helsinki, Finland, 2017.
56. Czepkiewicz, M.; Heinonen, J.; Ottelin, J. Why do urbanites travel more than do others? A review of associations between urban form and long-distance leisure travel. *Environ. Res. Lett.* **2018**, *13*, 073001. [CrossRef]
57. Czepkiewicz, M.; Jankowski, P.; Młodkowski, M. Geo-questionnaires in urban planning: Recruitment methods, participant engagement, and data quality. *Cartogr. Geogr. Inf. Sci.* **2016**, *44*, 551–567. [CrossRef]
58. Solon, G.; Haider, S.J.; Wooldridge, J.M. What Are We Weighting For? *J. Hum. Resour.* **2015**, *50*, 301–316. [CrossRef]
59. Söderström, P.; Schulman, H.; Ristimäki, M. *Urban Form in the Helsinki and Stockholm City Regions: Development of Pedestrian, Public Transport and Car Zones*; Finnish Environment Institute: Helsinki, Finland, 2015.

60. Esri. How Spatial Autocorrelation (Global Moran's I) Works. Available online: http://desktop.arcgis.com/en/arcmap/10.3/tools/spatial-statistics-toolbox/h-how-spatial-autocorrelation-moran-s-i-spatial-st.htm (accessed on 17 November 2018).

61. Esri. How Hot Spot Analysis (Getis-Ord Gi*) Works. Available online: http://desktop.arcgis.com/en/arcmap/10.3/tools/spatial-statistics-toolbox/h-how-hot-spot-analysis-getis-ord-gi-spatial-stati.htm (accessed on 13 December 2018).

62. Shen, J.; Saijo, T. Reexamining the relations between socio-demographic characteristics and individual environmental concern: Evidence from Shanghai data. *J. Environ. Psychol.* **2008**, *28*, 42–50. [CrossRef]

63. Diamantopoulos, A.; Schlegelmilch, B.B.; Sinkovics, R.R.; Bohlen, G.M. Can socio-demographics still play a role in profiling green consumers? A review of the evidence and an empirical investigation. *J. Bus. Res.* **2003**, *56*, 465–480. [CrossRef]

64. Arslan, T.; Yilmaz, V.; Aksoy, H.K. Structural Equation Model for Environmentally Conscious Purchasing Behavior. *Int. J. Environ. Res.* **2012**, *6*, 323–334. [CrossRef]

65. Ambrosius, J.D.; Gilderbloom, J.I. Who's greener? Comparing urban and suburban residents' environmental behaviour and concern. *Local Environ.* **2014**, *20*, 836–849. [CrossRef]

66. Berenguer, J.; Corraliza, J.A.; Martín, R. Rural-Urban Differences in Environmental Concern, Attitudes, and Actions. *Eur. J. Psychol. Assess.* **2005**, *21*, 128–138. [CrossRef]

67. Steg, L.; Vlek, C. Encouraging pro-environmental behaviour: An integrative review and research agenda. *J. Environ. Psychol.* **2009**, *29*, 309–317. [CrossRef]

68. Kyrö, R.; Heinonen, J.; Säynäjoki, A.; Junnila, S. Occupants have little influence on the overall energy consumption in district heated apartment buildings. *Energy Build.* **2011**, *43*, 3484–3490. [CrossRef]

69. Heinonen, J.; Junnila, S. Residential energy consumption patterns and the overall housing energy requirements of urban and rural households in Finland. *Energy Build.* **2014**, *76*, 295–303. [CrossRef]

70. Kennedy, E.H.; Krogman, N.; Krahn, H. Sustainable Consumption and the Importance of Neighbourhood: A Central City/Suburb Comparison. *Can. J. Sociol.* **2013**, *38*, 359–382.

71. Ala-Mantila, S.; Heinonen, J.; Junnila, S. Relationship between urbanization, direct and indirect greenhouse gas emissions, and expenditures: A multivariate analysis. *Ecol. Econ.* **2014**, *104*, 129–139. [CrossRef]

72. Reichert, A.; Holz-Rau, C.; Scheiner, J. GHG emissions in daily travel and long-distance travel in Germany—Social and spatial correlates. *Transp. Res. Part D Transp. Environ.* **2016**, *49*, 25–43. [CrossRef]

73. Stevens, M.R. Does Compact Development Make People Drive Less? *J. Am. Plan. Assoc.* **2017**, *83*, 7–18. [CrossRef]

74. Anable, J. 'Complacent Car Addicts' or 'Aspiring Environmentalists'? Identifying travel behaviour segments using attitude theory. *Transp. Policy* **2005**, *12*, 65–78. [CrossRef]

75. Flamm, B. The impacts of environmental knowledge and attitudes on vehicle ownership and use. *Transp. Res. Part D Transp. Environ.* **2009**, *14*, 272–279. [CrossRef]

76. Barr, S.; Prillwitz, J. Green travellers? Exploring the spatial context of sustainable mobility styles. *Appl. Geogr.* **2012**, *32*, 798–809. [CrossRef]

77. Brand, C.; Preston, J.M. '60-20 emission'—The unequal distribution of greenhouse gas emissions from personal, non-business travel in the UK. *Transp. Policy* **2010**, *17*, 9–19. [CrossRef]

78. Ottelin, J.; Heinonen, J.; Junnila, S. Greenhouse gas emissions from flying can offset the gain from reduced driving in dense urban areas. *J. Transp. Geogr.* **2014**, *41*, 1–9. [CrossRef]

79. Große, J.; Olafsson, A.S.; Carstensen, T.A.; Fertner, C. Exploring the role of daily "modality styles" and urban structure in holidays and longer weekend trips: Travel behaviour of urban and peri-urban residents in Greater Copenhagen. *J. Transp. Geogr.* **2018**, *69*, 138–149. [CrossRef]

80. Limtanakool, N.; Dijst, M.; Schwanen, T. The influence of socioeconomic characteristics, land use and travel time considerations on mode choice for medium- and longer-distance trips. *J. Transp. Geogr.* **2006**, *14*, 327–341. [CrossRef]

81. Dargay, J.M.; Clark, S. The determinants of long distance travel in Great Britain. *Transp. Res. Part A Policy Pract.* **2012**, *46*, 576–587. [CrossRef]

82. Næss, P. Urban Planning: Residential Location and Compensatory Behaviour in Three Scandinavian Cities. In *Rethinking Climate and Energy Policies*; Springer: Cham, Switzerland, 2016; pp. 181–207. [CrossRef]

83. Hodkinson, P.; Hodkinson, H. The Strengths and Limitations of Case Study Research. In Proceedings of the Learning and Skills Development Agency Conference—Making an Impact on Policy and Practice, Cambridge, UK, 5–7 December 2001.

84. Eisenhardt, K.M.; Graebner, M.E. Theory building from cases: Opportunities and challenges. *Acad. Manag. J.* **2007**, *50*, 25–32. [CrossRef]

85. Næss, P. Are Short Daily Trips Compensated by Higher Leisure Mobility? *Environ. Plan. B Plan. Des.* **2006**, *33*, 197–220. [CrossRef]

86. Holden, E.; Linnerud, K. Troublesome Leisure Travel. *Urban Stud.* **2011**, *48*, 3087–3106. [CrossRef]

87. Richards, G. Vacations and the Quality of Life: Patterns and Structures. *J. Bus. Res.* **1999**, *44*, 189–198. [CrossRef]

88. Dolnicar, S.; Lazarevski, K.; Yanamandram, V. Quality of life and tourism: A conceptual framework and novel segmentation base. *J. Bus. Res.* **2013**, *66*, 724–729. [CrossRef]

89. Saxe, H.; Larsen, T.M.; Mogensen, L. The global warming potential of two healthy Nordic diets compared with the average Danish diet. *Clim. Chang.* **2013**, *116*, 249–262. [CrossRef]

90. Young, W.; Hwang, K.; McDonald, S.; Oates, C.J. Sustainable consumption: Green consumer behaviour when purchasing products. *Sustain. Dev.* **2009**. [CrossRef]

91. Akenji, L. Consumer scapegoatism and limits to green consumerism. *J. Clean. Prod.* **2014**, *63*, 13–23. [CrossRef]

92. Whitmarsh, L.; Seyfang, G.; O'Neill, S. Public engagement with carbon and climate change: To what extent is the public 'carbon capable'? *Glob. Environ. Chang.* **2011**, *21*, 56–65. [CrossRef]

93. Gignac, R.; Matthews, H.D. Allocating a 2 °C cumulative carbon budget to countries. *Environ. Res. Lett.* **2015**, *10*, 075004. [CrossRef]

94. IPCC. *Global Warming og 1.5 °C: An IPCC Special Report on the Impacts of Global Warming of 1.5 °C above Pre-Industrial Levels and Related Global Greenhouse Gas Emission Pathways, in the Context of Strengthening the Global Response to the Threat of Climate Change, Sustainable Development, and Efforts to Eradicate Poverty*; World Meteorological Organization: Geneva, Switzerland, 2018; p. 32.

 © 2019 by the authors. Licensee MDPI, Basel, Switzerland. This article is an open access article distributed under the terms and conditions of the Creative Commons Attribution (CC BY) license (http://creativecommons.org/licenses/by/4.0/).

Article

Household Sharing for Carbon and Energy Reductions: The Case of EU Countries

Diana Ivanova * and **Milena Büchs**

School of Earth and Environment, University of Leeds, Leeds LS2 9JT, UK; M.M.Buchs@leeds.ac.uk
* Correspondence: d.ivanova@leeds.ac.uk

Received: 15 January 2020; Accepted: 20 February 2020; Published: 14 April 2020

Abstract: As households get smaller worldwide, the extent of sharing within households reduces, resulting in rising per capita energy use and greenhouse gas (GHG) emissions. This article examines for the first time the differences in household economies of scale across EU countries as a way to support reductions in energy use and GHG emissions, while considering differences in effects across consumption domains and urban-rural typology. A country-comparative analysis is important to facilitate the formulation of context-specific initiatives and policies for resource sharing. We find that one-person households are most carbon- and energy-intensive per capita with an EU average of 9.2 tCO_2eq/cap and 0.14 TJ/cap, and a total contribution of about 17% to the EU's carbon and energy use. Two-person households contribute about 31% to the EU carbon and energy footprint, while those of five or more members add about 9%. The average carbon and energy footprints of an EU household of five or more is about half that of a one-person average household, amounting to 4.6 tCO_2eq/cap and 0.07 TJ/cap. Household economies of scale vary substantially across consumption categories, urban-rural typology and EU countries. Substantial household economies of scale are noted for home energy, real estate services and miscellaneous services such as waste treatment and water supply; yet, some of the weakest household economies of scale occur in high carbon domains such as transport. Furthermore, Northern and Central European states are more likely to report strong household economies of scale—particularly in sparsely populated areas—compared to Southern and Eastern European countries. We discuss ways in which differences in household economies of scale may be linked to social, political and climatic conditions. We also provide policy recommendations for encouraging sharing within and between households as a contribution to climate change mitigation.

Keywords: household size; household economies of scale; carbon footprint; energy footprint; consumption; European Union; urban; rural; population density; climate change mitigation

1. Introduction

We need rapid and effective climate action to reduce global greenhouse gas (GHG) emissions and avoid catastrophic climate change. Annual emissions must decrease to close to half of their 2010 levels by 2030, and reach net-zero by 2050 to increase the probability of limiting temperature changes to 1.5 °C above preindustrial levels [1]. Yet there are some socio-demographic trends that may make it more difficult to achieve this.

One such trend is the shrinking of household sizes globally. Together with the rise in global emissions, the number of households has also been increasing, outpacing population growth. Several studies have shown that there is a strong link between household size and per capita energy use and GHG emissions [2–6] in both developed and developing countries [7]. When individuals live together, there are "economies of scale"—people tend to share appliances, tools and equipment, cook together and heat and cool common living spaces. These acts of sharing allow for the per capita energy use to diminish with rising household size. Thus, as households get smaller, the extent of sharing within households reduces, while the per capita energy use and emissions rise. Some domains, such as energy consumption for heating, cooling and lighting, show substantially higher potential for household economies of scale [3,4,8] compared to others such as transport, clothing, and services [2,4,8]. There may also be social benefits associated with shared living and larger household sizes, as they tend to counteract trends of isolation and loneliness and build stronger communities [9,10]. Furthermore, recent research shows that members of grassroots initiatives, which may involve communal living such as eco-villages and Transition towns, manage to reconcile lower carbon footprints and less materialistic living with higher life satisfaction [11,12]. Recognizing the important role of household economies of scale and their social and environmental implications, researchers have advocated policies and initiatives that encourage larger households and sharing within and across households [13].

Yet, the majority of research evidence focusing on the role of household size for consumption-based energy and GHG emissions is restricted to single country studies. A notable exception is a comparative multivariate analysis of household energy requirements in Australia, Brazil, Denmark, India and Japan conducted by Lenzen and colleagues dating from 2006 [14]. There is a lack of up to date comparative studies between countries [5], examining these trends in a broader context and discussing the potential contextual differences across countries. An up-to-date country comparative perspective is important from a policy perspective: is advice on supporting sharing within and across household equally valid across all EU countries, or do these strategies need to vary and be adjusted to different contexts?

Furthermore, average household sizes differ between rural and urban areas and opportunities to share may also vary with urban-rural context [15,16]. Yet, studies that examine the interaction between household size and population density in a country-comparative setting are lacking. This article addresses this gap, analyzing the role of household size and its interaction with urban-rural typology across EU countries.

Our main finding is that household economies of scale vary substantially across consumption categories, urban and rural typology and EU countries. High household economies of scale are noted for home energy, real estate services, and miscellaneous services such as waste treatment and water supply; yet, some of the weakest household economies of scale occur in high carbon domains such as transport. Furthermore, Northern and Central European states are more likely to report strong household economies of scale—particularly in sparsely populated areas—compared to Southern and Eastern European countries. We discuss possible reasons for these patterns, as well as policy strategies to encourage sharing within and between households to contribute to climate change mitigation.

1.1. Cross-Country Differences in Household Economies of Scale

There may be various factors explaining the potential differences in the household economies of scale across EU countries. Some of these are related to the distribution of household size and composition. Adding another member to a household is likely to reduce per capita energy use and carbon footprints at a decreasing rate with rising household size; that is, increasing the household size from one to two members may drastically reduce home energy use and the associated carbon footprint, while a change from three to four members has been shown to produce a smaller effect on average [2]. Furthermore, the household composition—e.g., the age and the gender of the new household member—may also play an important role [3,5].

Several social, political and cultural factors are also likely to influence the effect that an additional household member has on energy and carbon footprints. Widely reported long-term changes include decreasing social trust, concern for others, conformity and religiosity, and increasing individualism, gender egalitarianism, materialistic and extrinsic values [17,18], all of which may have implications for household dynamics and sharing practices. Yet, following the global financial crisis, more recent changes in values towards greater importance of conservation (security, tradition) and concerns for close others (benevolence) have been noted in Europe [17]. As countries with extensive social nets report lower value changes following the financial crisis [17], we discuss social welfare systems as an important country-specific factor that influences the potential for sharing within and between households. Welfare regimes that promote individual independence, female participation in the labor force, and countries with higher levels of secularization [19] may stand out with lower household sizes, which may also affect the potential for household economies of scale. Differences in consumption patterns across countries, stemming from differences in culture, social norms, geography and climate, infrastructural and institutional contexts, may also explain some of the variation in household economies of scale.

While we cannot test these theories directly in our analysis, they offer potential explanations for the country clustering of household economies of scale in our analysis.

1.2. Interaction between Household Size and Population Density

Urban areas are associated with high population and employment densities, compact and mixed land uses, and high degrees of connectivity and accessibility [20–22]; as such they have higher potential for collaborative consumption and sharing of resources between households, and more efficient uses of infrastructure [5], the so-called "compact" or "density effect" hypothesis [16]. This is because urban areas with narrower streets and smaller city blocks, compact and connected design, pleasant and safe urban space and mixed land uses generally reduce travel distance and promote active travel (walking and biking) and public transport [5,20,22]. Furthermore, urban dwellings are associated with smaller sizes, a higher proportion of apartments and multi-family houses and the presence of district heating, which are overall less carbon and energy intense per unit of area [3,22]. While there is strong evidence for this density effect on per capita carbon and energy footprints in the European context, this is largely compensated by higher income levels in cities [23]. Urban cores are generally preferred by more affluent and younger adults with greater consumption opportunities and smaller household sizes (and hence higher per capita carbon and energy footprints), while suburban areas benefit from larger household sizes and economies-of-scale effects at the household level [15,16]. This clearly complicates the established view that dense urban environments are more sustainable [5].

Furthermore, household economies of scale are likely to differ between rural and urban areas [15,16]. A recent study from the USA found household economies of scale to be about twice as large in rural compared to urban contexts (up to 8% reduction in per capita carbon emissions when adding an adult in rural contexts compared to 3% reduction in dense urban contexts) [24]. Lower household economies of scale in urban areas have also been found in a European context [25]. An explanation for this trend is that both household and urban economies of scale "are driven by proximity and realized through sharing" [24]. Adding a member in a rural detached house will bring about higher savings through sharing walls, living space and heating and cooling, compared to adding a member in a shared apartment building, where walls are already shared between more households, living space is smaller and common district heating may be present. Urban context is associated with proximity between households and thus higher potential to share resources outside of the household, which may in turn partially offset the household size effect. We explore differences in the household economies of scale between urban and rural context through an interaction term between household size and population density in the model.

1.3. This Study

In this article, we calculate the total and the average per capita EU carbon and energy footprints for various household sizes. We examine the inter-country differences in household economies of scale across 26 EU countries as a way to uncover sharing opportunities and support reductions in energy use and GHG emissions. This analysis considers differences in effects across consumption domains, as well as between rural and urban areas.

Prior studies generally focus on a single country, while a comparative perspective is lacking. A comparative perspective allows for a more robust discussion of the potential energy and GHG emission cuts that could be achieved through within- and between-household sharing—and may help formulate context-specific initiatives and policies for resource sharing on a regional and country level.

Studies usually focus on either carbon or energy. In this study, we examine both in order to enable a wider comparison.

2. Data and Methods

2.1. Databases

The Household Budget Surveys (HBS), harmonized and disseminated through Eurostat, collect information about household consumption expenditure across EU countries. This study utilized data from 2010, which is the latest available. Price coefficients were used to adjust household expenditure to the reference year of 2010 and EUR/purchasing power standard (PPS) units, thus accounting for price differences across countries and time (for the countries, which collected expenditure in a different year) [26]. A detailed overview of the HBS accuracy (sampling and non-sampling errors), timeliness, comparability and representativeness is provided elsewhere [26]. We transformed household expenditure into per capita expenditure and proceeded with carbon and energy footprint calculations.

We calculated annual carbon and energy footprints on the household level, utilizing the multiregional input-output database EXIOBASE (version 3.7) [27]. We applied the Global Warming Potential (GWP100 [28]) metric to convert various GHGs (carbon dioxide, methane, nitrous oxide and sulphur hexafluoride) to kilograms of CO_2-equivalents per year (kgCO_2eq). Annual energy use was calculated using the net energy extension measures in terajoules (TJ). There is no double counting with regards to the conversion from primary sources (derived directly from nature, e.g., coal) into secondary sources (coal-generated electricity, for instance) [29]. In this paper, we used the terms "carbon footprints" and "GHG emissions", as well as "energy footprints" and "energy use" interchangeably. We expected that the two environmental indicators would depict similar trends in terms of the effect of household size, as the majority of GHG emissions are related to energy use (e.g., burning of fossil fuels).

The EXIOBASE database covers high sectoral detail (200 products), 49 countries (including all EU countries) and rest-of-the-world regions, and a wide range of environmental and social satellite accounts [27,30]. We matched the HBSs household expenditure in 2010 with the environmental and economic structure in EXIOBASE for the same year. For a detailed overview of the harmonization steps between consumption from HBSs and the environmental intensities from EXIOBASE, see SM1 and elsewhere [4,31].

2.2. The Model

In order to examine inter-country differences in household size effects, we performed the regression analysis for each EU country c separately (see SM4 for a robustness check through a model including all of the countries). We also performed the analysis on EU level. We applied the household weights disseminated by Eurostat. The analysis is conducted on a per capita level for each household i, with the following specified model:

$$ln(\widetilde{ENVF}_{ci})$$
$$= \beta_{c0} + \beta_{c1}(LNINCOME_{ci}) + \beta_{c2}(HHSIZE_{ci}) + \beta_{c3}(DENSE_{ci}) + \beta_{c4}(INTERMEDIATE_{ci}) + \beta_{c5}(HHSIZE_{ci} \times DENSE_{ci}) + \beta_{c6}(REGION_{ci}) + \epsilon_{ci}$$

ENVF stands for the estimated environmental footprint, namely the annual carbon or energy footprint per capita measured in kgCO_2eq and TJ, respectively, in logarithmic form. The log-transformation was done to achieve normally distributed regression residuals, which previously had a positively skewed distribution.

LNINCOME measures the role of net disposable household income [32] (not equivalized) for the environmental footprint. The income coefficient can be interpreted as income elasticity as both the dependent and independent variables are measured in logarithmic form. As the Italian HBS does not include the income variable used for other countries, we employed the logarithm of total expenditure instead as an independent variable, similar to other studies [14,24].

HHSIZE presents the number of household members. The term *household* refers to people with a common use of an address, usually sharing space and practices [9]. In the HBSs, sharing common accommodation and expenses was also central to the household definition.

The dummy variables for population density (*DENSE* and *INTERMEDIATE*) utilize the Eurostat's measure of the degree of urbanization [33], based on Local Administrative Units level 2 (LAU2). LAU are low level administrative divisions below that of a province, region or state [34], where LAU2 is the lowest consisting of municipalities or equivalent units in the 28 EU Member States (formerly NUTS 5 level) [35]. The degree of urbanization defined by Eurostat classifies LAU2 into sparsely, intermediate and densely populated areas, using as a criterion the geographical contiguity in combination with the population density in the different types of areas [33]. A map of the degree of urbanization in 2011 for all of the EU and a detailed explanation of the undertaken steps for the LAU2 classification can be found elsewhere [33]. In this article, variable *DENSE* takes the value of one for households that live in areas with at least 500 inhabitants/km^2, and zero otherwise (cities). *INTERMEDIATE* takes the value of one for households that live in areas between 100 and 499 inhabitants/km^2, and zero otherwise (towns and suburbs). The base category *SPARSE* is associated with rural or sparsely populated areas with less than 100 inhabitants/km^2 according to the HBS classification.

Similar to a prior study [24], we added an interaction term between household size and population density (*HHSIZE×DENSE*) in order to explore the potential variability in household economies of scale by urban-rural typology.

We also included spatial controls—a set of regional dummy variables (*REGION*)—aiming to account for regional differences such as technological (e.g., energy efficiency or infrastructure, type of dominant industries) as well as geographical and climatic context [4] (see SM1 for an overview of all regions). The regional distribution is the first-level NUTS of the EU for most countries.

Prior work has discussed the selected variables in the model as key socio-demographic, economic and geographical determinants of environmental footprints [4,5,24]. While additional factors such as dwelling size and type, vehicle ownership, energy sources and prices [3,21] among others are important, the HBSs do not collect such data. We also did not explore the role of household composition, while prior studies found education, gender and age to have small and mixed effects [2–5,36]. For example, females have been found to have lower carbon footprints associated with transport and food, and higher energy use at home [3,36]. Single parent households (mostly headed by women) were found to be more likely to experience fuel and energy poverty [37]. Age has been found to be positively associated with energy use [3,38], although this effect may slow down or even change direction when people reach their later years [2,36]. Education and social status may also redesign preferences towards more or less emission- and energy-intensive consumption [2,4,39].

We estimated the regression model based on household surveys from 25 EU countries (excluding Sweden and the Netherlands due to lack of consumption data and Romania due to lack of population density), with a total sample of 243,911 observations.

2.3. Limitations

Our analysis was affected by limitations regarding the representativeness, harmonization and measurement errors of the HBSs. A detailed account of these limitations [26] and their implications for the carbon and energy footprint calculations can be found elsewhere [3,31]. There may be higher sampling error and inflated variation associated with infrequent purchases [26], for instance second homes [40], personal vehicles, flights or furniture, and their associated environmental impacts.

There are some limitations regarding the environmental impact assessment. EXIOBASE offers details of 200 products and services across 44 countries and five rest-of-the-world regions, and can thus only distinguish the country-level carbon and energy intensities of largely heterogeneous product groups. Particularly in the context of household dynamics, the product detail was insufficient to distinguish between consumption of items that are more likely to be shared within and between households (e.g., use of shared appliances vs. individual equipment). Difficulties in allocating land use change emissions to specific economic activities have been previously recognized [41,42].

Some products and services may also be purchased directly by households in some countries but are provided through governmental spending in others. Focusing solely on household expenditure may thus result in substantial variation in terms of spending on health, social work, education and transport services, disregarding impacts associated with public provision, which affects comparative analysis [43]. As a result, our analysis may not capture well country differences in the between-household sharing opportunities through the provision of public infrastructure.

Furthermore, as household carbon and energy footprints are based on monetary expenditure, there are limitations due to potential price differences within products. Therefore, we likely overestimated the environmental impact of expensive products (wealthier individuals) and underestimated the impact of cheap products (and less wealthy individuals) [44]. In addition, we could not examine the effect of "green consumerism" [16] on carbon and energy intensities, e.g., buying a fuel-efficient car, opting for a green energy provider or a more expensive but energy efficient dwelling. Larger households may also be more likely to purchase items in bulk and, thus, pay lower prices per item. Prior work discusses the limitations associated with the monetary-based approach [2,31,44].

The HBS uses household size or type in the stratification criteria for most countries in order to make the survey sampling more accurate [26,32]. Yet, there may be an under-representation of less common household types such as intentional communities (e.g., eco-villages, co-housing). All collective households such as elderly homes, boarding schools and others, where individual spending cannot be distinguished from collective spending, have been excluded from the HBSs [26].

Furthermore, the population density variable and interaction effect are based on the LAU2 classification and as such it can only capture potential consumption and footprint differences between cities, towns and suburbs and rural areas. We cannot capture differences in the between-household sharing potential and opportunities on dwelling-, close community- or neighborhood levels.

3. Results

3.1. Descriptive Statistics and Bi-Variate Regressions

3.1.1. Household Size, Carbon and Energy Footprints

In per capita terms, one-person households have the highest average carbon and energy footprints in the EU at 9.2 tCO_2eq/cap and 0.14 TJ/cap per year (Figure 1). They contribute 17-18% of the EU's total carbon and energy footprints, but constitute less than 13% of the EU population. Two-person households are most numerous with 27% of the EU population. They also contribute the largest share of the EU's total carbon and energy footprints with 31-32%. The EU per capita average of carbon and energy footprints for two-person households amounts to 8.4 tCO_2eq/cap and 0.12 TJ/cap, respectively. The largest households (>4 persons) contribute about 9-10% to total EU emissions and energy use and represent 14% of the population. They have the lowest average carbon and energy footprints of 4.6 tCO_2eq/cap and 0.07 TJ/cap, respectively (Figure 1).

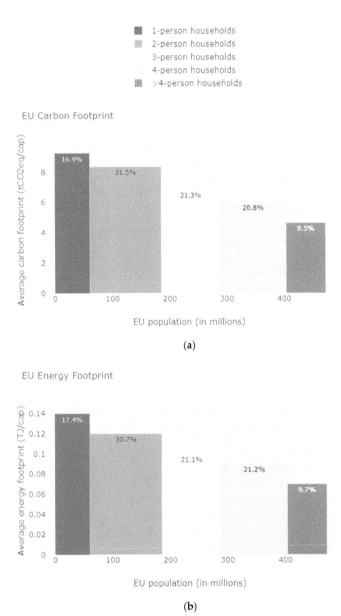

Figure 1. Distribution of EU carbon (**a**) and energy (**b**) footprint shares by household size. The total carbon and energy contribution can be split into two parts: the average carbon and energy footprints per capita (y-axis) and the number of people within the household cohort in the EU (x-axis). The %-s represent the share of total EU carbon and energy footprints by household sizes. Source: own calculations based on country population from the World Bank for 2010.

Figure 2 depicts the relationship between average per capita carbon and energy footprints and average household sizes across EU countries. The figure shows a negative trend across countries, suggesting a substantial overlap between countries with high average carbon and energy footprints and relatively low household sizes. The average household size in EU amounts to 2.4, varying between

2.2 and 2.9 across countries. The supplementary material (SM2) provides more detail about the distribution of carbon and energy footprints, and household sizes across EU countries.

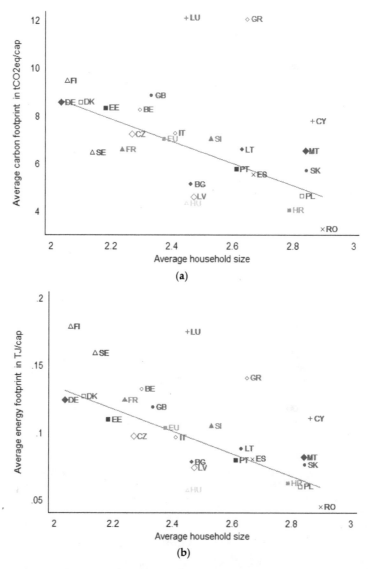

Figure 2. Association between average household size and average per capita carbon (**a**) and energy (**b**) footprints in the EU. The carbon footprints are measured in tCO_2eq/cap and energy footprints in TJ/cap. Household weights provided by the HBS have been applied.

The countries with the highest per capita carbon and energy footprints in the EU include Luxembourg, Greece (previously found to have one of the highest carbon footprints in the EU [4,43], with a large vessel fleet in relation to its size, requiring a high use of fuel from bunkers [45]), Ireland, Finland, United Kingdom, Belgium, Germany and Denmark, with carbon footprints between 14.1 and 9.1 tCO_2eq/cap, and energy footprints between 0.2 and 0.13 TJ/cap (Figure 2, SM2). These are also the countries with some of the lowest household sizes: Germany (2.0), Denmark and Finland (2.1), Belgium and the United Kingdom (2.3). Finland and Denmark have the highest share of one-person households from the total number of households at 40%, followed by Germany at 39%. These observations broadly agree with the Eurostat statistics on household sizes (SM3).

The countries with the lowest per capita carbon and energy footprints include Romania, Croatia, Hungary, Latvia, Poland, Bulgaria, Spain, Portugal and Slovakia, with carbon footprints between 3.6 and 6.2 tCO$_2$eq/cap, and energy footprints between 0.05 and 0.09 TJ/cap. The countries with the highest household sizes include Romania and Cyprus (2.9), Slovakia, Malta, Poland and Croatia (2.8), and Spain (2.7). Romania, Malta and Spain have the lowest share of one-person households (19%) from the total number of households.

Figure 3 shows average per capita carbon and energy footprints per household size across EU countries. It confirms a drop in the environmental per capita impact with rising household size within EU countries. While the slopes vary in steepness, we consistently confirm this trend for all EU countries. For example, the average carbon footprint of Luxembourg ranges from 18.8 to 7.4 tCO$_2$eq/cap for one-person and six-or-more persons households, respectively. Similarly, the per capita energy footprint of the average one-person household in Luxembourg is 0.27 TJ/cap, while that of an average six-or-more persons household amounts to 0.11 TJ/cap. According to Figure 3, the spread of the average carbon and energy footprints across EU countries is much larger for smaller household sizes compared to larger household sizes. Additionally, the absolute change in environmental impacts with the addition of one more household member is decreasing in magnitude with the rising household size.

3.1.2. Household Size and Population Density

The countries with lower average household sizes—Belgium, Germany, the United Kingdom and Finland—are also some of the most densely populated (Figure 4). At the same time, countries with larger average household sizes are more sparsely populated—e.g., Slovakia, Croatia and Poland.

Notable exceptions are Malta (with high average household size and a predominantly urban sample (92%) and Denmark (with low average household size and a largely rural sample, with as much as 43% of the sample living in sparsely populated areas). Denmark has a long tradition of a social-democratic welfare regime [46] with more liberal attitudes to family relationships and lower levels of religiosity, which may explain the relatively lower household sizes at lower population density. Compared to Western Europe, there is higher religious participation in Malta, attaching great importance to teachings regarding family life, the morality of abortion, divorce and other matters [47], which may explain the relatively large average household size. In addition, there may also be geographical reasons for the relatively high population density, with Malta being a small island.

Similar to other studies [23], we find that population density is important for per capita carbon and energy footprints (see SM2). Descriptive statistics should be interpreted with caution as they do not control for the differences in income levels and other relevant factors, which tend to vary substantially between urban and rural areas.

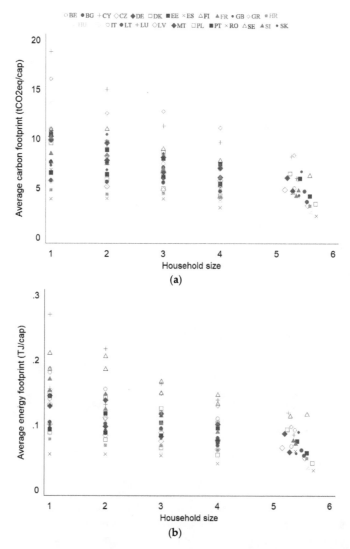

Figure 3. Mean per capita carbon (**a**) and energy (**b**) footprints by EU country by household size. Households with household sizes >5 have been aggregated in the same group. The carbon footprints are measured in tCO$_2$eq/cap and energy footprints in TJ/cap. Household weights provided by the HBS have been applied.

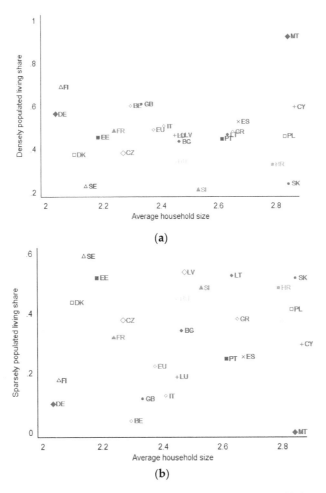

Figure 4. Association between average household size and share of households living in densely (**a**) and sparsely (**b**) populated areas in the EU. In cases where the shares do not add up to one, the difference amounts to the share of households living in intermediately populated areas. Household weights provided by the HBS have been applied.

3.1.3. Bi-Variate Regressions

Table 1 presents an overview of the standardized bi-variate Ordinary Least Squares (OLS) regression coefficients and statistical significance between household size (as a dependent variable) and urban-rural typology, carbon and energy footprints, and income per capita (as independent variables) across EU countries. Table 1 confirms a strong negative relationship between household size and per capita energy and carbon footprints within countries. The EU coefficients amount to −0.17 and −0.20 for carbon and energy footprints, respectively. Across countries, the coefficients vary between −0.11 (in Romania) and −0.39 (in Luxembourg) for carbon, and between −0.12 (in Romania) and −0.44 (in Czech Republic) for energy.

Table 1. Standardized bi-variate regression coefficients (can be interpreted as pairwise correlation coefficients) between household size and other variables by EU country.

Country Code	Country Name	Coefficients for Household Size (HHSIZE)				
		Densely Populated	Sparsely Populated	Carbon Footprint	Energy Footprint	Income
EU	European Union	−0.040***	0.042***	−0.170***	−0.196***	−0.208***
BE	Belgium	−0.102***	0.011	−0.310***	−0.341***	−0.297***
BG	Bulgaria	−0.007	−0.025	−0.132***	−0.195***	−0.356***
CY	Cyprus	−0.072***	0.01	−0.274***	−0.293***	−0.276***
CZ	Czech Republic	−0.083***	0.054**	−0.384***	−0.437***	−0.291***
DE	Germany	−0.179***	0.114***	−0.169***	−0.182***	−0.196***
DK	Denmark	−0.114***	0.087***	−0.162***	−0.228***	−0.154***
EE	Estonia	−0.009	−0.003	−0.196***	−0.241***	−0.239***
ES	Spain	−0.046***	0.016*	−0.191***	−0.217***	−0.416***
FI	Finland	−0.150***	0.128***	−0.159***	−0.195***	−0.181***
FR	France	−0.082***	0.101***	−0.229***	−0.294***	−0.242***
GB	United Kingdom	0.017	−0.000	−0.139***	−0.141***	−0.161***
GR	Greece	−0.026	−0.008	−0.193***	−0.190***	−0.263***
HR	Croatia	−0.095***	0.048**	−0.156***	−0.200***	−0.326***
HU	Hungary	−0.147***	0.118***	−0.282***	−0.264***	−0.415***
IE	Ireland	−0.052***	0.082***	−0.261***	−0.236***	−0.261***
IT	Italy	−0.053***	0.013*	−0.273***	−0.259***	–
LT	Lithuania	−0.152***	0.150***	−0.143***	−0.146***	−0.325***
LU	Luxembourg	−0.109***	0.084***	−0.391***	−0.379***	−0.391***
LV	Latvia	−0.076***	0.076***	−0.157***	−0.224***	−0.214***
MT	Malta	−0.001	–	−0.253***	−0.245***	−0.240***
PL	Poland	−0.187***	0.144***	−0.296***	−0.306***	−0.295***
PT	Portugal	−0.02	−0.044***	−0.127***	−0.134***	−0.243***
RO	Romania	–	–	−0.116***	−0.122***	−0.422***
SE	Sweden	−0.011	−0.002	−0.184***	−0.170***	−0.231***
SI	Slovenia	−0.079***	0.061***	−0.277***	−0.316***	−0.179***
SK	Slovakia	−0.098***	0.052***	−0.202***	−0.216***	−0.355***

Note: * $p < 0.05$, ** $p < 0.01$, *** $p < 0.001$. The variables densely populated (*DENSE*) and sparsely populated (*SPARSE*) are dummies. In the context of this table, *HHSIZE* can be interpreted as a dependent variable, and the rest of the variables—as independent variables. Household weights provided by the HBS have been applied.

Furthermore, densely populated contexts (cities) are associated with smaller household sizes, and sparsely populated rural contexts – with larger household sizes in most EU countries (Table 1). The lowest regression coefficients between household size and densely populated context are found in Poland (−0.19) and Germany (−0.18). The opposite is true for sparsely populated areas, with the highest significant coefficient between household size and sparsely populated context found in Poland (0.14). Portugal shows an exceptional trend, being the only country with a negative and significant coefficient for household size and sparsely populated context.

While we note substantial inter-country differences, household dynamics should clearly be analyzed controlling for other socio-demographic trends (such as income and population density) [16]. For example, the analysis confirms a strong negative relationship between income and household size across all EU countries—suggesting an association between lower household sizes and higher incomes—with a coefficient amounting to −0.21 for the EU.

3.2. Household Economies of Scale for Total Carbon and Energy Footprints

Figure 5 portrays results from a multi-variate OLS regression on the role of *HHSIZE* for per capita carbon and energy footprints in logarithmic form (dependent variables). There are additional variables in the models such as income, urban-rural typology and geographical region (see the Data and Methods section for the model specification). The figure shows two model specifications, including (in blue) and excluding (in red) the *HHSIZE×DENSE* interaction terms.

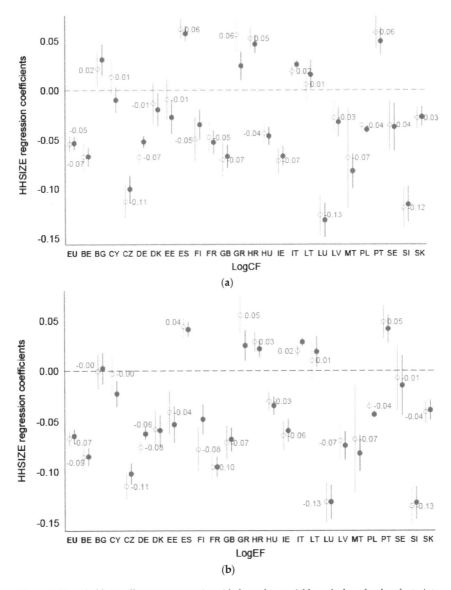

Figure 5. Household size effect across countries with dependent variables—the log of carbon footprints per capita (**a**) and energy footprint per capita (**b**). The blue coefficients depict the *HHSIZE* coefficient acquired from the model including interaction effect (*HHSIZE×DENSE*) and the red coefficient—the *HHSIZE* coefficient from the model without any interaction term. All models control for income, rural-urban typology and region. See Data and Methods for the model specification. Household weights provided by the HBS have been applied.

Figure 5 shows considerable variation across countries: while most countries display strong and moderate household economies of scale, there are also countries with no household economies of scale, or even with positive *HHSIZE* effects. Most countries (15 out of 25) in the EU sample show a negative and significant *HHSIZE* effect, which is in line with our initial hypothesis.

An increase in the EU household size by one member brings about a 5%-reduction in the carbon footprint and 7%-reduction in the energy footprint (Figure 5, in blue). The countries with the strongest household economies of scale include Luxembourg, Slovenia and Czech Republic, described by negative and significant *HHSIZE* at the 5% level coefficients, ranging from −0.11 to −0.13. The coefficients suggest that an increase in household size by one member decreases the per capita carbon and energy footprint by up to 12% (taking the exponent of the coefficient). Other countries—such as Belgium, Germany, Finland, France and the United Kingdom—are characterized by moderate household economies of scale. Their *HHSIZE* effects vary between −0.03 and −0.10, suggesting that an increase in the household size by one member reduces per capita carbon and energy footprints by 3–10%.

However, Figure 5 also points to countries—such as Cyprus and Lithuania—with no visible household economies of scale for the total carbon and energy footprint per capita. Against our initial hypothesis, several countries even stand out with positive and significant *HHSIZE* coefficients such as Spain, Italy, Greece, Portugal and Croatia. There are no significant differences between the *HHSIZE* coefficients for carbon and energy footprints in most countries (see SM Figure S9), suggesting similar economies of scale for energy and emissions.

The 95% confidence intervals of the *HHSIZE* coefficients in blue and red are also largely overlapping across EU countries, meaning that there is no significant difference of the *HHSIZE* effect magnitude regardless of whether or not the interaction term is included.

The following two sections explore these inter-country differences (1) for different consumption domains; and (2) in their interaction with population density. We consider contextual differences between countries to discuss these results in the Discussion section.

3.3. Household Economies of Scale by Consumption Categories

Figure 6 provides an overview of the *HHSIZE* regression coefficients across the various consumption categories with the logarithm of the carbon footprint by consumption category as a dependent variable. We note substantial differences between EU countries within each consumption category, both in terms of household economies of scale and carbon contribution. Figure 7 shows the *HHSIZE* regression coefficients and their 95% confidence intervals across the EU countries. A detailed overview of the sectors included in each consumption category can be found in the supplementary material.

The coefficient ranges highlight the differences of the magnitude of household economies of scale and point to some of the products and services associated with higher sharing rates compared to others. For example, the strongest household economies of scale are noted for housing categories such as rents and mortgages, electricity and household services. These housing categories have median carbon shares of 5%, 8% and 4%, respectively (Figure 6). At the same time, some of the weakest household economies of scale are noted in the transport domain, which is also characterized with the highest median carbon share of 25%.

Actual and imputed rent

Household services (e.g. waste, water supply, insurance)

Gas, liquid and solid fuels

Appliances, equipment and furniture

Electricity

Food

Other services and manufactured products

Transport

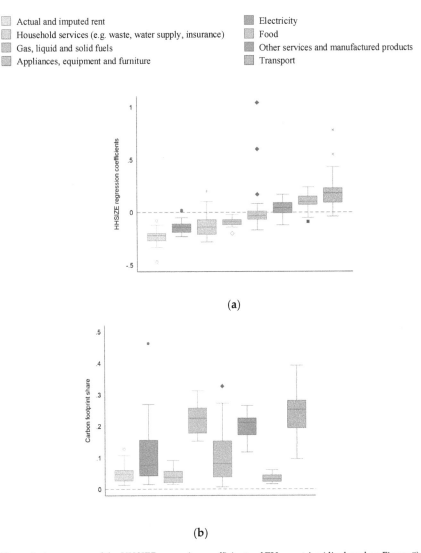

(a)

(b)

Figure 6. A summary of the *HHSIZE* regression coefficients of EU countries (displayed on Figure 7) with the logarithm of the per capita carbon footprint by consumption category as dependent variables (**a**) and the proportion of the individual consumption categories of the overall carbon footprint of EU countries (**b**). The categories are ordered by the median *HHSIZE* effect depicting the importance of the household economies of scale from the strongest to the weakest.

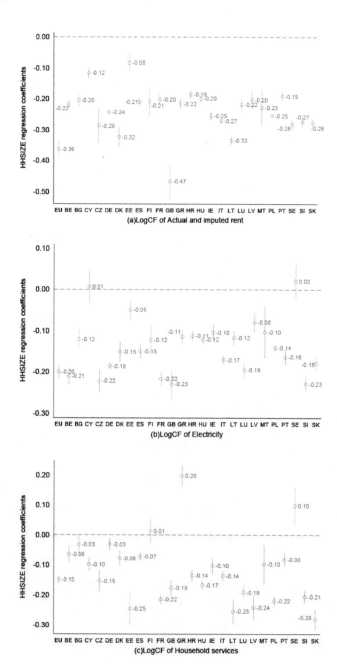

Figure 7. *Cont.*

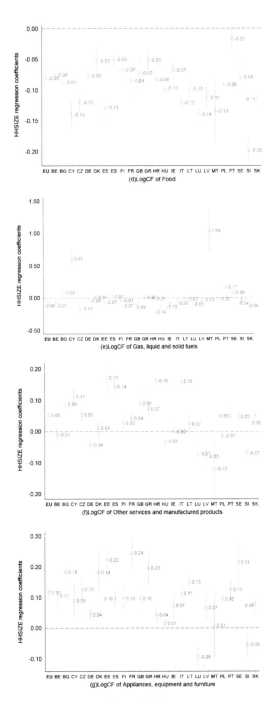

Figure 7. *Cont.*

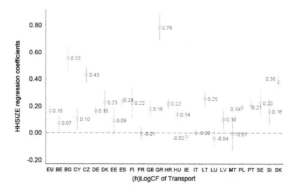

Figure 7. Regression coefficients for household size effects on the logarithm of the per capita annual carbon footprint by consumption category. Categories: (**a**) Actual and imputed rent; (**b**) Electricity; (**c**) Household services, e.g., waste treatment, water supply, insurance; (**d**) Food; (**e**) Gas, liquid and solid fuels; (**f**) Other services and manufactured products; (**g**) Appliances, equipment and furniture; and (**h**) Transport. The categories are ordered by the median *HHSIZE* effect depicting the importance of the household economies of scale from the strongest to the weakest. Household weights provided by the HBS have been applied.

3.3.1. Housing

Substantial household economies of scale are noted for home- and housing-related categories, particularly housing rent or real estate services (Figure 7(a)), electricity (Figure 7(b)) and household services such as waste treatment, water supply and insurance (Figure 7(c)). The *HHSIZE* effect associated with rents and mortgages vary between −0.08 (for Estonia) and −0.47 (for the United Kingdom) (the category includes development of building projects, management and support services). This means that an increase in the household size by one member is associated with an 8–37% reduction (taking the exponent of the coefficient) in the carbon footprint associated with real estate services. With regards to electricity, negative and significant *HHSIZE* coefficients between −0.05 for Estonia and −0.23 for the United Kingdom and Slovenia are noted; this suggests a 3–21% reduction in the related per capita carbon footprint with an additional household member. Cyprus and Sweden stand out with insignificant *HHSIZE* effects (the Swedish HBSs offered a lower level of consumption detail aggregating all home-related energy consumption). Similarly, strong household economies of scale are noted in terms of household services with the largest (negative) coefficients noted for Slovakia (−0.28), Lithuania and Estonia (−0.25). That is, the increase of household size by one member results in a reduction of the household services emissions by as much as 24%.

While similar ranges of the household economies of scale are noted for electricity and housing fuels (Figure 6), the strong positive outliers in terms of *HHSIZE* effects lower the median household economies of scale for housing fuels. We found negative and significant *HHSIZE* coefficients varying between −0.17 (for Czech Republic) and −0.04 (for Germany and Slovenia) across most EU countries (Figure 7(e)). The positive and significant effects—especially for Malta and Cyprus—could potentially be explained by product allocation inconsistencies of fuel use from marine bunkers [45] (where we do not expect household economies of scale) being inaccurately allocated to household fuels in the national accounts.

The strong household economies of scale in the household domain are in line with prior claims that household size is one of the largest determinants of domestic energy consumption [48] and shelter carbon footprints [4]. They result from the sharing of space and embodied energy in buildings, energy for heating, cooling, lighting and shared appliances and activities [9].

3.3.2. Food

Food-related economies of scale in larger households may occur when household members prepare (e.g., when sharing food ingredients) and manage food together (e.g., when they better manage food waste [49], which we were not able to test in this study). Furthermore, larger households may be more likely to buy food in larger quantities, which may cost less per unit [50]. While this may allow for a reduction in embodied emissions, e.g., through reduced packaging, in our model we were unable to capture any differences in carbon intensities within food products. As we applied monetary-based carbon intensities, any reduction in food spending due to lower price is reflected in our model in lower carbon footprints, which may be misleading in cases of large price variation within products. Finally, there may be other carbon reduction potential associated with the use of common utensils, appliances for cooking and storing food and shared shopping for larger households. These effects are included in the estimates for housing and transport in our analysis.

Figure 7(d) denotes significant negative coefficients between −0.20 (for Slovenia) and −0.05 (for Denmark, Spain and Greece), suggesting that an increase in the household size with one member leads to a decrease in the food-related carbon footprint by 5–18%.

3.3.3. Equipment, Transport and Other Consumption

While we expected substantial household economies of scale for shared appliances, equipment and furniture, we find that most EU countries report positive *HHSIZE* regression coefficients (Figure 7(g)). A potential explanation of this result is that while some appliances, machinery and furniture are shared within households, the sectoral detail of EXIOBASE does not allow us to distinguish between typically shared and individually-used items. Furthermore, this category only includes the purchase of items (and hence their embodied carbon footprint), while the direct emissions associated with the use phase is included in the analysis of electricity and housing fuels. Notable exceptions with moderate household economies of scale for home appliances and equipment include Luxembourg and Slovenia with regression coefficients of −0.09 and −0.05, respectively.

We did not find consistent household economies of scale for transport—with positive or insignificant coefficients for all EU countries (Figure 7(h)). Larger households have potential to stabilize car ownership [51,52], where additional household members do not require additional number of cars. Prior longitudinal analysis of French car sharing practices shows that while household car sharing is a regular practice concerning almost half of the French car fleet, this trend is decreasing [53]. Their analysis further highlighted gender differences in terms of car sharing within households, with a higher proportion of main users being male and a higher proportion of secondary users being female [53].

However, our analysis suggests that the benefits of shared travel within the household are not realized in many countries in Europe (Figure 7(h)). The lack of household economies of scale with regards to personal vehicles and equipment (SM4) suggests that additional household members may also activate a need for another household car, e.g., following a partnership formation [54]. There may also be offsetting effects such as using the car more intensively or having a larger car in single-car households [55]. Furthermore, no household economies of scale were noted for other transport modes such as air travel, for which there is a growing demand with rising incomes in Europe [31].

Finally, we did not observe substantial household economies of scale with regards to other services and manufactured products (Figure 7(f)). There may also be additional factors that strongly correlate with household size (e.g., demographic, social, cultural and economic characteristics) that we could not include in our model due to lacking data, which may explain the variation in coefficients.

3.4. Household Size and Population Density Interaction

In this section, we discuss the magnitude and significance of interaction effects depicted in Figure 8 (*HHSIZE×DENSE*) across EU countries (the model in blue in Figure 5, controlling for income, household size, population density and region). The majority of EU countries show insignificant interaction coefficients, suggesting no significant differences in the *HHSIZE* effect between densely and sparsely populated areas in the EU.

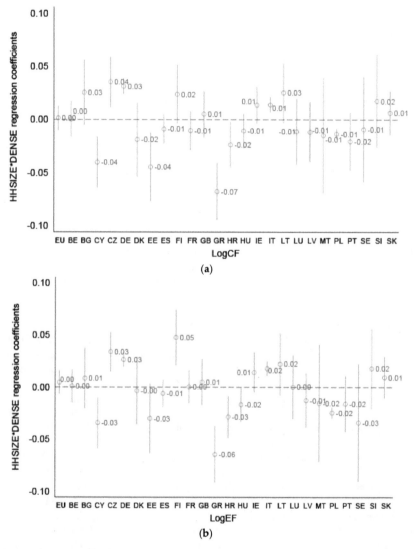

Figure 8. Interaction effect between household size and population density (*HHSIZE×DENSE*) across countries. Dependent variables—the log of per capita carbon (**a**) and energy (**b**) footprints. We excluded the *HHSIZE×INTERMEDIATE* interaction term as no significant differences of the household size effects between intermediately and sparsely populated areas were noted. See Data and Methods for the model specification. Household weights provided by the HBS have been applied.

However, several countries such as Czech Republic and Germany demonstrate negative *HHSIZE* effects and positive interaction effects (*HHSIZE×DENSE*), both of which are significant at the 5% level. This result suggests that adding another household member in a sparsely populated (rural) environment is associated with larger household economies of scale compared to doing so in a densely populated (urban) environment. While adding a household member to a rural household reduces per capita energy footprints by 7–11%, adding a household member to a dense urban household reduces them by 4–7% (Figure 5, Figure 8). The lower household economies of scales in densely populated environments are noted particularly for electricity, housing fuels, appliances, equipment and furniture, and food. This is plausible because these types of environmental impacts tend to be higher in rural areas in these countries, compared to urban areas, so that greater household sizes can reduce these impacts more in rural areas.

We find negative interaction effects for other countries, particularly for Greece, Estonia, Cyprus and Croatia, suggesting that households in densely populated regions encounter higher household economies of scale in these countries, compared to sparsely populated areas. The analysis of consumption categories suggests that these negative interaction effects are primarily associated with consumption of household services (e.g. water and waste), other services and manufactured products.

These negative interaction effects may contradict our previous hypothesis that the interaction between household and urban economies of scale leads to higher household economies of scale in rural and sparsely populated areas [24,25]. However, these are all countries where per capita environmental footprints tend to be higher in urban compared to rural areas (SM2), so it is plausible that adding a household member in urban areas leads to greater reductions of per capita environmental footprints there compared to rural areas.

4. Discussion and Conclusions

4.1. Household Dynamics within the EU

One-person households are the most carbon and energy intensive in per capita terms, contributing to 17-18% of the EU total carbon and energy footprint. The per capita carbon and energy footprint of a one-member household is about twice that of a five- or more person household in the EU. The share of those living in one-person households varies from 40% in Finland and Denmark to 19% in Spain, Malta and Romania, with an EU average of 31% from the total number of households.

We note substantial differences in household sizes across various EU countries as well as the role of household size for per capita carbon and energy impacts. Adding an additional household member results in a carbon and energy reduction of above 10% on average in some EU countries. This result confirms that shrinking household sizes across the EU and globally are of key concern for climate change mitigation. They should thus be adequately considered in modelling work, e.g., prospective scenarios of socio-demographic trends and their influence on carbon and energy footprints and pathways to meet carbon targets. Household dynamics should also be regarded in the context of mitigation solutions and experimentation with alternative household formations.

Substantial differences in the household economies of scale are noted for various consumption domains, with a higher potential in housing-related items such as electricity use (up to 21% reduction with an additional household member), real estate services (up to 37%) and household services such as waste collection and water supply (up to 24%). Food and fuel consumption show moderate household economies of scale with up to 18% reduction of the carbon footprint with an additional household member in some EU countries. We note lower or no household economies of scale in other domains of consumption (e.g., transport, manufactured products and services), where an increase in the household size likely corresponds to an increase in consumption needs (e.g., second household vehicle, more clothing, educational or health services with an additional household member).

Furthermore, the majority of EU countries have comparable household economies of scale between urban and rural areas (insignificant interaction term). Other countries such as Czech Republic and Germany report higher household economies of scale in sparsely populated areas, in line with prior evidence [24] (positive interaction term). We also found a negative interaction effect between household size and population density for a third group of countries, which counters our original hypothesis; yet, these are countries in which per capita emissions and energy use tend to be higher in urban compared to rural areas, unlike most other EU countries.

4.2. Country Clusters and Contextual Factors

Table 2 summarizes our observations regarding the household economies of scale by various consumption domains and the interaction with population density. Two clusters of countries emerge—one with strong or moderate household economies of scale, and one with lower or no household economies of scale.

Table 2. A summary of country clusters with regards to household economies of scale and other contextual differences.

	Country Clusters	Example Countries	Mean Household Size and T-test	Household Economies of Scale by Consumption Domains	Interaction with Population Density
1	Countries with high/moderate/low household economies of scale	LU, SI, CZ, BE, DE, FI, FR, GB, MT, DK, HU, IE, LV, PL, SE, SK	2.54 (0.003)	Strong household economies of scale for actual and imputed rent (GB, CZ, DK, SE), electricity (GB, BE, CZ, DK, FR, SI), household services (SK, LV), food (MT, SI, LU), housing fuels (CZ, HU), other goods and services (MT, LU, LV), appliances and equipment (LU, SI);	Higher household economies of scale in rural areas compared to urban areas (DE, CZ)
2	Countries with no household economies of scale/Countries with positive *HHSIZE* effect	CY, LT, EE, ES, IT, GR, PT, HR, BG	2.64 (0.005)	Some of the lowest household economies of scale (or positive coefficients) for actual and imputed rent (EE, CY), electricity (CY), household services (GR), food (PT, ES, GR), housing fuels (CY), other goods and services (EE, ES, LT, IT), appliances and equipment (EE, BG, GR, LT, IT) and transport (GR, BG);	Higher household economies of scale in urban areas (GR, EE, CY, HR), relatively low share of urban population and higher environmental impacts in urban areas.
	Difference		***		

Note: One-sided two-sample unweighted t-test is performed in order to compare the average household sizes between the country clusters under the following hypotheses: H_0: $\mu_{cluster2} - \mu_{cluster1} = 0$, H_A: $\mu_{cluster2} - \mu_{cluster1} > 0$. We estimated separate variances to control for significant differences in sample sizes between the country clusters. Standard errors are presented in parenthesis. T-test significance levels: * $p < 0.1$, ** $p < 0.05$, *** $p < 0.01$.

The first cluster—with high and moderate household economies of scale—consists of predominantly Northern and Central European countries. An increase in the household size by one member results in a reduction of the total carbon and energy footprint by 3–13% (Figure 5). This cluster is characterized by strong welfare regimes that promote individual independence and female labor market participation [19]—which may explain the lower household sizes in these countries. The cluster includes Belgium, Denmark, Sweden, Finland, France, Germany and the United Kingdom, which are similar in terms of socio-demographic context [56]. The small countries of Malta and Luxembourg are exceptions in terms of welfare regime [47,56]; the regression coefficients of Malta in particular are characterized by relatively high error ranges across most consumption categories, and results should thus be interpreted with caution. Finally, the Czech Republic, Poland, Slovakia, Slovenia and Hungary (and Croatia, which is allocated to the second cluster in terms of household economies of scale in our analysis) are characterized by the Central Europe welfare model, associated with lower income inequality, lower rates of unemployment, higher labor market flexibility and higher social contributions and government expenditure as a share of the Gross Domestic Product compared to the Eastern European countries in the second cluster [56].

The second cluster—with lower or no household economies of scale—consists of predominantly Southern and historically Catholic countries as well as some Eastern European states. An increase in the household size by one member does not change the total per capita carbon and energy footprint, or even increases in the per capita environmental impact (Figure 5). These countries already have higher household sizes, and emphasize the role of the family for mutual support or are more "collectivistic". Greece, Spain, Italy, Cyprus and Portugal stand out from other EU countries in terms of their welfare regimes previously described as the Mediterranean welfare model [56] with stronger influence of Catholicism and traditional family values [57–59]. The Eastern European welfare model—including Lithuania, Estonia and Bulgaria (and also Latvia, which is included in the first cluster in our analysis)—is associated with strong nuclear family institutions, low social protection expenditure primarily on old-age pensions, high income inequality, rigid and discriminatory labor markets and lower government capacity for generous social policies [56,60]. This might also contribute to higher family dependency for financial and welfare support, and hence higher household sizes. The reliance on extended family for assurance against risks of ill health, unemployment or poverty could be reduced with higher standards of living and the provision of stronger social-security systems in these countries [61].

These clusters show significant differences in terms of the average household sizes, with the second cluster denoting a significantly higher household size (Table 2, Figure 2). Considering the decreasing rate of household economies of scale with rising household sizes, this may partly explain the lower household economies of scale in these countries—where there already is a lot of within-household sharing, thus, there is less to gain by adding a household member.

Heating degree days are positively correlated with the housing-related energy use (and carbon footprints), with dwellings in colder regions requiring more energy to heat over the year [4]. This effect is partly mediated by stricter building standards in northern European countries, which reduces the amount of energy for heating per heating degree day [62]. Nevertheless, colder countries are likely to report higher household economies of scale particularly due to the high importance of home energy for the overall household economies of scale, which is also in line with the country clustering. This might also explain why we find significant positive *HHSIZE* effects in countries such as Spain, Italy, Greece, Portugal and Croatia. Not only are these countries with relatively large average household sizes already (and hence less scope for further within-household sharing), but there is also less of a requirement for heating, which is associated with some of the strongest capacity for household economies of scale.

The positive *HHSIZE* coefficients for some of the categories, where we expect relatively low possibilities for sharing is likely driven by other socio-demographic, infrastructural and economic factors that vary with household size, that we cannot explicitly control for in our model because they are not captured in the HBSs.

4.3. Policy Recommendations

Targeting the trend towards smaller households and under-occupation of homes in the EU and globally is a key option to reduce per capita carbon and energy contributions, with a higher mitigation potential compared to efficiency improvements such as upgrading the thermal insulation or more efficient appliances [42,63]. Understanding needs and expectations about personal space as well as changing social norms [18] are key for the upscaling of "downsizer homes" [63] and other alternatives to encourage within household sharing. Household sharing has an important gender dimension [53] as well; sharing may support the depersonalization of objects allowing for them to be managed and used jointly, thus encouraging even more (and more gender equal) sharing [53].

Yet, the trend of smaller households results from a myriad of processes, some of which cannot be reversed (e.g., falling birth rates or liberation from norms), or which we consider valuable for other reasons (e.g., female emancipation, financial independence or residential autonomy) [48,61]. For example, higher divorce rates worldwide may result in an increase of energy use and GHG emissions per capita [13]; however, the freedom to divorce is also a matter of human rights and social justice. This makes it crucial for policy interventions to realize the complexity of household dynamics and the inter-connections with social and environmental wellbeing.

Proximate causes of the reduction in household sizes worldwide include lower fertility rates, higher divorce rates and a decline in the frequency of multi-generational families with increasing non-family provision of care among others [61,64]. There is some evidence that the trend of decreasing fertility rates and increasing divorce rates is reversing since the early 2000s [65,66], which may also stabilize or even reverse the trend of smaller households. This suggests that the trend towards smaller families over the past half century did not result from a lasting change of family preferences, but rather from a change in women's roles and labor market participation when institutions and partnerships had not yet adapted [65]. To successfully promote parenthood and female labor force participation, there is a need for a strong investment in childcare services, flexible workplace support and other family support [65,66]. Such policies may help reconcile work and family responsibilities and promote gender equity [65].

Additional social and psychological factors that may have influenced the reduction in household sizes include liberation from strict norms, less religiosity and increased importance of individual autonomy, self-actualization and privacy [48,61]. Support and increased visibility [67] for alternative household types—such as intentional communal living—may encourage larger households, which share lifestyles, cultural elements and common sense of purpose. Such alternative forms of living may thus be less challenging in terms of these social and psychological factors [12], compared to traditional family living. Yet alternative living arrangements may also be associated with difficulties in negotiating common and personal items, space and time [9]. Partnerships between policymakers and sharing initiatives may help tackle such difficulties by alleviating structural and institutional constraints and reducing social distance (e.g., by fostering care for the community) and geographical distance (e.g., by improving connectivity), which impede sharing [9,11]. Sharing emerges as an opportunity to act collectively on growing social, political and environmental awareness and steadily transforms social norms and routines [68].

The complexity of household dynamics and the low household economies of scale in high-carbon consumption domains such as transport encourage the consideration of additional ways to share resources between households as well. For example, while sharing a car may reduce the energy use and emissions associated with travel *within* the household (particularly in car-dependent areas outside urban cores [22]), in the presence of an excellent public transport system, the mitigation potential may actually be higher through sharing *between* households. Further research on household sharing in the context of public infrastructure and sharing initiatives at a higher spatial resolution—in both urban and rural context—is needed to explore the carbon mitigation potentials associated with sharing. Such wider sharing practices for de-carbonization and low energy demand require the provision of social and technological infrastructure such as investment in public spaces, green areas, mass transportation and new forms of peer-to-peer sharing [9,24]. The establishment of collective systems (e.g., universal basic services [69])—as opposed to highly individualized energy service delivery—also enables more resilient societies and prevents future emission lock-in [70].

In this paper, we explore possible impacts of household dynamics on per capita emissions, and examine difference in within household economies of scale across EU countries. Our main finding is that household economies of scale vary substantially across consumption categories, urban and rural typology and EU countries. We identify potential explanations associated with the sharing potential of various products and services, contextual differences in terms of social and cultural norms, geographic context, infrastructural and political context. Targeting trends towards smaller households and under-occupation of homes and encouraging sharing offers substantial potential to mitigate climate change with already available technologies and infrastructure.

Supplementary Materials: The following are available online at http://www.mdpi.com/1996-1073/13/8/1909/s1, SM1: Household Budget Surveys, SM2: Descriptive statistics by countries, SM3: Eurostat statistics, SM4: Total carbon and energy footprint determinants, Supplementary spreadsheet including the overview of consumption categories.

Author Contributions: Conceptualization, D.I. and M.B.; Formal analysis, D.I.; Funding acquisition, D.I. and M.B.; Investigation, D.I. and M.B.; Methodology, D.I. and M.B.; Software, D.I.; Supervision, M.B.; Visualization, D.I.; Writing—original draft, D.I.; Writing—review and editing, M.B. All authors have read and agreed to the published version of the manuscript.

Funding: This research was funded by the European Union's Horizon 2020 research and innovation program under Marie Sklodowska-Curie grant agreement, grant number 840454. The authors also received support from the UK Research Councils under the Centre for Research on Energy Demand Solutions.

Energies **2020**, *13*, 1909

Acknowledgments: We thank the whole EXIOBASE team for the effort to build the database and make it available for other researchers to use. In particular, we would like to thank Richard Wood for his assistance in the early stages of the environmental footprint analysis and Arkaitz Usubiaga-Liaño for his effort in compiling and communication the energy extensions. We would also like to thank Sylke Schnepf and two anonymous reviewers for their valuable feedback.

Conflicts of Interest: The authors declare no conflict of interest.

Data Statement: The data associated with this paper is available from University of Leeds at https://doi.org/10. 5518/785. The dataset includes the per capita carbon and energy footprint calculations (generated by the authors of this study) together with household and country IDs from the HBS dataset disseminated by Eurostat. Please use the following data citation when referring to the dataset [71]: Diana Ivanova and Milena Büchs (2020): Carbon and energy footprints of European households (EU HBS) University of Leeds. [Dataset]. https://doi.org/10.5518/785.

References

1. Masson-Delmotte, V.; Zhai, P.; Pörtner, H.-O.; Roberts, D.; Skea, J.; Shukla, P.R.; Pirani, A.; Moufouma-Okia, W.; Péan, C.; Pidcock, R.; et al. *IPCC Special Report 1.5—Summary for Policymakers*; IPCC: Geneva, Switzerland, 2018.

2. Büchs, M.; Schnepf, S.V. Who emits most? Associations between socio-economic factors and UK households' home energy, transport, indirect and total CO2 emissions. *Ecol. Econ.* **2013**, *90*, 114–123. [CrossRef]

3. Ivanova, D.; Vita, G.; Wood, R.; Lausselet, C.; Dumitru, A.; Krause, K.; Macsinga, I.; Hertwich, E. Carbon mitigation in domains of high consumer lock-in. *Glob. Environ. Chang.* **2018**, *52*, 117–130. [CrossRef]

4. Ivanova, D.; Vita, G.; Steen-Olsen, K.; Stadler, K.; Melo, P.C.; Wood, R.; Hertwich, E.G. Mapping the carbon footprint of EU regions. *Environ. Res. Lett.* **2017**, *12*, 1–13. [CrossRef]

5. Wiedenhofer, D.; Smetschka, B.; Akenji, L.; Jalas, M.; Haberl, H. Household time use, carbon footprints, and urban form: A review of the potential contributions of everyday living to the 1.5 °C climate target. *Curr. Opin. Environ. Sustain.* **2018**, *30*, 7–17. [CrossRef]

6. Druckman, A.; Jackson, T. Household energy consumption in the UK: A highly geographically and socio-economically disaggregated model. *Energy Policy* **2008**, *36*, 3177–3192. [CrossRef]

7. Liddle, B. Impact of population, age structure, and urbanization on carbon emissions/energy consumption: Evidence from macro-level, cross-country analyses. *Popul. Environ.* **2014**, *35*, 286–304. [CrossRef]

8. Underwood, A.; Zahran, S. The carbon implications of declining household scale economies. *Ecol. Econ.* **2015**, *116*, 182–190. [CrossRef]

9. Yates, L. Sharing, households and sustainable consumption. *J. Consum. Cult.* **2018**, *18*, 433–452. [CrossRef]

10. Demey, D.; Berrington, A.; Evandrou, M.; Falkingham, J. Living alone and psychological well-being in mid-life: Does partnership history matter? *J. Epidemiol. Community Health* **2014**, *68*, 403–410. [CrossRef]

11. Vita, G.; Ivanova, D.; Dumitru, A.; García-mira, R.; Carrus, G.; Stadler, K.; Krause, K.; Wood, R.; Hertwich, E.G. Happier with less? Members of European environmental grassroots initiatives reconcile lower carbon footprints with higher life satisfaction and income increases. *Energy Res. Soc. Sci.* **2020**, *60*, 101329. [CrossRef]

12. Grinde, B.; Nes, R.B.; MacDonald, I.F.; Wilson, D.S. Quality of Life in Intentional Communities. *Soc. Indic. Res.* **2018**, *137*, 625–640. [CrossRef]

13. Yu, E.; Liu, J. Environmental impacts of divorce. *Proc. Natl. Acad. Sci. USA* **2007**, *104*, 20629–20634. [CrossRef] [PubMed]

14. Lenzen, M.; Wier, M.; Cohen, C.; Hayami, H.; Pachauri, S.; Schaeffer, R. A comparative multivariate analysis of household energy requirements in Australia, Brazil, Denmark, India and Japan. *Energy* **2006**, *31*, 181–207. [CrossRef]

15. Ottelin, J.; Heinonen, J.; Junnila, S. New Energy Efficient Housing Has Reduced Carbon Footprints in Outer but Not in Inner Urban Areas. *Environ. Sci. Technol.* **2015**, *49*, 9574–9583. [CrossRef] [PubMed]

16. Gill, B.; Moeller, S. GHG Emissions and the Rural-Urban Divide. A Carbon Footprint Analysis Based on the German Official Income and Expenditure Survey. *Ecol. Econ.* **2018**, *145*, 160–169. [CrossRef]

17. Hamamura, T. Cross-temporal changes in people's ways of thinking, feeling, and behaving. *Curr. Opin. Psychol.* **2020**, *32*, 17–21. [CrossRef]

18. Easthope, H.; Liu, E.; Burnley, I.; Judd, B. Changing perceptions of family: A study of multigenerational households in Australia. *J. Sociol.* **2017**, *53*, 182–200. [CrossRef]

19. Three, T.; Economies, P. The Three Political Economies of the Welfare State. In *Three Worlds of Welfare Capitalism*; Polity Press: Cambridge, UK, 1995.

20. Creutzig, F.; Fernandez, B.; Haberl, H.; Khosla, R.; Mulugetta, Y.; Seto, K.C. Beyond Technology: Demand-Side Solutions for Climate Change Mitigation. *Annu. Rev. Environ. Resour.* **2016**, *41*, 173–198. [CrossRef]

21. Jones, C.M.; Kammen, D.M. Spatial distribution of U.S. household carbon footprints reveals suburbanisation undermines greenhouse gas benefits of urban population density. *Environ. Sci. Technol.* **2014**, *48*, 895–902. [CrossRef]

22. Poom, A.; Ahas, R. How does the environmental load of Household consumption depend on residential location? *Sustainability* **2016**, *8*, 799. [CrossRef]

23. Ottelin, J.; Heinonen, J.; Nässén, J.; Junnila, S. Household carbon footprint patterns by the degree of urbanisation in Europe. *Environ. Res. Lett.* **2019**, *14*, 114016. [CrossRef]

24. Fremstad, A.; Underwood, A.; Zahran, S. The Environmental Impact of Sharing: Household and Urban Economies in CO2 Emissions. *Ecol. Econ.* **2018**, *145*, 137–147. [CrossRef]

25. Ala-Mantila, S.; Ottelin, J.; Heinonen, J.; Junnila, S. To each their own? The greenhouse gas impacts of intra-household sharing in different urban zones. *J. Clean. Prod.* **2017**, *163*, S79–S90. [CrossRef]

26. Eurostat EU Quality Report of the Household Budget Surveys 2010. Available online: http://epp.eurostat.ec.europa.eu/portal/page/portal/eurostat/home (accessed on 27 January 2020).

27. Stadler, K.; Wood, R.; Bulavskaya, T.; Södersten, C.-J.; Simas, M.; Schmidt, S.; Usubiaga, A.; Acosta-Fernández, J.; Kuenen, J.; Bruckner, M.; et al. EXIOBASE 3: Developing a Time Series of Detailed Environmentally Extended Multi-Regional Input-Output Tables. *J. Ind. Ecol.* **2018**, *22*, 502–515. [CrossRef]

28. Solomon, S.; Qin, D.; Manning, M.; Marquis, M.; Averyt, K.; Tignor, M.M.B.; LeRoy Miller, H.; Chen, Z. *Contribution of Working Group I to the Fourth Assessment Report of the Intergovernmental Panel on Climate Change: Climate Change 2007 The Physical Science Basis*; Cambridge University Press: Cambridge, UK, 2007.

29. Schenau, S. The Dutch Energy Accounts. Available online: https://unstats.un.org/unsd/envaccounting/londongroup/meeting10/LG10_10a.pdf (accessed on 27 January 2020).

30. Wood, R.; Stadler, K.; Bulavskaya, T.; Lutter, S.; Giljum, S.; de Koning, A.; Kuenen, J.; Schütz, H.; Acosta-Fernández, J.; Usubiaga, A.; et al. Global sustainability accounting-developing EXIOBASE for multi-regional footprint analysis. *Sustainability* **2015**, *7*, 138–163. [CrossRef]

31. Ivanova, D.; Wood, R. The unequal distribution of household carbon footprints in Europe and its link to sustainability. *Rev. Glob. Sustain.* **2020**.

32. EUROSTAT. *Description of the Data Transmission for HBS (Reference Year) 2010 Version: Final*; Eurostat: Brussels, Belgium, 2012.

33. Eurostat Degree of Urbanisation Classification -2011 Revision. Available online: https://ec.europa.eu/eurostat/statistics-explained/index.php/Degree_of_urbanisation_classification_-_2011_revision (accessed on 3 February 2020).

34. Eurostat Glossary: Local Administrative Unit (LAU). Available online: https://ec.europa.eu/eurostat/statistics-explained/index.php?title=Glossary:LAU2 (accessed on 3 February 2020).

35. Eurostat Local Administrative Units (LAU). Available online: https://ec.europa.eu/eurostat/web/nuts/local-administrative-units (accessed on 3 February 2020).

36. Zhang, X.; Luo, L.; Skitmore, M. Household carbon emission research: An analytical review of measurement, influencing factors and mitigation prospects. *J. Clean. Prod.* **2015**, *103*, 873–883. [CrossRef]

37. Galvin, R.; Sunikka-Blank, M. Economic Inequality and Household Energy Consumption in High-income Countries: A Challenge for Social Science Based Energy Research. *Ecol. Econ.* **2018**, *153*, 78–88. [CrossRef]

38. Dubois, G.; Sovacool, B.; Aall, C.; Nilsson, M.; Barbier, C.; Herrmann, A.; Bruyère, S.; Andersson, C.; Skold, B.; Nadaud, F.; et al. It starts at home? Climate policies targeting household consumption and behavioral decisions are key to low-carbon futures. *Energy Res. Soc. Sci.* **2019**, *52*, 144–158. [CrossRef]

39. Chancel, L.; Piketty, T. *Carbon and Inequality: From Kyoto to Paris*; Paris School of Economics: Paris, France, 2015.

40. Strandell, A.; Hall, C.M. Impact of the residential environment on second home use in Finland—Testing the compensation hypothesis. *Landsc. Urban Plan.* **2015**, *133*, 12–23. [CrossRef]

41. Hertwich, E.; Peters, G. Carbon footprint of nations: A global, trade-linked analysis. *Environ. Sci. Technol.* **2009**, *43*, 6414–6420. [CrossRef] [PubMed]

42. Ivanova, D.; Barrett, J.; Wiedenhofer, D.; Macura, B.; Callaghan, M.; Creutzig, F. Quantifying the potential for climate change mitigation of consumption options. *Environ. Res. Lett.*. under review. [CrossRef]

43. Ivanova, D.; Stadler, K.; Steen-Olsen, K.; Wood, R.; Vita, G.; Tukker, A.; Hertwich, E.G. Environmental impact assessment of household consumption. *J. Ind. Ecol.* **2016**, *20*, 526–536. [CrossRef]

44. Girod, B.; De Haan, P. More or Better? A Model for Changes in Household Greenhouse Gas Emissions due to Higher Income. *J. Ind. Ecol.* **2010**, *14*, 31–49. [CrossRef]

45. Usubiaga, A.; Acosta-Fernández, J. Carbon emission accounting in MRIO models: The territory vs. the residence principle. *Econ. Syst. Res.* **2015**, *27*, 458–477. [CrossRef]

46. Schaffrin, A.; Reibling, N. Household energy and climate mitigation policies: Investigating energy practices in the housing sector. *Energy Policy* **2015**, *77*, 1–10. [CrossRef]

47. Abela, A.M. Youth, religion and community care in Malta. *Soc. Compass* **1995**, *1*, 59–67. [CrossRef]

48. Ellsworth-Krebs, K. Implications of declining household sizes and expectations of home comfort for domestic energy demand. *Nat. Energy* **2019**, 1–6. [CrossRef]

49. Quested, T.; Ingle, R.; Parry, A. *Household Food and Drink Waste in the UK*; WRAP: Oxon, UK, 2012.

50. Ricciuto, L.; Tarasuk, V.; Yatchew, A. Socio-demographic influences on food purchasing among Canadian households. *Eur. J. Clin. Nutr.* **2006**, *60*, 778–790. [CrossRef] [PubMed]

51. Ritter, N.; Vance, C. Do fewer people mean fewer cars? Population decline and car ownership in Germany. *Transp. Res. Part A Policy Pract.* **2013**, *50*, 74–85. [CrossRef]

52. Soltani, A.; Pojani, D.; Askari, S.; Masoumi, H.E. Socio-demographic and built environment determinants of car use among older adults in Iran. *J. Transp. Geogr.* **2018**, *68*, 109–117. [CrossRef]

53. Papon, F.; Hivert, L. Adulterous behaviour within the car-owner couple: Some analyses from french panel data on car rental and car sharing within households. *IATSS Res.* **2008**, *32*, 6–15. [CrossRef]

54. Clark, B.; Chatterjee, K.; Melia, S. Changes in level of household car ownership: The role of life events and spatial context. *Transportation* **2016**, *43*, 565–599. [CrossRef]

55. ONS National Travel Survey: 2010. Available online: https://assets.publishing.service.gov.uk/government/uploads/system/uploads/attachment_data/file/8938/nts2010-07.pdf (accessed on 13 February 2020).

56. Lauzadyte-Tutliene, A.; Balezentis, T.; Goculenko, E. Welfare state in central and eastern Europe. *Econ. Sociol.* **2018**, *11*, 100–123. [CrossRef]

57. Ferrera, M. The "southern model" of welfare in social Europe. *J. Eur. Soc. Policy* **1996**, *6*, 17–37. [CrossRef]

58. Voicu, M.; Voicu, B.; Strapcova, K. Housework and gender inequality in European countries. *Eur. Sociol. Rev.* **2009**, *25*, 365–377. [CrossRef]

59. Tavora, I. The southern European social model: Familialism and the high rates of female employment in Portugal. *J. Eur. Soc. Policy* **2012**, *22*, 63–76. [CrossRef]

60. Gentile, M.; Tammaru, T.; Van Kempen, R. Heteropolitanization: Social and spatial change in Central and East European Cities. *Cities* **2012**, *29*, 291–299. [CrossRef]

61. Keilman, N. Biodiversity: The threat of small households. *Nature* **2003**, *421*, 489–490. [CrossRef]

62. Balaras, C.A.; Gaglia, A.G.; Georgopoulou, E.; Mirasgedis, S.; Sarafidis, Y.; Lalas, D.P. European residential buildings and empirical assessment of the Hellenic building stock, energy consumption, emissions and potential energy savings. *Build. Environ.* **2007**, *42*, 1298–1314. [CrossRef]

63. Ellsworth-Krebs, K.; Reid, L.; Hunter, C.J. Home Comfort and "Peak Household": Implications for Energy Demand. *Hous. Theory Soc.* **2019**, 1–20. [CrossRef]

64. Liu, J.; Daily, G.C.; Ehrlich, P.R.; Luck, G.W. Effects of household dynamics on resource consumption and biodiversity. *Nature* **2003**, *421*, 530–533. [CrossRef] [PubMed]

65. Esping-Andersen, G.; Billari, F.C. Re-theorizing Family Demographics. *Popul. Dev. Rev.* **2015**, *41*, 1–31. [CrossRef]

66. OECD. *Doing Better for Families: United States*; OECD Publishing: Paris, France, 2011; ISBN 9789264098732.

67. Nyborg, K.; Anderies, J.M.; Dannenberg, A.; Lindahl, T.; Schill, C.; Schlüter, M.; Adger, W.N.; Arrow, K.J.; Barrett, S.; Carpenter, S.; et al. Social norms as solutions: Policies may influence large-scale behavioral tipping. *Science* **2016**, *354*, 42–43. [CrossRef] [PubMed]

68. Freudendal-Pedersen, M.; Kesselring, S. Sharing mobilities. Some propaedeutic considerations. *Appl. Mobilities* **2018**, *3*, 1–7. [CrossRef]

69.	The Social Prosperity. Network Social Prosperity for the Future: A Proposal for Universal Basic Services. 2017, p. 55. Available online: https://www.ucl.ac.uk/bartlett/igp/sites/bartlett/files/universal_basic_services_-_the_institute_for_global_prosperity_.pdf (accessed on 3 March 2020).
70.	Kwan, S.C.; Tainio, M.; Woodcock, J.; Sutan, R.; Hashim, J.H. The carbon savings and health co-benefits from the introduction of mass rapid transit system in Greater Kuala Lumpur, Malaysia. *J. Transp. Heal.* **2017**, *6*, 187–200. [CrossRef]
71.	Ivanova, D.; Büchs, M. *Carbon and Energy Footprints of European Households (EU HBS)*; University of Leeds: Leeds, England, 2020; [Dataset]. [CrossRef]

© 2020 by the authors. Licensee MDPI, Basel, Switzerland. This article is an open access article distributed under the terms and conditions of the Creative Commons Attribution (CC BY) license (http://creativecommons.org/licenses/by/4.0/).

 *energies*

Article

A Comparative Analysis of House Owners in Need of Energy Efficiency Measures but with Different Intentions

Robert Baumhof, Thomas Decker and Klaus Menrad *

Chair of Marketing and Management of Biogenic Resources, University of Applied Sciences
Weihenstephan-Triesdorf, TUM Campus Straubing, Petersgasse 18, 94315 Straubing, Germany;
robertbaumhof@gmail.com (R.B.); thomas.decker@hswt.de (T.D.)
* Correspondence: klaus.menrad@hswt.de

Received: 1 May 2019; Accepted: 8 June 2019; Published: 13 June 2019

Abstract: Existing private homes in Germany and throughout Europe often are in need of energy efficient refurbishment measures (EERMs). However, these EERMs are not realized on the required level in order to achieve environment-related political targets. Therefore we investigate, based on an online survey of 1085 German owner-occupiers, the factors that differentiate two groups of single- and two-family house owners in need of EERM. Using an extended version of the Theory of Planned Behavior as a research framework, the performed logistic regression analysis shows that e.g., behavioral beliefs are significant factors for differentiating "Future-Refurbishers" from "Non-Refurbishers". Based on our results we suggest an enhancement of practice-orientated initiatives, e.g., refurbishment workshops or best-practice presentations. By presenting the aesthetic appearance of refurbished buildings or providing knowledge, other owner-occupiers could be motivated to engage in EERM. In addition to funding programs, initiatives like this can be used to increase the general energy efficiency of buildings and specifically of those in cities and urban districts, where a high share of the mentioned houses is located and greenhouse gas emissions are caused to a great extent.

Keywords: energy efficient refurbishment measures; residential buildings; decision-making; Theory of Planned Behavior

1. Introduction

Energy efficiency in the building sector plays a crucial role in Germany and in other European countries. Both Germany and the EU have passed several laws and regulations to improve the energy efficiency of buildings. As examples the 2010 Energy Performance of Buildings Directive [1], the 2012 Energy Efficiency Directive [2] of the European Union, the German National Action Plan on Energy Efficiency [3] and the German Federal Government's energy concept [4] can be mentioned. The stipulations and objectives in these frameworks deal with the high energy demand of the existing building stock and consequently its negative effects on the climate as well as the environment. In total, the European building stock accounts for 40% of the European final energy consumption as well as 36% of the overall European greenhouse gas emissions (GHGE) [5]. For Germany, these figures are similar, with the total building stock accounting for 38% of the final energy consumption and 30% of the overall GHGE [6]. In order to achieve significant reductions in consumption and emissions, the stock of owner-occupied single- and two-family houses is of special importance in Germany. Compared to the more complex ownership structure associated with multi-family houses, owner-occupiers of single- and two-family houses are more independent in their decision-making related to energy efficient refurbishment measures (EERM) [7]. Additionally, these house owners are responsible for 11% of the total final energy consumption in Germany what also suggests a high energy saving potential [8]. Based on an average energy consumption of 177 kWh/m^2·a, the estimated potential savings could range between 50% and 70% by 2050 [6].

However, despite several governmental actions such as setting legal requirements, grants or low interest loans [9], the refurbishment rate in Germany has currently not yet reached the politically focused target value of 2% p. a. [4,8]. With regard to residential buildings, Rein and Schmidt [10] actually point out a decline of more than 6 billion Euros between 2010 (EUR 40.9 billion) and 2014 (EUR 34.8 billion) in the financial investment in EERM.

In order to achieve an almost climate-neutral building stock by 2050, as determined in the existing German regulations, and moreover benefitting from multiple societal benefits (e.g., decreased energy import dependency, lower residential energy bills and increased residential comfort [11–13]), a better understanding of house owners' reluctance towards EERM is essential. Against this background, the present study considers owner-occupiers of single- and two-family houses in Germany with a specific focus on two groups of owner-occupiers. Next to owner-occupiers who stated their intention to conduct specific EERM in the next years, hereinafter called "Future-Refurbishers," the second group consists of "Non-Refurbishers", who stated a need for EERM but also a lack of intention to take action. For the comparative analysis of these groups we analyze data gained from an online survey. Within this survey we considered influencing factors derived from the scientific literature which are related to the Theory of Planned Behavior [14], Building conditions and individuals' Environmental awareness.

Based on this research framework, our research target is the identification of those factors allowing for a differentiation and consequently a better understanding of "Future-Refurbishers" and "Non-Refurbishers" (research target 1). Furthermore, we intend to provide ideas on how relevant identified factors can be utilized to trigger increased energy-related refurbishment activities among owner-occupiers of single- and two-family houses in Germany and beyond (research target 2). This is of special relevance for cities and urban districts where globally 70% of all GHG originate from [15] and where 57% of all single-family houses are located in Germany [16].

By focusing on willing house owners pre-refurbishment ("Future-Refurbishers") and house owners who do not intend to take actions despite a perceived need ("Non-Refurbishers"), this study is a contribution to the still lacking understanding of decisions regarding EERM [17]. In contrast to our study, which is focused on future refurbishment activities, the existing decision-making literature focused on EERM is, as pointed out in the review of Kastner and Stern [18], primarily characterized by studies considering past decisions (retrospective studies) or experimental/hypothetical approaches. As examples the retrospective studies of Zundel and Stieß [19], Stieß and Dunkelberg [20], Michelsen and Madlener [21] or Black et al. [22] can be mentioned. Experimental/hypothetical approaches are followed in the studies of Achtnicht [23], Achtnicht and Madlener [24], Grösche and Vance [25] or e.g., Alberini et al. [26].

In [19,20], the authors pursued a comparative concept by comparing German homeowners with different refurbishment activities, i.e., energy-efficient and standard refurbishment activities. Michelsen and Madlener [21] also conducted an analysis among German homeowners but with a focus on motivational factors that influence the decision-making in the context of residential heating systems. In the study of Black et al. [22] various energy-related efficiency measures were considered in order to investigate relevant factors that determine the decisions of the analyzed US citizens. Next to insulation activities also activities referring to the heating system were considered.

As a prominent experimental/hypothetical approach, the analysis of Achtnicht [23], who conducted a choice experiment among German house owners, can be mentioned. Besides the role of environmental benefits, this study also analyzed the willingness-to-pay for CO2 savings. The study of Achtnicht and Madlener [24] is a continuation of Achtnicht [23] and differs with regard to the considered choice sets. Grösche and Vance [25] analyzed data of German homeowners who conducted one or more EERM (e.g., roof insulation, façade insulation, replacement of the heating system or replacement of windows). Based on this measures and further details, the authors elicited the households' willingness to pay per kWh saved. Alberini et al. [26] surveyed Swiss owner-occupiers of houses that haven't been renovated in the past years. The considered owner-occupiers had to choose between hypothetical refurbishments during the conducted conjoint choice experiments. These refurbishments were defined by different attributes such as upfront cost, rebate offered by the government or savings on the energy bills per year.

While there is a number of retrospective and hypothetical/experimental studies, only a few studies considering future refurbishment activities can be identified in the existing literature. As examples, the studies of Klöckner and Nayum [27] and Friege [28] can be mentioned. In their study of 3787 Norwegian households, Klöckner and Nayum [27] considered drivers and barriers (in different stages of the decision-making process) referring to planned EERM such as e.g., insulation activities or the replacement of windows. Insulation activities were also regarded in the study of Friege [28] who considered planned refurbishment activities as well as past refurbishment activities in his study among 275 private German homeowners. On the one hand, we want to contribute to the limited understanding of decisions regarding EERM [17] by adding a study using a future-orientated approach in a research field that so far was predominantly analyzed with retrospective and experimental/hypothetical studies. On the other hand, the present study aims to enhance the insights related to the current political activities focused on increasing the refurbishment activities in Germany.

The study is structured as follows: the theoretical and methodological background is outlined in the Sections 2 and 3. Our results related to research target 1 are presented and discussed in Section 4. Finally, we provide conclusions and implications in Section 5 based on our results to meet research target 2.

2. Research Framework of the Study

This section conveys the theoretical research framework of our analysis, including an introduction of the Theory of Planned Behavior (TPB) which is the main guideline for the identification of relevant factors within the scientific literature. This section also introduces additionally considered predictors which were identified when screening relevant literature.

Built upon the Theory of Reasoned Action (TRA) [29], the Theory of Planned Behavior was developed by Icek Ajzen [30]. This was done by adding the predictor 'Perceived behavioral control' to the TRA predictors 'Attitude toward the behavior' and 'Subjective norms' [14]. With these predictors, the TPB is intended to deal with behaviors over which people have incomplete control. In the context of the TPB, the predictor 'Attitude toward the behavior' refers to the extent of which a person has a favorable or unfavorable evaluation or appraisal of the behavior in question. The second predictor is named 'Subjective norm'. This predictor refers to the perceived social pressure to perform or not perform the behavior. The third factor is the degree of 'Perceived behavioral control' and refers to the perceived ease or difficulty of performing the behavior and it is assumed to reflect past experience, individuals' resources and related anticipated barriers. In general, the greater the 'Perceived behavioral control' and the more favorable the 'Attitude' and 'Subjective norm' with respect to a behavior, the stronger is an individual's intention to perform the behavior in question [14]. Thereby, the individual contributions of the three predictors are expected to vary across situations and behaviors [14].

However, according to Ajzen, the developer of the TPB, and Driver [31], the TPB postulates–at the most basic level of explanation–that performance or non-performance of behaviors depends on the beliefs behind the introduced TPB predictors. In addition to *Behavioral beliefs*, which are assumed to affect the predictor 'Attitudes toward the behavior,' these are *Normative beliefs* and *Control beliefs*. While *Normative beliefs* constitute the underlying determinants of 'Subjective norms,' *Control beliefs* refer to the predictor 'Behavioral control' [31].

Based on the TPB we utilized factors associated to these beliefs for the differentiation of "Future-Refurbishers" and "Non-Refurbishers". These factors as well as additional contextual aspects were identified by a screening of the existing scientific literature. The identified additional aspects refer to individuals' *Environmental awareness* and *Building conditions*. The latter were also considered by Organ et al. [32] as important for understanding house owners' motivation in the context of EERM.

In addition, Black et al. [22] also pointed out a building's physical structure as relevant in the context of capital investments in residential energy efficiency. Considering of house owners' *Environmental awareness* in the analysis is supported by two reasons. The first relates to the interaction of energy consumption and environmental damages and the perceived high relevance of environmental and climate protection in Germany but also other European countries [33]. The second and more important reason is the identified relationship between environmental awareness and related attitudes in previous empirical research considering the adoption of measures to reduce the environmental impact of buildings [34,35]. Thus Rajaie et al. [36] explicitly suggest that environmental awareness should be addressed in research that considers technological advancements for the reduction of the energy demands of buildings and consequently their impact on the environment.

Finally, a legitimization for the utilization of the TPB as a basis framework can be found in the studies of Wang et al. [37], Wu et al. [38] or Abrahamse and Steg [39], in which the TPB was already used successfully in similar contexts (energy efficiency and buildings).

3. Data Collection and Analysis

To analyze our research questions an online survey was conducted using a questionnaire with statements considering *Environmental awareness aspects, Building conditions* as well as *Behavioral, Normative* and *Control beliefs* of the TPB model. Finally, this extended form of the TPB served as a guideline for the identification of relevant influencing factors within the existing literature. In the following we introduce the precise statements and questions asked based upon the identified influencing factors. Moreover we provide information on the procedure of data acquisition and the method used to statistically analyze the collected data.

3.1. Survey Content

The factors and statements used in this study were either drawn directly from the available scientific literature in the context of energy efficiency and residential buildings (such as e.g., [19,20,24]) or were specifically created based on factors identified as relevant. Moreover, we utilized statements from Bearden et al. [40] to assess the potential influence of individuals' *Environmental awareness*. The *Building conditions* [22,32] were examined using self-developed statements related to the structural condition, the energy efficiency as well as a variable representing the comfort in the building and its visual appearance.

The wording of the statements used in our questionnaire can be derived from Table 1. While "Non-Refurbishers" were asked to refer their answers to hypothetical energy-related refurbishment activities on their buildings, "Future-Refurbishers" were asked to refer their answers to those measures stated as intended for the near future.

Table 1. Statements used in the questionnaire of this study (wording for "Non-Refurbishers").

Factors	Predictor and Statements
	Behavioral Beliefs
All in all reasonable *	The expenditure for EERM is justified …
Indoor comfort *	all in all.
Energy bills *	because of an associated enhancement of the indoor comfort.
Reasonable for environment *	because of the cost savings afterwards.
Doubts about desired effects	because of the resulting benefits for the environment.
	I would have doubts regarding the desired effects of EERM.
Susceptibility repairs	Energy-related refurbishment projects make a house less susceptible to repairs.
	Normative Beliefs
Esteem friends/family	Among my friends and my family refurbishments are seen as useful.
Social esteem	Energy-related refurbishments raise the social esteem.
Esteem neighborhood	In my neighborhood refurbishments are seen as useful.

Table 1. *Cont.*

Factors	Predictor and Statements
Control Beliefs	
Experience	I have experience with energy-related refurbishment projects.
Time planning	I would have enough time for planning the refurbishment.
Time conduction	I would have enough time for conducting the refurbishment measures.
Own capabilities	I could renounce on professional help regarding EERM due to my own capabilities.
Support family	My family would support me during an energy-related refurbishment project.
Financing problems	I would have problems financing the EERM.
No loan	I wouldn't want to take up a loan.
Appropriate craftsmen	It surely would be hard to find appropriate craftsmen.
Complex promotion	The governmental promotions for EERM are onerous and bureaucratic.
Legal requirements	Complying with the legal regulations would be difficult.
Dust / dirt no problem	Dust and dirt are no problem for me.
Objective information	Getting objective information in the context of EERM would be difficult.
Complex case	My house would be a complex refurbishment case.
Consulting during conduction	I would use professional help during the conduction of EERM.
Consulting during planning	I would use professional help for the planning of EERM.
Insecurity during refurbishment	I would often be insecure during the planning and conducting of EERM.
Environmental Awareness	
Environmental harm products	It is important to me that the products I use do not harm the environment.
Impacts of decisions	I consider the environmental impact of my actions when making many of my decisions.
Purchase habits	My purchase habits are affected by my concern for our planet.
Waste of resources	I am concerned about the resource wastage on our planet.
Environmental responsibility	I would describe myself as environmentally responsible.
Discomfort Eco-friendliness	I would accept discomfort in exchange for more environmental friendliness.
Building Conditions	
	In terms of the ...
Energy efficiency **	... energy efficiency of the building I ought to take actions ...
Comfort and appearance **	... comfort in the building and its visual appearance I ought to take actions ...
Building fabric **	... structural condition I ought to take actions ...

Answer-scales: I totally agree/I agree/Neither agree nor disagree/I don't agree/I don't agree at all. * Yes/Not sure/No. ** I should take actions ... as soon as possible (asap)/ ... in the next years/there is no need. Source: Content adapted and adopted from Zundel and Stieß [19], Stieß and Dunkelberg [20], Achtnicht and Madlener [24], Bearden et al. [40], Black et al. [22] and Organ et al. [32].

3.2. Data Collection

For the purpose of our study, a Germany-wide online survey was conducted during June and July 2016 using an online panel provided by a market research institute. Our target group were house owners of single- and two-family houses in Germany who lived in these houses at the time of data collection. By asking the house owners whether a refurbishment project was planned or not, the group of "Future-Refurbishers" and "Non-Refurbishers" were identified. Subsequently, "Future-Refurbishers" were asked whether they plan to undertake EERM on the upper or lower building envelope, the façade, windows and/or doors. Only those house owners who stated their intention to realize at least one EERM related to these building components or intended to modernize the heating system (e.g., via solar thermal systems, installation of a ventilation system with heat recovery) were considered as "Future Refurbishers" for the present study. "Future-Refurbishers" without energy-related measures were not considered for this study.

Those individuals who stated to have no refurbishment intentions were considered for this study when a need for EERM was indicated. This need was identified by asking a question considering the perceived energy-related status of those building components.

Only those owner-occupiers (without refurbishment intentions) who stated a "need" or an "immediate need" for improving the energy efficiency of the heating system or of at least one of the mentioned building components were considered for the group of "Non-Refurbishers".

Finally, after data cleaning and sorting out owner-occupiers without energy-related refurbishment intentions (75 respondents) or needs (627 respondents) 351 "Non-Refurbishers" and 734 "Future-Refurbishers" were available for statistical data analysis. The data cleaning procedure followed a combined approach characterized by an analysis of the respondents' answers to the individual question sets as well as the time respondents devoted for answering the questions. After marking questionnaires in which mainly identical answers and/or short processing times were evident, an individual case-by-case examination of suspicious but also incomplete data sets finally led to the exclusion of questionnaires of 320 "Future-Refurbishers" and 345 "Non-Refurbishers".

The characteristics of the respondents of both groups are presented in the Figures 1–4 indicating statistically significant differences between the two groups in terms of age (Figure 1), education (Figure 2), average monthly net household income (Figure 3) and in terms of the construction periods (Figure 4) of the participants' buildings.

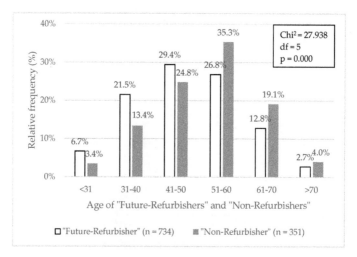

Figure 1. Age groups of "Future-Refurbishers" and "Non-Refurbishers".

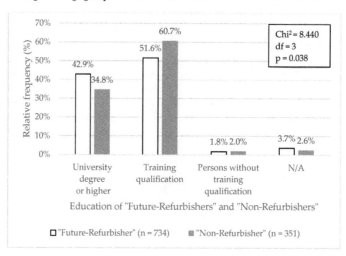

Figure 2. Education levels of "Future-Refurbishers" and "Non-Refurbishers".

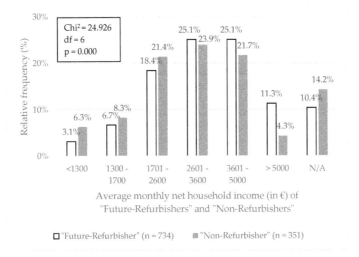

Figure 3. Average monthly net household income (in €) for "Future-Refurbishers" and "Non-Refurbishers".

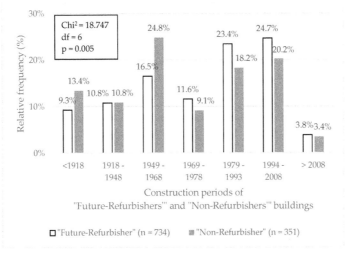

Figure 4. Construction periods of "Future-Refurbishers" and "Non-Refurbishers" buildings.

Figures 2 and 3 show that "Future-Refurbishers" are not only more likely to have a university degree, but also a higher income than "Non-Refurbishers." Since EERM often result in substantial costs, it seems that people with a higher income are more capable of realizing EERM in the future. Moreover, the group of "Non-Refurbishers" is older than the group of "Future-Refurbishers." Further, there are significant differences between the two groups related to the age of their houses with the average construction year of "Future-Refurbishers" buildings being 1968 compared to 1963 for houses of "Non-Refurbishers". This implies that a higher share of "Non-Refurbishers" buildings were built before the 'Thermal Insulation Ordinance' came in place in 1977 in order to enhance the energy efficiency of new buildings in Germany.

The answers of the "Future-Refurbishers" and "Non-Refurbishers" to the statements presented in Section 3.1 were analyzed using binary logistic regression. This method is intended to reveal factors— beyond socio-demographic aspects—that allow for a differentiation of both analyzed groups and potentially for deriving recommendations for overcoming the reluctance concerning residential EERM in Germany.

3.3. Mathematical Approach for Data Analysis

In general, logistic regression is a form of multiple regression with a categorical outcome variable and categorical or continuous predictor variables. In its simplest form it is possible to forecast which of two categories a person is likely to belong to given some other details [41]. In this study, the two outcome categories are represented by "Future-Refurbishers" and "Non-Refurbishers." The predictor variables, in turn, are represented by the underlying factors of the questions and statements presented in Section 3.1.

In multiple linear regression, Y is, as presented in Equation (1), predicted by a combination of predictor variables multiplied by their respective regression coefficients:

$$Y_i = b_0 + b_1 X_{1i} + b_2 X_{2i} + \ldots + b_n X_{ni} + \varepsilon_i \tag{1}$$

Instead of predicting the value of a variable Y from several predictor variables X_n, in binary logistic regression a probability P(Y) of Y occurring given known values of X_n is determined with Equation (2):

$$P(Y) = \frac{1}{1 + e^{-(b_0 + b_1 X_{1i} + b_2 X_{2i} + \ldots + b_n X_{ni} + \varepsilon)}} \tag{2}$$

In this equation e is the base of the natural logarithm and the other coefficients form a linear combination. By expressing the multiple linear regression equation in logarithmic terms (called the logit) the results of the equation vary between 0 and 1. Thus, a value close to 1 means that Y is very likely to have occurred while a value close to 0 expresses the opposite [41]. The coefficients of the predictor variables are determined by using maximum-likelihood estimation. This estimation method selects coefficients that make the observed values most likely to have occurred [41]. Based on these values so-called "odds" and "odds ratios" (the proportionate change in odds due to a unit change in the predictor variable) can be calculated [41]. These odds ratios and the regression coefficients are presented hereinafter in Section 4.

For identifying relevant factors behind the introduced statements, we used the IBM SPSS Statistics 23 analysis program. Due to the high amount of initially considered influencing factors, a stepwise logistic regression was used for identifying the most important factors capable of distinguishing the survey participants into "Future-Refurbishers" and "Non-Refurbishers." Due to potential suppressor effects (those effects occur when a predictor has a significant effect but only when another variable is held constant) we used the stepwise backward method. In [42], this method is described as follows: "With this method, the initial model contains all of the terms as predictors. At each step, terms in the model are evaluated, and any terms that can be removed without significantly detracting from the model are removed. In addition, previously removed terms are reevaluated to determine if the best of those terms adds significantly to the predictive power of the model. If so, it is added back into the model. When no more terms can be removed without significantly detracting from the model, and no more terms can be added to improve the model, the final model is generated." The thresholds for this procedure were $P_{IN} = 0.05$ and $P_{OUT} = 0.10$. The stepwise backward method was used in order to reduce the risk of a Type II error (i.e., missing a predictor that does in fact predict the outcome) which would be more likely with the alternative method of stepwise forward selection [41]. This method in essence follows an opposite procedure than the stepwise backward method but starts with no model terms (except the constant) in the equation. The third general method available in SPSS when conducting a binomial logistic regression is the default mode called 'enter'. This method simply adds all terms into the equation [42].

4. Results and Discussion

In order to gain a better understanding of the differences between house owners who are aware of their need to conduct EERM but differ with regard to their intention to take action, we compared reluctant "Non-Refurbishers" with house owners who plan to take action, i.e., "Future-Refurbishers." The results of the applied binary logistic regression analysis as well as a discussion are presented in the following subsections.

4.1. Differentiating Influencing Factors

The results of the binary logistic regression analysis are provided in Table 2. For all significant influencing factors not excluded via the stepwise regression, the odds ratios (Exp(B)), the regression coefficients (β) and p-values are presented. A significant Exp(B) value (p-value ≤ 0.05) greater (less) than 1.0 indicates that, as the predictor increases, the odds of the outcome occurring (being a "Future-Refurbisher") increase (decrease). Statistically insignificant results are printed in non-bold letters.

Table 2. Results for the numeric and categorical variables of being a "Future-Refurbisher".

Factors	Predictors and Statements		Exp (B)/β (*p*-value)
	Behavioral beliefs		
	The expenditure for EERM is justified ...		
All in all reasonable	all in all.	YES vs. NO	1.62/0.48 (0.411)
		DON'T KNOW vs. NO	0.92/−0.086 (0.881)
Indoor comfort	because of an associated enhancement of the indoor comfort.	YES vs. NO	**5.37/1.68 (0.000)**
		DON'T KNOW vs. NO	**3.33/1.20 (0.013)**
Energy bills	because of the cost savings afterwards.	YES vs. NO	**2.09 /0.74 (0.043)**
		DON'T KNOW vs. NO	1.13/0.125 (0.722)
Reasonable for environment	because of the resulting benefits for the environment.	YES vs. NO	**0.15/−1.92 (0.000)**
		DON'T KNOW vs. NO	**0.29/−1.26 (0.013)**
Doubts about desired effects	I would have doubts regarding the desired effects of EERM.		**2.06/0.723 (0.000)**
	Normative beliefs		
Esteem friends/family	Among my friends and my family refurbishments are seen as useful.		**0.64/−0.439 (0.004)**
Social esteem	Energy-related refurbishments raise the social esteem.		0.81/−0.212 (0.089)
Esteem neighborhood	In my neighborhood refurbishments are seen as useful.		0.79/−0.240 (0.089)
	Control beliefs		
Experience	I have experience with energy-related refurbishment projects.		1.22/0.202 (0.060)
Time planning	I would have enough time for planning the refurbishment.		**0.74/−0.302 (0.028)**
Time conduction	I would have enough time for conducting the refurbishment measures.		**0.66/−0.422 (0.001)**
Own capabilities	I could renounce on professional help regarding EERM due to my own capabilities.		**0.74/−0.305 (0.015)**
Financing problems	I would have problems financing the EERM.		**2.43/0.888 (0.000)**

Table 2. *Cont.*

Factors	Predictors and Statements		Exp (B)/β (*p*-value)
Appropriate craftsmen	It surely would be hard to find appropriate craftsmen.		0.58/−0.545 (0.000)
Complex promotion	The governmental promotions for EERM are onerous and bureaucratic.		0.67/−0.399 (0.000)
Legal requirements	Complying with the legal regulations would be difficult.		1.36/0.310 (0.008)
Complex case	My house would be a complex refurbishment case.		1.24/0.218 (0.044)
Consulting during conduction	I would use professional help during the conduction of EERM.		1.43/0.357 (0.011)
Consulting during planning	I would use professional help for the planning of EERM.		1.34/0.295 (0.025)
Environmental awareness			
Impacts of decisions	I consider the environmental impact of my actions when making many of my decisions.		0.64/−0.453 (0.001)
Discomfort Eco-friendliness	I would accept discomfort in exchange for more environmental friendliness.		1.30/0.261 (0.069)
Building conditions			
	In terms of the ...		
Energy efficiency	energy efficiency of the building I ought to take actions ...	ASAP vs. NO NEED	10.60/2.36 (0.000)
		NEXT YEARS vs. NO NEED	4.09/1.41 (0.000)
Comfort and appearance	comfort in the building and its visual appearance I ought to take actions ...	ASAP vs. NO NEED	7.25/1.98 (0.000)
		NEXT YEARS vs. NO NEED	3.50/1.25 (0.000)
Building fabric	structural condition I ought to take actions ...	ASAP vs. NO NEED	1.49/0.398 (0.455)
		NEXT YEARS vs. NO NEED	1.91/0.647 (0.012)
Constant term			N/A/−1.61 0.143

Reference-category: "Non-Refurbishers"; Source: own calculation.

Regarding *Behavioral beliefs*, the factors *Indoor comfort, Reasonable for environment, Energy bills* and *Doubts about desired effects* were significant and thus included in the regression model. The affiliated Exp(B) values for these factors suggest that it is more likely to be in the group of "Future-Refurbishers," given house owners assume that EERM enhance the housing comfort and that EERM lead to a reduction of the energy bill. Belonging to this group is also more likely for individuals, who are not or less skeptical regarding the doubts about the pursued effects of EERM. The Exp(B) value associated with the factor *Reasonable for environment* is smaller than 1.0. This indicates that house owners who think that EERM are good for the environment are less likely to be part of the group of "Future-Refurbishers."

When considering *Normative beliefs*, only the factor *Esteem friends/family* is significant and included in the regression model. The calculated Exp(B) value suggests that belonging to the group of "Non-Refurbishers" is more likely with a decreased appreciation of EERM by house owners' friends and family.

A look at the *Control beliefs* shows that there are ten significant factors identified as being relevant for predicting group membership. Among these factors the most differentiating factors with Exp(B) values bigger than 1.0 are *Financing problems, Consulting during conduction, Legal requirements* and *Consulting during planning*. These results indicate that being a member of the group of "Future-Refurbishers" is more likely the lower house owners perceive financial problems to be associated with EERM. Implementing EERM is, furthermore, more likely for those house owners who have a lower demand of consultation. Further, the results of the factors *Legal requirements* but also *Complex case* imply that the uptake of EERM is more probable if complying with legal requirements in connection with EERM is perceived as less complex and also when the building does not appear to be hard to treat.

Significant Exp(B) values smaller than 1.0 are calculated for the factors *Appropriate craftsmen*, *Time conduction* as well as *Complex promotion*, *Own capabilities* and *Time planning*. With respect to the wording of our statements and the answer scales used in the questionnaire, this can be interpreted as follows: the more positive a house owner's expectation is to find appropriate craftsmen for conducting EERM, the more likely this person belongs to the group of "Non-Refurbishers." This also applies to the perceived difficulty connected to governmental promotion—if individuals perceive governmental promotion as not complex, their belonging to the group of "Non-Refurbishers" is more likely. In contrast to the latter two rather surprising results, we also find that limited time for conducting and planning EERM and low *Own capabilities* of the house owners in this area increase the odds of belonging to the group of "Non-Refurbishers."

Along with factors associated with the TPB we included *Environmental awareness* factors and *Building conditions* as additional contextual aspects in our study. When considering the results related to the *Environmental awareness* aspects, there is only one significant factor, which is *Impacts of decisions*. The associated Exp(B) value suggests that belonging to the group of "Non-Refurbishers" is more probable if house owners do not or hardly consider the potential environmental impacts of their actions when making decisions.

With respect to *Building conditions,* the factors *Energy efficiency* and *Comfort and appearance* are included, significant and connected to strong Exp(B) values greater than 1.0. These results suggest that being a "Future-Refurbisher" is more likely if house owners perceive an immediate need or a need within the next few years to take actions to improve the energy efficiency, the appearance or the comfort of their buildings. A perceived need to take care of a buildings structural condition in the foreseeable future (*Building fabric*) was also identified as increasing the likeliness of being part of the "Future-Refurbishers."

The factors which have been excluded via stepwise backward algorithm are presented in Table 3. In total 10 factors were excluded by the stepwise regression algorithm in SPSS.

Table 3. Excluded factors/statements.

Factors	Predictors and Statements
Behavioral beliefs	
Susceptibility repairs	Energy-related refurbishment projects make a house less susceptible to repairs.
Normative beliefs	
—	
Control beliefs	
Support family	My family would support me during an energy-related refurbishment project.
No loan	I wouldn't want to take up a loan.
Dust/dirt no problem	Dust and dirt are no problem for me.
Objective information	Getting objective information in the context of EERM would be difficult.
Insecurity during refurbishment	I would often be insecure during the planning and conducting of EERM.
Environmental awareness	
Environmental harm products	It is important to me that the products I use do not harm the environment.
Purchase habits	My purchase habits are affected by my concern for our planet.
Waste of resources	I am concerned about the resource wastage on our planet.
Environmental responsibility	I would describe myself as environmentally responsible.
Building conditions	
—	

Source: own figure.

4.2. Overall Classification

This section is intended to allow a better evaluation of the quality of the analysis results. Next to the actual and predicted group membership via binary logistic regression in Table 4 we furthermore provide additional information on specific quality indicators.

Table 4. Classification table showing the predicted and actual groups from the sample.

Actual Membership	Predicted Membership		
	Future-Refurbishers	Non-Refurbishers	Correctly Classified
Future-Refurbishers (N = 734)	671	63	91.4%
Non-Refurbishers (N = 351)	93	258	73.5%
	Overall:		85.6%

Source: own figure.

From 734 respondents who stated their willingness to conduct relevant refurbishment measures in the future, 91.4% were assigned to the correct group. In the case of the "Non-Refurbishers," this value is 73.5%. In total, the binary logistic regression function assigned 85.6% of the sample participants correctly. By comparing this proportion of correctly classified observations with the proportion expected by chance, known as proportional chance criterion (56.2%) [43], our model improves this indicator by almost 30%.

The pseudo R^2 value that determines the amount of variance in the dependent variable explained by the independent variables of 0.649 (Nagelkerke) also indicates a very good quality of the analysis [44]. The finally computed significance levels associated with the model chi-square value (678.8) of $p = 0.000$ and the Hosmer and Lemeshow test with $p = 0.960$ (>0.05) also suggest a good model fit. For the assessment of multicollinearity among the considered variables, the variance inflation factors (VIF; details on VIFs can be derived from [44]) were calculated. None of these VIFs was higher than 3, which leads to the conclusion that multicollinearity does not negatively affect the quality of our results.

4.3. Discussion

In this study we analyzed multiple factors that influence the realization of EERM in owner-occupied single- and two-family houses in Germany. The specific subjects of our empirical analysis, which is based on a relatively highly educated sample, were owner-occupiers of single- and two-family houses who stated their intention to conduct EERM ("Future-Refurbishers") and those owner-occupiers of such houses who stated a need to undertake EERM but do not intend to take action ("Non-Refurbishers").

Utilizing an extended version of the TPB as a framework for our analysis appears justified in our point of view as it has already been previously used successfully in the context of buildings and energy efficiency and factors of all predictor domains contribute to group differentiation in our study. Additionally, Wilson and Dowlatabadi [45] state, that "Residential energy use is characterized by a wide range of decision types and contexts, as well as psychological and contextual influences on behavior. [Thus] Decision models from different research traditions are all relevant to some aspect of residential energy use". Adding further aspects in connection with the original TPB is not unusual and provides, as Kastner and Stern [18] state, the possibility to improve and adapt the purpose of the analysis. Additionally, considering house owners' perceived specific *Building conditions* and *Environmental awareness* in this study contributed to a better differentiation of "Future-Refurbishers" and "Non-Refurbishers".

Before discussing the results of our study some limitations and methodological aspects need to be addressed. As outpointed earlier, our data was collected with an online survey in June and July 2016. Choosing this time of the year might have led to a bias of our results due to an omission or an overrepresentation of certain house owners. Evidence for such effects can be found in [46]. Additionally, some limitations refer to the depth of further statistical evaluations, e.g., carrying out a more detailed analysis of our research framework differentiated by older or younger respondents in interaction with their income. The reason for not realizing such type of analysis relates to the limited sample size. Even though the number of respondents was suitable for the statistical analyses presented, the sample size was not sufficient for such more specific statistical analyses. The limited sample size was also the reason why further statistical tests to underpin the predictive power (e.g., cross-validation; for details see [47]) were omitted.

Related to our results, specifically referring to the considered *Behavioral beliefs*, the literature states that individuals are likely to perform energy efficiency measures in order to increase indoor comfort and to reduce energy bills and their environmental impact [32]. However, the results of our study regarding the last aspect suggest the opposite as the perception that EERM do have a positive effect on the environment is more characterizing for the group of "Non-Refurbishers." A reason for this result could originate from house owners' thoughts about the necessary building components and the origin of the materials for these components that are required for carrying out EERM. While "Non-Refurbishers" might only consider the usually desired positive effects of EERM on the environment, "Future-Refurbishers" answers could be influenced by their higher involvement and know-how about the refurbishment such as the necessary amount of insulation material or construction material for windows and doors, which are often based on fossil fuels. Regarding the factors *Indoor comfort* and *Energy bills*, our results are congruent with the thesis of Organ et al. [32]. Further underpinning results referring to these aspects originate from empirical studies conducted in Ireland [48] and Sweden [49]. The Irish study concluded that EERM are mainly driven by monetary goals while comfort gains were identified to be of secondary relevance. Environmental benefits of EERM were identified to be of low relevance in both studies. In terms of *Doubts about desired effects*, our results go along with the cause-effect relationship stated by Zundel and Stieß [19] who identified doubts concerning the results of EERM as a hindering aspect.

Regarding the *Normative beliefs*, our results associated with the factor *Esteem friends/family* indicate that a supportive opinion of friends and family favors the uptake of EERM, what is supported by Earl and Peng [50] who state that the desire of an enhanced standing within the social surrounding (e.g., friends and family) is a motivating factor for the uptake of EERM. Furthermore, a case study carried out in British communities [51] also suggests that 'social capital' is important for home energy innovations what partly is related to the wish of individuals to gather information from people they know—e.g., from friends or family members who value such home energy innovations or EERM.

When considering *Control beliefs* and the factor *Financing problems*, our results go along with Organ et al. [32] and Zundel and Stieß [19], who state a lack of financial resources as a barrier for energy efficiency measures. Concerning the factors *Consulting during conduction* and *Consulting during planning*, our results indicate that a refurbishment is more probable in the case of a low demand of professional help or advice. This could be influenced by the house owners' *Own capabilities*, but also by low trust in energy advisers. Support for the latter reason can be found in the study of Risholt and Berker [52] who identify a lack of knowledge and expectation of bad advice from professionals as impeding aspects for homeowners. Lacking possibilities to conduct EERM by themselves is also stated as impeding factor in our study. A further result in the field of the *Control beliefs* shows that high availability of time results in a higher probability of realizing EERM (*Time conduction, Time planning*), what is in line with the findings of Zundel and Stieß [19] who show that house owners who conducted EERM have had more time to deal with the planning than those who conducted standard refurbishment measures. A higher time intensity for larger home improvement projects is also outlined in [53]. Further support for our findings can be found in empirical studies conducted in Greece [54], Norway [55] and The Netherlands [56]. In the latter two studies financial aspects were also identified as barriers for the adoption of EERM. Moreover, in [54] a missing expertise or knowledge was identified as an impairing factor, too. Further critical influencing factors identified were a lack of reliable experts and information, time and effort to find information and complexities in the refurbishment process. The latter aspects found in [56] do not only support our finding regarding the relevance of time to carry out EERM but also our findings referring to the trust in energy advisers.

Besides the TPB components we also analyzed *Environmental awareness* aspects in the study on hand. From six initial factors, only the factor *Impacts of decisions* was identified to contribute significantly to a differentiation of "Future-Refurbishers" and "Non-Refurbishers." This factor indicates that individuals who do not put high relevance on environmental aspects during decision-making rather belong to the group of "Non-Refurbishers." When additionally considering the results associated with the factor *Reasonable for environment*, both findings together allow for the conclusion that even though "Non-Refurbishers" might support the idea that EERM are good for the environment, it might be less likely that environmental aspects are of high relevance during the decision-making in terms of EERM for this group. This conclusion suggests to regard political initiatives critically that emphasize the environmental benefits of energy-related refurbishment activities to influence house owners' decisions positively in order to persuade them to conduct EERM.

When considering the predictor *Building conditions*, our analysis shows that the perceived *Energy efficiency* as well as the *Comfort and visual appearance* strongly contribute to a differentiation between the analyzed groups. At a first glance, it is reasonable that those house owners who perceive a greater need for actions belong to the group of "Future-Refurbishers." However, when considering the construction periods of the houses of the analyzed groups, it comes up that the houses of "Non-Refurbishers" are on average older compared to those of "Future-Refurbishers" and thus should generally call for a higher need of action. Taking into account the finding of Stieß and Dunkelberg [20] who conclude that house owners with standard refurbishment measures are more likely to believe their house to be in a good condition, this might support the assumption that the actual (energy) status of the houses of "Non-Refurbishers" is more negative than perceived by their owners even though they have performed some efforts to reduce the energy consumption of their houses in the past.

German and European goals and legislations have become steadily more important to fulfill the *Legal requirements* in the context of EERM. Our results suggest that a future refurbishment is more likely the lower the perceived problems are to comply with existing regulations. According to the review of Kastner and Stern [18] neither approving nor disproving results could be detected in the existing literature for this factor.

Further initially surprising results refer to the variables *Complex promotion* and *Appropriate craftsmen*. Our findings suggest that house owners are more likely to belong to the group of "Non-Refurbishers" if they think it is easy to find appropriate craftsmen for carrying out EERM or if they do not perceive governmental promotions as complex. These results might be explained by the low involvement and experience of "Non-Refurbishers" related to the practice of refurbishment activities. Thus, such house owners might not be very concerned when it comes to aspects as finding craftsmen or dealing with governmental promotions. This might originate from a lack of a threat of "Non-Refurbishers" compared to house owners who intend to undergo EERM and who not only risk losing time but also money, due to potential incorrect craftsmen-work, missed grants and subsidies because of non-compliance with legal requirements. This reasoning is supported by Pepels [57],who points out that extensive investments (such as in EERM) are associated with more extensive risk evaluations or intensified search for information.

5. Conclusions

In order to increase the currently rather low energy efficiency-related refurbishment activities in Germany it is necessary to take a wider range of measures into account. While it is widely acknowledged that private house owners and their respective buildings play a key role for achieving the climate targets until 2050 set by the German Government [4] and elsewhere, the results of this study show that pure political appeals to house owners to conduct specific energy-related measures are not expedient.

Based on the results of our analysis and with respect to our second research target, we suggest that, along with already existing financial support *(Financing problems)* that was identified as relevant, an increased non-monetary support might supplement existing efforts to trigger individual house owners towards increased energy-related refurbishment activities. An enhanced presentation of refurbished "best-practice houses" and their owners, who already have mastered the task of refurbishment, could be such an additional non-monetary support activity.

These kind of measures could supplement existing information and capacity building measures that are provided by the German Energy Agency (Dena, "Deutsche Energieagentur") or the KfW

("Kreditanstalt für Wiederaufbau"), which support interested house owners inter alia during financing EERM activities. An enhanced provision of best-practice houses could be provided by regional contact points for energy efficiency or by the German Energy Agency itself, as their objectives involve the design of campaigns in the context of energy efficiency, the distribution of information to the public, and the support of the building sector (architects, craftsmen, etc.) in order to ensure aligned work with current standards and regulations [58].

Directed towards "Future-Refurbishers," a presentation of already refurbished houses in collaboration with energy advisors and craftsmen could be used to level up the currently low refurbishment efficiency in the residential building sector in Germany. Since our results indicate a rather low acceptance of advice from professionals (*Consulting during planning, Consulting during conduction*), providing more neutral information during such best-practice events could foster additional efforts from those house owners who already intend to take specific individual energy-related refurbishment measures. Thus, potential doubts (*Doubts about desired effects*) about the implementation and the effects of additional measures of "Future-Refurbishers" could be eliminated. A key role in this regard is assigned to the owners of the refurbished best-practice houses. While professionals could take care of the presentation of the individually conducted measures and the overall refurbished building, or answer specific questions from the visiting house owners, these hosting house owners could ensure the trustworthiness of the professionals and provide further credible answers. Besides information on promised and actual costs and energy savings, those owners can also provide reliable information on technical aspects such as the effort associated with technical systems (e.g., in terms of operation and maintenance aspects) or the refurbishment process itself.

Such a trustworthy and informative situation can also be used to inform and persuade house owners who are aware of energy-related deficiencies, but also perceive financial problems (*Financing problems*) and thus neglect the uptake of efficiency measures. By lowering these house owners' doubts regarding financial savings or costs associated with certain efficiency measures, this could also reduce these house owners' perceived financial problems. Additionally, information on technical aspects provided by the professionals but also the best-practice-house owners can also lower their concerns due to a perceived lack of skills and capabilities (*Own capabilities*).

A further promising activity could be providing Do-It-Yourself workshops to individual house owners. During such workshops, energy advisors and craftsmen could present measures that allow for identification and removal of energy-related weak points of residential buildings. This could involve for example, the insulation behind radiator niches, or, for technically skilled house owners, the insulation of neuralgic spots like cellar ceilings. In addition to the direct effect of such measures, meaning the provision of capabilities and skills (*Own capabilities*) to "Non-Refurbishers" but also "Future-Refurbishers," there are also indirect effects connected to such workshops, i.e., multiplier effects among house owners, since applied know-how very likely will be spread within the neighborhood and among friends (*Esteem friends/family*). Additionally, such workshops might have positive effects related to trust in and the image of EERM since "Future Refurbishers" as well as "Non-Refurbishers" are likely to look for approval from their social network (e.g., families, friends, neighbors) instead of trusting highly unknown governmental or professional experts.

Workshops of this nature can also be used to provide information on legal obligations (*Legal requirements*) that have to be met according to the German "Energieeinsparverordnung" (energy saving ordinance) when implementing specific EERM. Other relevant information could concern e.g., legal obligations, when old or polluting heating systems need to be replaced. In addition to "Non-Refurbishers" and "Future-Refurbishers," another group of house owners could be targeted with such workshops, namely those who are basically not aware of the energy efficiency of their houses. By providing information on average energy consumptions for houses of different construction periods as well as information on energy savings associated with different kinds of EERM, all groups of house owners could be triggered to re-evaluate their actual need for energy efficiency measures and their intentions to take measures. This is also true for "Non-Refurbishers" who perceive a lower need for actions (*Building conditions*) but live on average in older houses with mostly lower energy efficiency standards.

A further opportunity associated with the presentation of best-practice refurbishment projects is the possibility to allow visiting house owners to experience a high level of indoor comfort and the nice appearance of a comprehensively refurbished building envelope. Such measures would address important influencing factors according to our results such as *Building conditions* and *Behavioral beliefs* and the factors *Comfort and appearance* and *Indoor comfort*, respectively.

Even though the extent and the effects of best-practice campaigns in private residential houses might be unknown, the realization of the proposed measures is a way forward to increase the energy efficiency in the existing building stock in Germany but also in other European countries. Furthermore, this kind of initiative would largely go along with Article 17, information and training, of the Energy Efficiency Directive 2012/27/EU [2], which demands that "Member States shall, with the participation of stakeholders, including local and regional authorities, promote suitable information, awareness-raising and training initiatives to inform citizens of the benefits and practicalities of taking energy efficiency improvement measures."

Due to the initially mentioned fact that a large share of single- and two-family houses is located in cities and urban districts, such measures might be especially promising when focused on these spatial and social environments. Since financial issues, capabilities and social acceptance were identified as relevant, enhanced initiatives considering these aspects could help to reduce the high energy consumption and GHG emissions in such conurbations. Thereby, the mentioned focus on specific districts is essential. Besides the possibility to enhance the outlined multiplier effect in the regional social surrounding, also regional-typical energy-related weak points of the commonly similar buildings could be addressed. These weak points could be covered during the mentioned practice-orientated workshops as well as in funding programs, e.g., for subsidized refurbishment management or for specific EERM. Increasing prices because of such funding programs, however, could be prevented by contractual arrangements with regional partners.

Nevertheless, the potential negative effects of such local initiatives also need to be considered, e.g., the fact that people with lower incomes might not be able to afford living in such houses or apartments anymore due to increased rental fees after refurbishment activities. Overcoming this phenomenon, however, is another aspect that is and needs to be considered by politicians and also scientists [59].

Author Contributions: Conceptualization, methodology, statistical analysis, writing—original draft preparation, writing—review and editing: R.B. supervision, project administration, funding acquisition: T.D., K.M.

Funding: This work was supported in part by a grant provided by the Bavarian State Ministry of Education, Science and the Arts [project number 1512-DW-78-01].

Conflicts of Interest: The authors declare no conflict of interest.

References

1. Directive 2010/31/EU of the European Parliament and of the Council of 19 May 2010 on the Energy Performance of Buildings. 2010. Available online: https://eur-lex.europa.eu/legal-content/EN/TXT/PDF/?uri=CELEX:32010L0031&from=EN (accessed on 12 June 2019).
2. DIRECTIVE 2012/27/EU OF THE EUROPEAN PARLIAMENT AND OF THE COUNCIL of 25 October 2012 on Energy Efficiency, Amending Directives 2009/125/EC and 2010/30/EU and Repealing Directives 2004/8/EC and 2006/32/EC: Energy Efficiency Directive 2012/27/EU. 2012. Available online: https://eur-lex.europa.eu/legal-content/EN/TXT/PDF/?uri=CELEX:32012L0027&from=EN (accessed on 12 June 2019).
3. Ein gutes Stück Arbeit. Mehr aus Energie machen—Nationaler Aktionsplan Energieeffizienz. 2014. Available online: https://www.bmwi.de/Redaktion/DE/Publikationen/Energie/nationaler-aktionsplan-energieeffizienz-nape.pdf?__blob=publicationFile&v=6 (accessed on 12 June 2019).

4. BMWi, BMU. Energiekonzept für eine umweltschonende, zuverlässige und bezahlbare Energieversorgung. 2010. Available online: https://www.bmwi.de/Redaktion/DE/Downloads/E/energiekonzept-2010.pdf?__blob=publicationFile&v=5 (accessed on 12 June 2019).

5. Artola, I.; Rademaekers, K.; Williams, R.; Yearwood, J. Boosting Building Renovation: What potential and value for Europe? Study for the ITRE Committee. 2016. Available online: http://www.europarl.europa.eu/RegData/etudes/STUD/2016/587326/IPOL_STU%282016%29587326_EN.pdf (accessed on 12 June 2019).

6. BMWi. Sanierungsbedarf im Gebäudebestand: Ein Beitrag zur Energieeffizienzstrategie Gebäude. 2014. Available online: https://www.bmwi.de/Redaktion/DE/Publikationen/Energie/sanierungsbedarf-im-gebaeudebestand.pdf?__blob=publicationFile&v=3 (accessed on 12 June 2019).

7. BPIE. EUROPE'S BUILDING UNDER THE MICROSCOPE: A country-by-country review of the energy performance of buildings. 2011. Available online: http://bpie.eu/wp-content/uploads/2015/10/HR_EU_B_under_microscope_study.pdf (accessed on 12 June 2019).

8. Walberg, D.; Gniechwitz, T.; Neitzel, M.; Austrup, S.; Gottschalk, W. Instrumentenkasten für wichtige Handlungsfelder der Wohnungsbaupolitik; Bauforschungsberichte Nr. 70, 2016. Available online: https://www.dgfm.de/wohnungsbaupolitik/sv/artikel/instrumentenkasten-fuer-wichtige-handlungsfelder-der-wohnungsbaupolitik.html (accessed on 12 June 2019).

9. Küchler, S.; Nestle, U. *Neue Finanzierungsmodelle für einen klimaneutralen Gebäudebestand. Strategien zur Modernisierung*; Heinrich-Böll-Stiftung: Berlin, Germany, 2012.

10. Rein, S.; Schmidt, C. Struktur der Bestandsmaßnahmen im Hochbau: Bestandsleistungen im Wohnungs- und Nichtwohnungsbau im Jahr 2014. 2016. Available online: http://www.bbsr.bund.de/BBSR/DE/Veroeffentlichungen/AnalysenKompakt/2016/ak-01-2016-dl.pdf?__blob=publicationFile&v=2 (accessed on 2 June 2016).

11. Bukarica, V.; Lončarević, A.K.; Pešut, D. Renovation in Buildings: Policy Brief. 2017. Available online: http://www.odyssee-mure.eu/publications/policy-brief/renovation-building-policy-brief.pdf (accessed on 7 March 2017).

12. Hall, M.R. *Materials for Energy Efficiency and Thermal Comfort in Buildings*; Woodhead Publishing Series in Energy; Elsevier Science: Cambridge, MA, USA; ProQuest: Ann Arbor, MI, USA, 2010; Volume 14.

13. *Global Energy Assessment: Toward a Sustainable Future*; Cambridge University Press: Cambridge, UK, 2012. [CrossRef]

14. Ajzen, I. The theory of planned behavior. *Organ. Behav. Hum. Decis. Process.* **1991**, *50*, 179–211. [CrossRef]

15. BBSR. CO2-Neutral in Cities and Neighbourhoods—The European and International Perspective. 2017. Available online: https://www.bbsr.bund.de/BBSR/EN/Publications/OnlinePublications/2017/bbsr-online-10-2017-dl.pdf?__blob=publicationFile&v=3 (accessed on 9 April 2019).

16. Effenberger, K.-H. Projektbericht Entwicklungsdynamik EFH: Arbeitsbaustein 4: Differenzierung der EFH-Bestände. 2015. Available online: http://homes-up.ioer.eu/fileadmin/files/PDF/IOER_Projektbericht_EFH_Bestaende_Effenberger.pdf (accessed on 17 March 2019).

17. Friege, J.; Chappin, E. Modelling decisions on energy-efficient renovations: A review. *Renew. Sustain. Energy Rev.* **2014**, *39*, 196–208. [CrossRef]

18. Kastner, I.; Stern, P.C. Examining the decision-making processes behind household energy investments: A review. *Energy Res. Soc. Sci.* **2015**, *10*, 72–89. [CrossRef]

19. Zundel, S.; Stieß, I. Beyond Profitability of Energy-Saving Measures—Attitudes Towards Energy Saving. *J. Consum. Policy* **2011**, *34*, 91–105. [CrossRef]

20. Stieß, I.; Dunkelberg, E. Objectives, barriers and occasions for energy efficient refurbishment by private homeowners. *J. Clean. Prod.* **2013**, *48*, 250–259. [CrossRef]

21. Michelsen, C.C.; Madlener, R. Motivational factors influencing the homeowners' decisions between residential heating systems: An empirical analysis for Germany. *Energy Policy* **2013**, *57*, 221–233. [CrossRef]

22. Black, J.S.; Stern, P.C.; Elworth, J.T. Personal and contextual influences on houshould energy adaptations. *J. Appl. Psychol.* **1985**, *70*, 3–21. [CrossRef]

23. Achtnicht, M. Do environmental benefits matter? Evidence from a choice experiment among house owners in Germany. *Ecol. Econ.* **2011**, *70*, 2191–2200. [CrossRef]

24. Achtnicht, M.; Madlener, R. Factors influencing German house owners' preferences on energy retrofits. *Energy Policy* **2014**, *68*, 254–263. [CrossRef]

25. Grösche, P.; Vance, C. *Willingness to Pay for Energy Conservation and Free Ridership on Subsidization: Evidence from Germany*; Ruhr Economic Papers; RWI: Essen, Germany, 2008; Volume 58.

26. Alberini, A.; Banfi, S.; Ramseier, C. Energy Efficiency Investments in the Home: Swiss Homeowners and Expectations about Future Energy Prices. *Energy J.* **2013**, *34*, 49–86. [CrossRef]

27. Klöckner, C.A.; Nayum, A. Specific Barriers and Drivers in Different Stages of Decision-Making about Energy Efficiency Upgrades in Private Homes. *Front. Psychol.* **2016**, *7*, 1362. [CrossRef] [PubMed]

28. Friege, J. Increasing homeowners' insulation activity in Germany: An empirically grounded agent-based model analysis. *Energy Build.* **2016**, *128*, 756–771. [CrossRef]

29. Fishbein, M.; Ajzen, I. *Belief, Attitude, Intention, and Behavior: An Indroduction to Theory and Research*; Addison-Wesley: Reading, MA, USA, 1975.

30. Ajzen, I. From intentions to actions: A theory of planned behavior. In *Action Control: From Cognition to Behavior*; Kuhl, J., Beckmann, J., Eds.; Springer: Heidelberg, Germany, 1985; pp. 11–39.

31. Ajzen, I.; Driver, B.L. Prediction of leisure participation from behavioral, normative, and control beliefs: An application of the theory of planned behavior. *Leis. Sci.* **1991**, *13*, 185–204. [CrossRef]

32. Organ, S.; Proverbs, D.; Squires, G. Motivations for energy efficiency refurbishment in owner-occupied housing. *Struct. Surv.* **2013**, *31*, 101–120. [CrossRef]

33. European Commission. Attitudes of European Citizens towards the Environment: Survey Requested by the European Commission, Directorate-General for Environment and Co-Ordinated by the Directorate-General for Communication. Special Eurobarometer 468—Wave EB88.1—TNS Opinion & Social. 2017. Available online: http://ec.europa.eu/commfrontoffice/publicopinion/index.cfm/ResultDoc/download/DocumentKy/83070 (accessed on 2 February 2019).

34. Liu, Y.; Hong, Z.; Zhu, J.; Yan, J.; Qi, J.; Liu, P. Promoting green residential buildings: Residents' environmental attitude, subjective knowledge, and social trust matter. *Energy Policy* **2018**, *112*, 152–161. [CrossRef]

35. Zuo, J.; Zhao, Z.-Y. Green building research–current status and future agenda: A review. *Renew. Sustain. Energy Rev.* **2014**, *30*, 271–281. [CrossRef]

36. Rajaie, M.; Hoseini, S.M.; Malekmohammadi, I. Proposing a socio-psychological model for adopting green building technologies: A case study from Iran. *Sustain. Cities Soc.* **2019**, *45*, 657–668. [CrossRef]

37. Wang, Z.; Zhang, B.; Li, G. Determinants of energy-saving behavioral intention among residents in Beijing: Extending the theory of planned behavior. *J. Renew. Sustain. Energy* **2014**, *6*, 53127. [CrossRef]

38. Wu, S.R.; Greaves, M.; Chen, J.; Grady, S.C. Green buildings need green occupants: A research framework through the lens of the Theory of Planned Behaviour. *Archit. Sci. Rev.* **2017**, *60*, 5–14. [CrossRef]

39. Abrahamse, W.; Steg, L. How do socio-demographic and psychological factors relate to households' direct and indirect energy use and savings? *J. Econ. Psychol.* **2009**, *30*, 711–720. [CrossRef]

40. Bearden, W.; Netemeyer, R.; Haws, K. *Handbook of Marketing Scales: Multi-Item Measures for Marketing and Consumer Behavior Research*; SAGE Publications: Thousand Oaks, CA, USA, 2011.

41. Field, A. *Discovering Statistics Using SPSS (Introducing Statistical Methods)*, 3rd ed.; SAGE Publications: Thousand Oaks, CA, USA, 2009.

42. IBM. IBM SPSS Modeler 18.1.1 Modeling Nodes. 2017. Available online: ftp://public.dhe.ibm.com/software/analytics/spss/documentation/modeler/18.1.1/en/ModelerModelingNodes.pdf (accessed on 20 May 2019).

43. Morrison, D.G. On Interpretation in Discriminant Analysis. *J. Mark. Res.* **1969**, *6*, 156–163. [CrossRef]

44. Backhaus, K.; Erichson, B.; Plinke, W.; Weiber, R. *Multivariate Analysemethoden: Eine anwendungsorientierte Einführung, 14. Aufl. 2016. SpringerLink: Bücher*; Springer: Berlin/Heidelberg, Germany, 2016.

45. Wilson, C.; Dowlatabadi, H. Models of Decision Making and Residential Energy Use. *Annu. Rev. Env. Resour.* **2007**, *32*, 169–203. [CrossRef]

46. Potoski, M.; Urbatsch, R.; Yu, C. Temperature Biases in Public Opinion Surveys*. *Weather Clim. Soc.* **2015**, *7*, 192–196. [CrossRef]

47. Morin, K.; Davis, J.L. Cross-validation: What is it and how is it used in regression? *Commun. Stat. Theory Methods* **2017**, *46*, 5238–5251. [CrossRef]

48. Aravena, C.; Riquelme, A.; Denny, E. Money, Comfort or Environment? Priorities and Determinants of Energy Efficiency Investments in Irish Households. *J. Consum. Policy* **2016**, *39*, 159–186. [CrossRef]

49. Mahapatra, K.; Gustavsson, L. Adoption of innovative heating systems—Needs and attitudes of Swedish homeowners. *Energy Effic.* **2010**, *3*, 1–18. [CrossRef]

50. Earl, E.P.; Peng, T.-C. Home improvements. In *Handbook on the Economics of Leisure*; Edward Elgar Publishing: Cheltenham, UK, 2011; pp. 197–220.

51. McMichael, M.; Shipworth, D. The value of social networks in the diffusion of energy-efficiency innovations in UK households. *Energy Policy* **2013**, *53*, 159–168. [CrossRef]

52. Risholt, B.; Berker, T. Success for energy efficient renovation of dwellings—Learning from private homeowners. *Energy Policy* **2013**, *61*, 1022–1030. [CrossRef]

53. Maller, C.J.; Horne, R.E. Living Lightly: How does Climate Change Feature in Residential Home Improvements and What are the Implications for Policy? *Urban Policy Res.* **2010**, *29*, 59–72. [CrossRef]

54. Karytsas, S. An empirical analysis on awareness and intention adoption of residential ground source heat pump systems in Greece. *Energy Policy* **2018**, *123*, 167–179. [CrossRef]

55. Sopha, B.M.; Klöckner, C.A. Psychological factors in the diffusion of sustainable technology: A study of Norwegian households' adoption of wood pellet heating. *Renew. Sustain. Energy Rev.* **2011**, *15*, 2756–2765. [CrossRef]

56. Ebrahimigharehbaghi, S.; Qian, Q.K.; Meijer, F.M.; Visscher, H.J. Unravelling Dutch homeowners' behaviour towards energy efficiency renovations: What drives and hinders their decision-making? *Energy Policy* **2019**, *129*, 546–561. [CrossRef]

57. Pepels, W. Einführung in das Konsumentenverhalten, 2. Auflage. Available online: http://rybarecords.de/eBooks/Marketing/einfuhrung-in-das-konsumentenverhalten.pdf (accessed on 12 June 2019).

58. D'Agostino, D.; Zangheri, P.; Cuniberti, B.; Paci, D.; Bertoldi, P. *Synthesis Report on the National Plans for Nearly Zero Energy Buildings (NZEBs): Progress of Member States towards NZEBs*; EUR, Scientific and Technical Research Series; Publications Office: Luxembourg, 2016; Volume 27804.

59. Bundesministerium für Bildung und Forschung (BMBF) Grundsatzfragen, Nachhaltigkeit, Klima, Energie53170 Bonn/11055 Berlin (2018) Nachhaltigkeitsforschung sozial-ökologisch gestalten: Agenda-Konferenz für die Sozial-ökologische Forschung19./20. September 2018, Kongress Palais Kassel. Available online: https://botanik.uni-greifswald.de/fileadmin/uni-greifswald/fakultaet/mnf/biologie/botanik/Umweltethik/FEH/BMBF_SOEF_Agenda2018_Programmheft_DinA4Einzelseiten.pdf (accessed on 12 June 2019).

 © 2019 by the authors. Licensee MDPI, Basel, Switzerland. This article is an open access article distributed under the terms and conditions of the Creative Commons Attribution (CC BY) license (http://creativecommons.org/licenses/by/4.0/).

Article

European Cities in the Energy Transition: A Preliminary Analysis of 27 Cities

Estitxu Villamor [1,2,*], **Ortzi Akizu-Gardoki** [1,3], **Olatz Azurza** [1,4], **Leire Urkidi** [1,5], **Alvaro Campos-Celador** [6], **Izaro Basurko** [1,7] **and Iñaki Barcena Hinojal** [1,7]

[1] EKOPOL Research Group, University of the Basque Country (UPV/EHU), 01006 Vitoria-Gasteiz, Spain; ortzi.akizu@ehu.eus (O.A.-G.); olatz.azurza@ehu.eus (O.A.); leire.urkidi@ehu.eus (L.U.); izaro.basurko@ehu.eus (I.B.); inaki.barcena@ehu.eus (I.B.H.)

[2] Department of Applied Physics II, University of the Basque Country (UPV/EHU), Paseo de la Universidad 7, 01006 Vitoria-Gasteiz, Spain

[3] Department of Graphic Design and Engineering Projects, University of the Basque Country (UPV/EHU), 01006 Vitoria-Gasteiz, Spain

[4] Department of Electrical Engineering, University of the Basque Country (UPV/EHU), 20018 Donostia, Spain

[5] Department of Geography, Prehistory and Archaeology, University of the Basque Country (UPV/EHU), 01006 Vitoria-Gasteiz, Spain

[6] Department of Thermal Engineering, University of the Basque Country (UPV/EHU), 20600 Eibar, Spain; alvaro.campos@ehu.eus

[7] Department Political and Administration Science, University of the Basque Country (UPV/EHU), 48940 Leioa, Spain

* Correspondence: estitxu.villamor@ehu.eus

Received: 22 January 2020; Accepted: 6 March 2020; Published: 12 March 2020

Abstract: Nowadays, there is a wide scientific consensus about the unsustainability of the current energy system and at the same time, social awareness about climate change and the IPCC's goals is increasing in Europe. Amongst the different pathways towards them, one alternative is the radical transition to a democratic low-carbon energy system where the local scale has a key leading role. Under this scope, this research is framed within the mPOWER project, financed by the European Commission's H2020 programme, which promotes collaboration among different European municipalities in order to boost the transition to a renewable-based participatory energy system. This paper presents the starting point of the mPOWER project, where the main energy features of 27 selected European municipalities are collected and analysed for the year 2016. An open public tender and selection process was carried out among European cities in order to choose the candidates to participate in mPOWER project. A view of this situation will be taken by the mPOWER project as a diagnostic baseline for the following steps: a peer-to-peer knowledge-sharing process among these European municipalities, and subsequently, among a more extensive group. The first finding of the paper is that, even if those municipalities are trying to reduce their greenhouse gas emissions, they are highly dependent on fossil fuels, even in cases where renewable energies have significant presence. Second, their energy consumption is logarithmically related to the human development index and gross domestic product but not to the size of the cities and their climate characteristics. Finally, despite the work that these cities are making towards energy transition in general and within the mPOWER project in particular, the paper shows a high difficulty mapping their energy systems. The lack of accurate and unified data by the municipalities is a sign of disempowerment at a local and public level in the energy sphere and makes difficult any strategy to advance towards a bottom-up energy transition. Among other goals, the mPOWER project aims to reveal these kinds of difficulties and help local authorities in managing their transition paths.

Keywords: energy transition; sustainable cities; transition roadmaps; renewable energies; policymaking; energy democracy; energy mapping

---

1. Introduction

The urgency for changing the current European energy model and transiting towards a more sustainable one is a well-accepted reality among European inhabitants, policy-makers and scientists. In line with this, it has been clearly detected that the elevated use of fossil fuels needs to be reduced in order to keep the temperature increase of the planet to under 2 degrees Celsius [1]. Furthermore, it has been accepted that the incoming transition will not be merely a technological transition towards renewable energy systems [2], but will require a change in our way of dealing with democracy, economy and social values [3,4]. Indeed, there is an on-going debate about how this multi-dimensional transition will take place [5]. The goals of energy democracy movements all over the world intend to resist the current energy agenda, and reclaim and restructure the energy sector [6], with desired outcomes such as shifting public resources away from fossil fuels, leaving fossil fuels on the ground and stopping extractivist infrastructures, ensuring public or social control of the energy sector, or not prioritising only the monetary benefit out of the energy system.

A number of different voices point to the need for a locally based energy transition, as the local scale is related to more participative, inclusive and socially accepted policies and actions. Van der Schoor et al. [7] argue that local communities should lead a bottom-up transition since they boost the use of local resources with democratic horizontal governance and own financial strength-based energy production and supply. Other similar studies maintain that the new energy system will be funded directly by citizens, since they are at the heart of this new transition based on decentralised renewable energy cooperatives [8]. In the same vein, Vita et el. [9] show that those individuals who are members of sustainability-oriented grassroots initiatives have a more sustainable lifestyle compared to their socio-demographic counterparts, which leads to a more satisfying life and lower carbon footprints in the analysed domains of housing, transport, clothing and food. Indeed, energy embedded in consumed products and services [10,11] is a major issue that goes beyond direct energy consumption and needs to be considered in local energy transitions in order to avoid global rebound effects. Beyond the influence of a single consumer [12], as Grabs et al. [13] point out, grassroots initiatives play a major role in this field. After analysing the nexus between individual motivation and collective action in the context of sustainable consumption, they concluded that individuals can be agents of societal change when they are organised in groups.

Furthermore, some authors attribute the progress of energy transitions in different countries to the presence of grassroots initiatives in such countries [14]. In the above-mentioned reference, Kooij et al. studied what the conditions are for grassroots initiatives to emerge, and how these initiatives create an impact upon these conditions. They observe that openness to alternative discourses and a shared knowledge are favourable conditions for the appearance of these kinds of initiatives. In turn, they argue that the influence they exert upon energy systems is low in the case of those systems with strong vested interests, and that the support by governments and institutions is crucial for those initiatives to make a change.

More specifically, in relation to local authorities, in the Sustainable Development Goals of 2015 [15], the United Nations clearly recognised the key role of local public institutions in the transition towards a more sustainable future. According to Sperling et al. [16], cities will be relevant in boosting locally produced and consumed energy systems based on renewables in different sectors. This change will occur by focusing our attention on underlying social drivers, and releasing the need for economic growth as a single scope [17]. However, they suggested that the role of municipalities needs to be outlined very clearly and that the state must provide municipalities with the necessary planning tools, establishing the required strategy, for the integration of a 100% renewable source-based decentralised system [16] or decarbonisation plans [18]. Comodi et al. [19] show that, even while the role of local authorities is relevant, the results of their actions can be merely partial within a multi-scalar energy transition. The support and energy policies of nations and states remain central in achieving decarbonisation goals under democratic principles [20].

This paper has been developed within the mPOWER project, which focuses on the strategies and actions that municipal authorities carry out towards a sustainable and democratic energy system [21]. Within the framework of the project and despite their limitations, municipalities are recognised as key political actors in the transformation of the energy system within the European context.

During the last decade, the EU has promoted a proactive climate policy, increasing renewables and improving energy efficiency [22]. Some of the leading EU countries, going beyond climate change on the direction of the conservation of the national and global environment, have also opted for nuclear phasing-out [23]. However, the results do not appear to be sufficient. In Europe (European Union 28, EU-28), non-renewable energy consumption (coal, oil, gas and nuclear energy) constitutes 85.3% of the total primary energy supply [24], consuming 23.18 MWh of non-renewable energy per inhabitant and year (MWh·cap^{-1}·yr^{-1}) out of the total of 27.16 MWh·cap^{-1}·yr^{-1}. Even though the consumed non-renewable energy in EU-28 is 26% less than the average for OECD countries, it is 68.7% greater than the world average value [24], which has already been considered 2–6 times above sustainable levels, making it beyond the planetary boundaries [25]. This underlines that there is an urgency to continue reducing the consumed non-renewable energy in EU-28.

According to Tagliapietra et al. [22], the cost of a fully-fledged energy transition in the EU would be similar to that of preserving the current non-renewable energy system, and adopting the right policies to mitigate the distributional effects of said transformation, could make it also socially desirable. Since the social and metabolic transformations required by a real decarbonisation process are to be so relevant [26], it will be determinant to control its distributional and democratic aspects. Nevertheless, concerning local experiences, there is a gap in the current energy system between the new theoretical sustainable energy systems and the reality that the cities are facing [8]. In order to build bridges among theoretical roadmaps and practical strategies, the active role of the municipalities is considered a key factor [9]. Furthermore, difficulties in modelling the impacts of citizens' behaviour on climate change have been detected [27], concluding that further collaboration between social scientists and economic developers are required.

Cities are said to be responsible for 70% of global emissions of CO$_2$eq [28], and different targets have been established in EU cities in order to face the energy transition towards a sustainable one. According to van den Dobbelsteen et al. [29], all targets at a municipal level should aim to research the current energy situation, reduce the total energy consumption, reuse energy (i.e., reuse flows, heat transfer) and produce renewable energy. To this effect, one of the first targets in the EU was established by the Swiss government, following the ETH researchers who estimate 17.5 MWh per capita per annum (equivalent of 2000 watt during 365 days and 24 h) as a sustainable amount [30]. This target is also aligned with the 1 eqtCO$_2$ emissions per person and year, which would allow us to avoid a climate change scenario [30]. The percentage of integration of renewable energy or electricity has also been established, and most European cities have the goal of integrating 20% of renewable energy into their electric mix by 2020 [29]. The European Commission goes beyond and targets a renewable energy share of 20% in the gross final energy demand [31,32]. It has also been common to use relative targets in percentages, such as reductions of CO$_2$eq emissions of 40% by 2030 [31,32] or 85–90% by 2050 [32] (compared to 1990). Another commonly used percentage target is a 27% increase in energy efficiency compared to a 'business-as-usual' projection of future energy demand [30,31]. The existence of different goals has generated a diversification of targets among different cities, with an absence of unified targets [33]. Nevertheless, despite the existence of targets, emission reductions in cities measured in consumption-based accounts do not always occur. In the study developed in six Japanese cities from 1980 to 2000, it was concluded that consumption-based emissions measured by carbon inventories have not been reduced, but rather increased from 8 to 9 eqtCO$_2$ per year and capita [28].

Furthermore, it has been also detected that the energy consumption and carbon emissions of cities are related to their economic performance, especially in developed countries such as China [34], thus a massive reduction of energy or emissions could happen to not be attractive or convenient for some cities, drawing us into a controversial panorama.

Despite these limitations, different initiatives are being developed on the roadmap to more sustainable cities. One such example is the European Energy Awards [35], given to municipalities for energy and climate protection activities at the European level. Those cities awarded can be considered exemplary in energy transition.

In this regard, different bottom-up movements have arisen in recent years to boost the necessary energy transition. The 'Covenant of Mayors' (CoM) [36] is one of the most relevant initiatives, a movement that involves more than 9000 cities in 131 countries, where local authorities voluntarily commit to meeting and exceeding the European goals for CO_2 emissions reductions [37]. In the same vein of work, 'Energy Cities', the European association of cities in energy transition, is a network of local authority representatives from 30 countries that gathers frontrunners and energy transition beginners, city officials and technical experts. Their principal goal is to support the creation of new policies through National Energy and Climate Plans (NECP) [38]. Similarly, Ursula von der Leyen presented the plan to make the EU the world's first 'climate-neutral' continent by 2050 [39].

Apart from the work that has been carried out on (and combined with) policy-making, from an academic perspective, several efforts to model a sustainable energy model have been made. The MEDEAS project [40] is one of the best examples, a tool to design the transition into a 100% renewable energy system (RES) in Europe. This initiative considers three different scenarios to model the energetic macro-economic system from 1995 to 2050: Business as Usual (BAU), Green Growth (GG) and the Post-Growth or degrowth approach (PG). Other tool to boost this transition in urban districts is the learning experience through the use of visualisation games, such as Go2Zero [41].

Within the framework of this European energy transition, the mPOWER project is funded by the European Commission Horizon 2020 Research and Innovation Framework Programme and aims to boost municipal actions, public engagement and the creation of routes towards the necessary Energy Transition [42]. The project is managed by seven partners (the University of Glasgow, Platform-London, the Stichting Transnational Institute, the Society for the Reduction of Carbon Limited, the Institute for Political Ecology, Energy Cities and the University of the Basque Country). Throughout the 48-month duration of the project, the partners will detect, through systematic peer review, the best replicable municipal practices in energy transitions and create a framework to share the different achievements in a peer-to-peer learning programme.

The central question of this paper is: What is the current situation, regarding energy, of the 27 municipalities that were selected for the initial stages of the learning programme? In addition, two sub-questions are defined, to be answered throughout the structure of the paper:

- What are the difficulties in describing the current situation?
- How can these difficulties help other authorities in their energy transition?

The analysis used in order to answer these questions is based on the statistical evaluation of various energy indicators and was carried out using the data provided by municipalities from an online survey related to energy consumption, renewable production and municipal policies and strategies of participatory energy transition. The data were collected in order to determine the baseline for year 2016 (in some cases, updated data of 2017 have been used), that is, the reference situation that will be compared with that of the end of the project. To this end, first, a description is given of the mPOWER project, as well as the methodology used in the research, which includes the baselining, standardisation and evaluation of the data. Following this, the results obtained from the 27 cities (i.e., municipalities) are presented and, finally, a summary provided of the conclusions drawn.

2. The mPOWER Project

The mPOWER project aims, by means of learning programmes participated in by more than 100 local public authorities, to replicate innovative best practices in municipal energy, and develop ambitious energy transition plans. The project relies on two learning programmes: first, a bespoke learning programme (referred to as mPOWER Exchange) in which 27 cities are participating and second, a peer-to-peer online learning programme (referred to as mPOWER Digital) where around 90 municipalities will participate. This publication deals with the first part of the project, the bespoke learning process, in which 27 cities are involved. In order to choose the cities, Covenant of Majors [36] and Energy Cities [43] platforms were used to share the possibility of participating in the project across all European cities. Furthermore, the institutions leading the mPOWER project (see Acknowledgments) offered hundreds of municipalities the possibility of applying to take part in the selection process.

Among all the candidate cities, a ranking was developed by the Glasgow University members so as to choose the most appropriate cities. The ranking was made following an online survey, interviews and online research and was developed a selection of main learning preferences of cities based on motivation and participation for an energy transition; experience in renewable energy integration; experience in energy efficiency and consumption organisation. It is important to note that the cities were selected not only for their expertise, but moreover for their interest in participating in a learning programme. The selected cities were classified into three topics: Local Energy Communities, Renewable Energy Integration and Energy Efficiency. Finally, in order to start the learning process, one or two working groups have been created for each of the topics. In each of the five different working groups created, a group leader was selected by the project organiser. The group leaders have the role of showing the rest of the members the initiatives that have been developed or are planned to be developed.

The mPOWER Exchange programme is based on city visits to share knowledge, and enables technicians and policy-makers to invest face-to-face time researching, understanding and contrasting existing and new energy infrastructures and projects, with the aim of promoting participation and enhancing the exchange of practical knowledge and expertise.

3. Methodology of the Research Baseline

At the initial stage, a baseline evaluation was planned within mPOWER in order to establish a reference framework to be compared with the situation at the end of the project. This baseline will serve to gain knowledge on the energy reality of the participating cities and to help to evaluate the expected impacts from the mPOWER project:

1. To increase energy savings;
2. To increase renewable energy production;
3. To increase the capabilities of public authorities on energy supply and production management;
4. To create city-based strategies for encompassing energy transition.

Because of the lack of a public European or worldwide database about energy consumption and production at the municipal level [36], and the fact that there is very little up-to-date online information in this field, our strategy was to directly collect the data via an online survey (see Appendix A Material for accessing the survey) to be completed by the municipal technicians or politicians in charge of the mPOWER project in each participating city.

The questions from the survey cover both qualitative and quantitative aspects related to the objectives and the expected impacts of the project: Amount and type of consumed energy; greenhouse gas emissions (GHG); renewable energy systems (RES); municipal public staff in the energy sector and in energy transition projects; municipal public investments related to energy transition; municipal plans for renewable energy power development; municipality led initiatives and policies for energy transition; citizenship/cooperative-led initiatives and campaigns for energy transition.

Taking into account the impacts for mPOWER and specific targets for energy transition listed above, several indicators were chosen to be analysed in this baseline. Some of them were directly obtained from the survey, some were found in the literature on the topic and some were calculated by the authors. The following table lists all the analysed indicators, relating them to the expected impacts and targets, as well as indicating where in the paper they can be found. Note that impact 3 is transversal to all targets that is why it is not appearing in Table 1.

The performance of these indicators, by assessing them at the beginning and at the end of the project, will be used to evaluate the impacts achieved and the success of different strategies and actions that will be carried out throughout the project. Some of the indicators, such as total energy consumption and RES percentage, are analysed in this paper in order to evaluate how cities are currently performing. However, others such as RES installation and production are left for a future analysis and comparison with the end-of-project situation. This is due to the difficulty in obtaining a reference target to compare with.

3.1. Survey Data Standardisation Methodology

As mentioned above, we faced difficulties with the data collection since some of the cities did not complete the survey (or part of it) and, among those cities that did, in some cases the collected data was not consistent. After compiling all the information on a database, the validity of the RES production, energy consumption and GHG emission data was assessed as explained below.

In the case of municipal RES production, we related the data on installed power (in MW) with the total annual production (in MWh) in order to obtain the capacity factor (CF), i.e., ratio of actual energy output over a whole year to the maximum possible energy output over that year [44]. We considered the data were consistent only when the CF ranged between 1 and 90%. In those cases where only installed power or annual production was given, the data could not be checked for consistency (which is regarded as a lack of data in Figure 1). See Table A1 from the Appendix B. for checking how the RES data were interpreted.

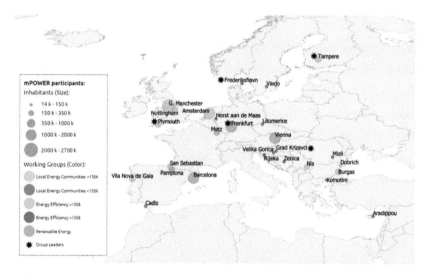

Figure 1. Municipalities selected for the mPOWER exchange programme. The selected 27 municipalities are classified in five different working groups.

In the case of the energy consumption and GHG emission data, first the values per capita were obtained by dividing the values given by each city by the number of inhabitants. We then compared them to the national per capita average consumption and emission data, taken from the International Energy Agency (IEA) database (2016) [24]. The data given by the cities were considered consistent when they were on the same order of magnitude as the ones taken from the IEA: specifically, when the data of the cities were no lower than one-third of the IEA data, or they were no higher than three times the IEA data. When the data were not considered consistent or when no information was given, the IEA data were used instead.

3.2. Survey Data Assessment Methodology

In this section, we analyse some of the above-mentioned indicators, comparing the obtained data across all the 27 cities. The number of resources that each municipality assigns to the energy transition (number of campaigns, people and budget) has been analysed as an indicator of energy democracy. Total energy consumption was analysed next (how much energy per capita is consumed in each city), quantifying also what the main energy sources are and in which sectors that energy is consumed. Hidden Energy Flows were included among the analysed sectors.

Energy consumption has been linked to GHG emissions by comparing the obtained emission and consumption data, and additionally by estimating the emissions that should be obtained from the consumed energy; this was done by taking into account each city's energy mix and the emission intensities of each type of fuel (eqtCO$_2$ per kWh) provided by the IPCC [45], as well as the electricity mix per country [24].

Finally, various economic, climatic or size indicators, such as the gross domestic product (GDP), the human development index (HDI), the heating and cooling degree days (HDD and CDD) and the number of inhabitants of each city were plotted as a function of the energy consumption and fitted to a logarithmic equation in order to try to find a correlation, following the methodology of Steinberger et al. [46], Arto et al. [10] and Akizu et al. [11].

4. Results and Discussion

The aim of this section is to provide an overview of the obtained data, in order to give the cities an insight into the steps needed for an energy transition, as well as to gain an indication of what to learn from each other, by comparing their energy consumption and GHG emission data. Nevertheless, before doing so, careful effort has been made to check the reliability of the data received.

4.1. Survey Data Standardisation

As can be observed, Figure 2 shows the ratio between valid and non-valid data, as well as the absence of any answer for the energy consumption, GHG emission and RES production data given by the cities, which was standardised as previously explained in Section 3.1. Regarding energy consumption, the highest uncertainty corresponds to the case of liquid fuels, where only 37% of the cities provided reliable data. In the case of coal, all of the received answers were considered valid, since the consumption of this fuel is very low and most of the cities reported no consumption. Apart from coal, natural gas consumption data present the highest reliability, with 63% of the answers considered valid.

Regarding GHG emissions, 59% of the cities provided reliable data. As for RES installation and production, we observe a better knowledge in the case of electric RES (48% of answers valid) as compared to thermal, where only 41% of the cities provided an answer, with a validity rate of 33%.

With respect to the total energy consumption per capita, Figure 3 shows the data that we were able to collect. Note that, in order to calculate this total, only the final consumptions of electricity, natural gas, liquid fuels and coal were included in the survey. This, in some cases, resulted in a gap between the total real energy consumption of a city and the total energy consumption calculated in this assessment. As a further check of the validity of the results, the direct energy consumption data obtained from the surveys is compared with the national total primary energy supply (TPES) per capita of the corresponding countries in Figure 2. The ratios between these two range from 26% to 95%, meaning that this standardisation process has allowed us to map a 49% average TPES per inhabitant of a country. The gaps, on the one hand, may be due to the fact that a specific city is being compared to its national average reality. On the other hand, the energy losses in transformation (in order to produce electricity and heat from coal, gas or biofuels and waste), the fuels employed for non-energy uses (crude oil for asphalt and oil products used in agriculture and chemical industry) and other fuels such as biofuels (biomass, biogas, bioethanol), butane gas or waste were not considered in the survey, which certainly led to differences.

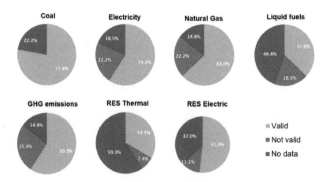

Figure 2. Data standardisation.

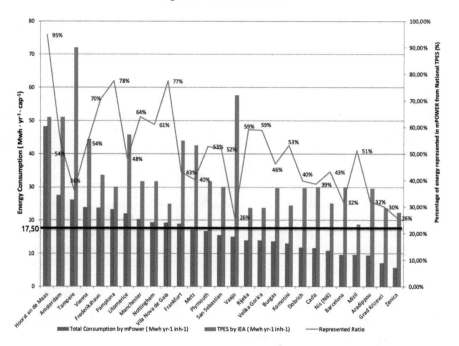

Figure 3. The total energy consumption by inhabitant computed for the selected cities (by mPOWER project) and the national reality reflected by the International Energy Agency averages. The goal in energy reduction of 17.5 MWh·cap^{-1}·yr^{-1} has been indicated [30].

Another difficulty in the calculation of the total energy consumption was the case of those cities with significant production by Combined Heat and Power (CHP) plants, commonly fed by natural gas. In CHPs, energy consumption is measured, such as the consumed amount of natural gas, but similarly the electricity produced by the CHPs is also taken into account when energy consumed at homes is measured. Thus, this could generate small amount of double accounting that this project has not been able to correct. For future research, a specific question could be included to understand the energy production from CHPs, and thus avoid this double accounting.

From this standardisation we obtained the data to be used in the evaluation of the results (Section 3.2), which is listed in Table A2 from the Appendix B.

4.2. Survey Data Assessment

Figure 4 shows some of the indicators related to energy democracy: the staff working on energy and transition, the municipal energy or transition campaigns, and the budget dedicated to energy transition (shown in Table A3 from Appendix B). These indicators are a measure of the resources dedicated to energy and transition by enrolled authorities at both the technical and the social level. With some exceptions, such as Barcelona, Frankfurt, Horst aan de Maas, Vienna and Zenica, most of the municipalities have from 0 to 20 employees working on energy and energy transition issues. Similarly, excluding Nis, Pamplona and Rijeka, most of the cities have from 5 to 15 annual campaigns. In the annual budget for the energy transition, the values differ much more. Whereas most of the cities dedicate several thousands of euros (within a broad range from 20,000 € to 792,000 €), some of the cities dedicate millions of euros to the energy transition. Such is the case of Mizil (1 M€) or Frankfurt (1.8 M€). The highest budgets correspond to Vila Nova de Gaia (5 M€), Manchester (7 M€) and Amsterdam (87.5 M€), which were left out of the Figure in order to make the rest of the cities visible. It is important to note that those budgets often depend on external projects (European or national, for instance), that make it difficult to define a fixed and constant annual budget. Some cities also pointed out the difficulty to define a budget solely related to energy transition, since this is normally spread out over the overall budget of the city.

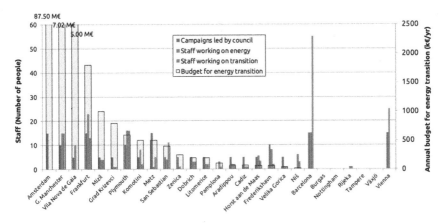

Figure 4. Annual budget, number of campaigns led by the city councils and number of people working on energy transition.

Regarding the total energy consumption per capita, and going back to Figure 3, we can observe how energy consumption differs among the cities analysed. Thus, Zenica (Bosnia and Herzegovina) is the city with the lowest consumption per capita (6 MWh·cap^{-1}·yr^{-1}) while in Horst aan de Maas (Netherlands) the consumption is as high as 48 MWh·cap^{-1}·yr^{-1}, meaning that Zenica consumes 87.5% less energy than Horst aan de Maas. Comparing it to the previously cited target of 17.5 Mwh per person and year [30], 17 out of 27 cities do reach the target. From the ones that do not reach it, the total energy consumption of Frankfurt (Germany), Vienna (Austria), Aradippou (Cyprus), Nottingham (United Kingdom) and Metz (France) is especially high. Alternatively, when national TPES data are taken into account, most of the values are higher than the total energy consumption mapped by mPOWER. For instance, the values change to 22 MWh·cap^{-1}·yr^{-1} in the case of Zenica and 51 MWh·cap^{-1}·yr^{-1} in the case of Horst aan de Maas, leading to a 57% smaller energy consumption in the former. In this case, all the consumptions are above the target level, meaning that none of the municipalities is able to reach it.

Figure 5 depicts the distribution of the municipal energy consumption by type of fuel, taking into account the national electric mix as that of the municipality. That assumption was made due to a lack of data on the RES production of some of the municipalities, based on the fact that the electricity consumed in each city is supplied by the national grid. This data changes considerably from city to city. It can be observed that in northern countries like Tampere (Finland) and Vaxjo (Sweden), around a 50% of the whole consumed energy is in the form of electricity. Other countries, such as the Netherlands (Amsterdam, Horst aan de Maas) and Austria (Vienna) present a stronger dependence on natural gas. It needs to be clarified that in Horst aan de Maas the high consumption of natural gas is due to the massive use of heated greenhouses for intensive vegetable production [47]. Finally, southern and eastern cities, such as Pamplona and Cadiz (Spain), Zenica or Krizevci (Croatia) make, in proportion, a higher use of liquid fuels, but this could be due to the generalised use of other fuels, such as biofuels or butane gas (instead of natural gas) that was not taken into account in the calculations. In Figure 5, the electric consumption has been disaggregated by source, according to the national electricity mix, in order to obtain the RES percentage of the total municipal energy consumption. It can be seen that only Vaxjo is above the target of 27% of renewable energy from the total energy consumption, with a 27.1% share. In the rest of the municipalities, renewable energies cover a maximum of 25.8% (Tampere) and a minimum of 1.5% (Horst aan de Maas) of the total energy consumed. Northern countries (Finland, Denmark and Austria) and Croatia show particularly high RES percentages. However, we have observed that a high renewable electricity mix (in green in Figure 5) does not assure low fossil fuel consumption. On the other hand, a lower energy consumption does not assure a high renewable share, i.e., none of the cities that are able to reduce their fossil fuel consumption to below 10 MWh·cap^{-1}·yr^{-1} (Aradippou -Cyprus-, Barcelona, Krizevci, Mizil -Romania-, Nis -Serbia-, Vila Nova de Gaia -Portugal- and Zenica) have an integration of renewable energy above 17.3%.

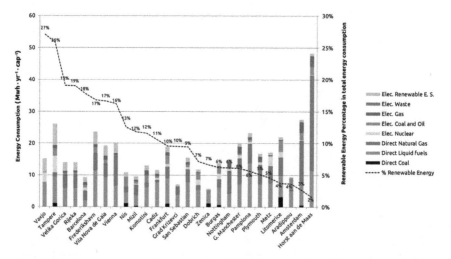

Figure 5. Energy consumption by fuel within the direct and indirect (in electric vector) energy consumptions by municipality (note that the total consumption of cities obtained from mPOWER survey differs, as shown in Figure 3, from the national average data provided by International Energy Agency (IEA)).

In order to complement the information given in Figure 5 (taking into account the differences shown in Figure 3), Figure 6 has been created, where sectorial national direct energy consumption averages have been included from IEA balances [24], and national hidden energy flows (HEF) have also been added from previous analyses carried out by the authors [11]. In order to take into account the displacements that the impacts related to the consumption of the citizens generate elsewhere, energy embodied in imported products and services in each country have been included using the latest data from the year 2014 to obtain the difference between total primary energy footprint (TPEF) and TPES per capita at a national level, adding it to each city (HEF = TPEF/TPES). The calculations have been developed using global multi-regional input-output (GMRIO) methodology, and data are available in Appendix B, Table A4. The accuracy of these calculations could be improved with municipal hidden energy flows data instead of national average ones, but this would require an input-output analysis at a local level. Although a methodology for local input-output analysis is currently being developed by Cazcarro et al. [48] as well as by our team [49], it is currently beyond the scope of this paper.

This last figure shows how only a small percentage of the energy consumption, between 9 and 24%, is consumed by private households in terms of electricity and heat (green numbers in Figure 5), whereas from 76% to 91% is not consumed in the residential sector (imported and national products and services, transportation needs for humans and trade, and transformation and distribution losses of energy).

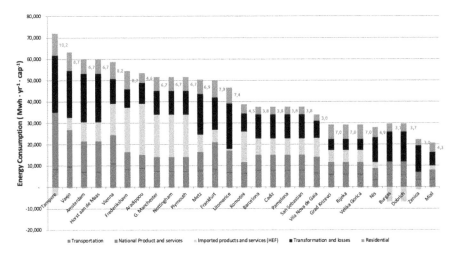

Figure 6. National energy consumptions by sector.

Figure 7 shows the relation between energy consumption (in red bars) and GHG emissions (in blue and green). The red bars correspond to the total per capita energy consumption calculated by mPOWER. The blue line corresponds to the per capita GHG emission data obtained from the survey and standardised using the IEA national values (as explained in Section 3.1). Finally, the green line corresponds to the GHG emissions calculated from the total energy consumption mapped from the surveys, taking into account the GHG emission intensity of each fuel given by the IPCC (tonnes of CO_2eq per kWh), as well as the emission intensity of the national electricity mix. This way, when the IEA standardised values and the IPCC estimated values are on the same order of magnitude, it can be regarded as a further check of the validity of the results. We consider that both GHG emission values are on the same order of magnitude when the IEA standardised values are within the IPCC estimated error bars, which cover a range from 50 to 150% of the IPCC estimated value. It can be observed in general trends that energy consumption and the corresponding CO_2eq emissions are related.

Even if the general trend is that the higher energy consumption, the higher the emissions, there are some exceptions, such as Litomerice, Manchester, Nottingham and Pamplona, which have a low IEA standardised GHG emission despite their high energy consumption. This can be explained by the use of different energy sources (a high natural gas and RES rate in the case of Manchester, Nottingham and Pamplona) or the uncertainty found in the data (low GHG emission data in the case of Litomerice). In some other cities, such as Frankfurt, Nis and Tampere, the opposite relationship is observed: the IEA standardised GHG emission data is high compared to the total energy consumption. This could be due to an overestimation of the GHG emissions or due to an underestimation of the energy consumption. In this last case, as well as in the case of Litomerice, we know the inconsistencies between IEA standardised GHG emissions and energy consumption are due to uncertainties in the data (and not due to the use of different energy sources), because the GHG emissions estimated from the IPCC intensities and those standardised with the IEA values are not on the same order of magnitude.

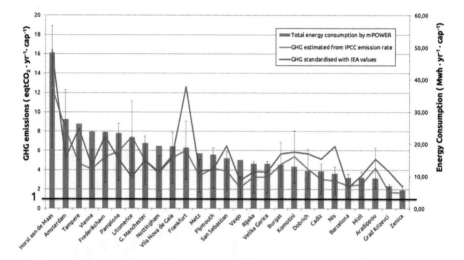

Figure 7. Energy consumption per capita by municipality, and the respective greenhouse gas (GHG) emissions obtained from the survey (IEA standardised) and calculated from the energy consumption and the IPCC emission intensities.

Finally, in order to understand the energy consumption differences in all the 27 cities, the total energy consumption detected by mPOWER has been related to the achieved national HDI [50] and national GDP [51], and also to physical conditions like the climate or the size of each city. All data were fitted to the equation "y = A ln(x) + B" following the methodology presented by Steinberger et al. [46], Arto et al. [10] and Akizu et al. [11]. Note that Horst aan de Maas was left out of the analysis because a large part of its energy consumption is used for industrial agriculture, making it difficult to correlate with the rest of the cities. This phenomenon could also occur in cities with a high presence of industrial production, but our results for rest of the analysed cities have not shown alterations as significant as those detected in Horst aan de Mass, so it has not been taken into account for the rest of the cities.

Figure 8 gives us a comparison of the consumed energy and the benefits obtained from it, using HDI and GDP indicators as they are the most commonly used in this respect [10,11]. The former, more related with human behaviours, allows us to understand how energy can affect education, life expectancy and economy, and the latter only focuses on national economy. The general trends among analysed cities show that life quality standards, measured in national HDI (Figure 8a) and GDP (Figure 8b), are directly related to consumed energy. Nevertheless, it can be observed that some cities can achieve high standards of living with markedly low energy (such as Vaxjo, Frankfurt and Frederikshavn). It must be noted that since HDI and GDP data are national averages, they are not fully sensitive to the realities of the cities, and it would be helpful to include city data for both indicators in the future.

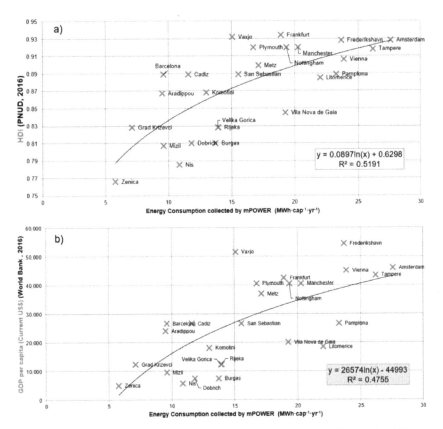

Figure 8. Energy consumption of each city compared to the corresponding national Human Development Index (HDI) (**a**) and the national Gross Domestic Product (GDP) (**b**).

In Figure 9a, the climate of each city was taken into account by using the heating degree day (HDD) and cooling degree day (CDD) factors [52]. In the analysed cities, according to the obtained fitting and R^2, there is a low correlation between the energy consumption and the HDD plus CDD, as shown in Figure 9a. Cities such as Zenica or Krizevci, with a high heating need, have a very low energy consumption per capita, whereas cities like Amsterdam and Pamplona have a higher energy consumption with a lower heating and cooling requirement. This could also be related to the difference in GDP. Figure 8b compares the size of each city (measured in inhabitants) and the energy consumption per capita, with the previous hypothesis that bigger cities might be more efficient than the smaller ones. However, Figure 9b shows that this assumption does not correspond to reality. Small cities like Aradippou show low energy consumption, whereas big cities such as Amsterdam are not especially efficient because of their large number of inhabitants.

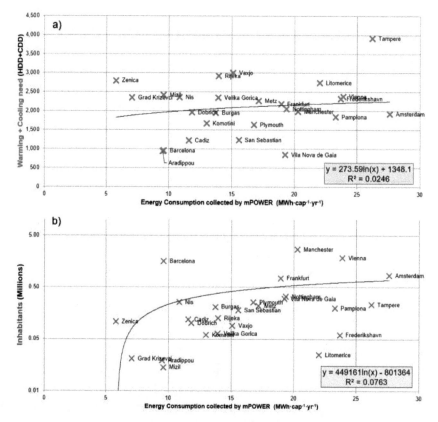

Figure 9. Energy consumption of each city, and the corresponding heating and cooling need according to the climate of each city (**a**), and the corresponding inhabitants (**b**).

Table 1. Indicators used in the paper in order to analyse and compare the 27 cities.

Indicator	Impact	Target	Description	Unit	Where
Validity of the gathered data	3	Energy democratisation	Indicates the level of knowledge of public energy employees on municipal energy issues.	%	Figure 2
Municipal campaigns	4	Energy democratisation	Indicates the number of campaigns that city has create in order to boost energy transitions.	No. $\cdot$ yr^{-1}	Figure 4, Table A3
Staff on energy	3,4	Energy democratisation	Indicates the human capacity of the cities in energy transition field.	No. $\cdot$ yr^{-1}	Figure 4, Table A3
Staff on transition	3,4	Energy democratisation	Indicates the human capacity of cities in ecological transition field.	No. $\cdot$ yr^{-1}	Figure 4, Table A3
Budget for transition	1,2,3,4	Energy democratisation	Amount of public resources dedicated to boost the energy transition: increase efficiency, increase RES or increase participation.	€ $\cdot$ yr^{-1}	Figure 4, Table A3
RES percentage	2	Increase of renewable share	RES percentage of the total mapped energy consumption by taking into account the national electricity mix.	%	Figure 5
Installed RES	2	Increase of renewable share	Total RES installation of the whole municipality.	MW	Table A2
RES production	2	Increase of renewable share	Annual RES production of the whole municipality.	MWh·yr^{-1}	Table A2
Plans for RES investment	2	Increase of renewable share	A measure of the increase of RES, by comparing the plans to the actual installed	MW for 2020	Table A3
Total energy consumption	1	Reduction of energy consumption	Total consumption of the municipality that mPOWER was able to map.	MWh·yr^{-1}·cap^{-1}	Figures 3, 5 and 7, Table A2
Total Primary Energy Supply	1	Reduction of energy consumption	Total average national energy consumption.	MWh·yr^{-1}·cap^{-1}	Figure 6
Total Primary Energy Footprint	1	Reduction of energy consumption	Total average national energy consumption, including energy embodied in imported/exported goods and services.	MWh·yr^{-1}·cap^{-1}	Figure 6
Hidden Energy Flows (HEF)	1	Reduction of energy consumption	Percentage energy embodied in imported/exported goods and services (HEF = TPEF/TPES).	(%)	Figure 6, Table A4
GHG emissions	1	Reduction of energy consumption	Total GHG emissions of the municipality.	eqtCO$_2$·yr^{-1}·cap^{-1}	Figure 7, Table A2
Human Development Index (HDI)	3,4	Reduction of energy consumption	This indicator allows to compare the acquired life quality in comparison of consumed energy.	HDI	Figure 8a
Gross Domestic Product (GDP)	3,4	Reduction of energy consumption	This indicator allows to compare the acquired national economic development in comparison of consumed energy.	US\$·yr^{-1}·cap^{-1}	Figure 8b
Heating Degree Day (HDD) and Cooling Degree Day (CDD)	1	Reduction of energy consumption	This indicator allows us to compare the consumed energy and need of heating and cooling due to the climate conditions.	Degree Days	Figure 9a
Inhabitants	1	Reduction of energy consumption	This indicator allows us to compare the energy consumption according the inhabitants of a city.	Number of inhabitants	Figure 9b

5. Conclusions

In relation to the difficulties in collecting municipal energy data, we have several considerations that may be relevant for the specific goals of the project and to be taken into account when boosting the general energy transition in Europe. The low quality of the data gathered by the municipalities (sometimes literally non-existent) is a clear sign of public disempowerment in energy issues. Despite the high effort of each municipality, there are not enough public up-to-date municipal data at the European level and the energy sector is mostly owned by private companies that manage the information according to their own interests [53]. Therefore, this project reflects how significant it is to have real energy consumption and production data in order to lead an energy transition at city level.

Nowadays, participation in different energy transition initiatives, such as the Covenant of Mayors, and thus, the sharing of energy consumption and GHG emission data with citizens is a voluntary act. However, in some regions, such as the Basque Country [54], the publication of data related to energy consumption is starting to become compulsory for their cities and villages. We claim this kind of law to provide citizens with information could boost the incoming energy transition. This knowledge could facilitate evaluating energy policies, analysing the real needs of each city, or creating roadmaps and energy plans for incoming sustainable energy transitions. We expect that this project will help in revealing these kinds of issues, enabling initiatives such as the creation of public databases, and empowering local public institutions in the management of low-carbon energy transition. Similarly, it is important to spread the know-how of the current energy reality among citizens and other agents in cities in order to boost citizen-led initiatives. As an example, and as an alternative to private energy management, renewable cooperatives could be an opportunity to start a transition towards a democratic and sustainable energy system [55–57].

Going back to the data collection, it has been observed that the mPOWER baseline survey has allowed us to map an average of 49% of the energy consumption per capita (in comparison with national average total primary energy supply values offered by the IEA) consumed by citizens. The remaining 52% is mainly due to transformation losses, and also, to a lesser extent, due to the lack of integration of non-common energy vectors such as biomass (like firewood or biofuels), butane gas, waste use for energy purposes and fuel oil boilers. In some cases, the use of CHPs could also generate alterations in results because of the double accountability they tend to cause when taking into account the gas they consume, but the electricity produced in homes is also taken into account.

The obtained results reveal that European cities still present a strong dependence on fossil fuels, ranging from 72% of fossil fuels in the total energy mix mapped in this paper to 98.4%. The low percentage of electricity in energy supply is also noteworthy, where renewable generation is still generally minimal. In addition, because of the small percentage of the total (renewable and non-renewable) energy that is consumed by private homes in the form of electricity and heat, it must be underlined that energy transition not only needs to be focused on the energy consumption of private dwellings, but it especially needs to challenge the current model of products and goods consumption. In this sense, this work provides a view of how consumers have the potential to improve the national energy system, partaking in shared responsibility with governments [58].

The comparison among the 27 cities analysed clearly relates the achieved human development index and gross domestic product in a city to the consumed energy, showing a dependence on energy consumption to maintain the current living standards, and improve them. However, some cities already show that they can achieve high GDP and HDI values with relatively low energy consumption (as Vaxjo and Plymouth); hence these cities should be taken as a reference. On the other hand, we can see that the climate and size of a city do not positively or negatively affect the energy efficiency, and thus, this gives various types of cities the opportunity to think about different strategies to improve their own energy systems.

Finally, in relation to the mPOWER project, this baseline has been shown as an effective tool to obtain an initial picture of the energy situation of different European cities. The results of the baseline and of this paper will help to improve the development of the project and can encourage participant cities to identify the above-mentioned key obstacles and information gaps in the transition to a participative low-carbon energy system.

Author Contributions: Conceptualization E.V., O.A.-G. and L.U.; Data curation E.V., O.A.-G. and O.A.; Formal analysis E.V. and O.A.-G.; Investigation E.V., O.A.-G., O.A., L.U., A.C.-C., I.B. and I.B.H.; Methodology E.V., O.A.-G. and O.A.; Writing—original draft E.V. and O.A.-G.; Writing—review & editing O.A., L.U., A.C.-C., I.B. and I.B.H. All authors have read and agreed to the published version of the manuscript.

Funding: This research was funded by the European Union's H2020 Research and Innovation programme under grant agreement 785171—mPOWER project. The research has been supported by 'Ekopol: Iraunkortasunerako Bideak' research group, recognised by the Basque Government (IT-1365-19) and the University of the Basque Country (GIC-18/22).

Acknowledgments: The authors would like to recognise the effort made by the technicians of the 27 analysed cities, during the data gathering process and also all the mPOWER research team from the University of Glasgow, Platform-London, Stitching Transnational Institute, The Society for the Reduction of Carbon Limited, Institute for Political Ecology and Energy Cities (Energy-Cities Association).

Conflicts of Interest: The authors declare no conflict of interest.

Appendix A. Online Survey

We need some data and information to carry out a baseline assessment of your municipality. This will allow us to calculate the evolution of the energy transition and the learning process in the coming years. Thank you very much for your involvement and the data you provide! *Required

1. Name*
2. Municipality*

Renewable energy data

Please fill in the 'data year', it is very important for us. The data should be from 2017 or as close as possible.

3. Installed renewable thermal power MW and (year)
4. Renewable thermal energy production MWh and (year)
5. Installed renewable electric power MW and (year)
6. Renewable electric energy production MWh and (year)

Non-renewable energy data

Please fill in the 'data year', it is very important for us. The data should be from 2017 or as close as possible.
7. Natural gas consumption MWh and (year)
8. Electricity consumption MWh and (year)
9. Liquid fuels MWh and (year)
10. Coal MWh and (year)
11. Greenhouse Gas Emissions eqCO_2 tonnes and (year)
12. If your city/municipality has any data documents with more information about energy data, you can share the link with us here! (or email to name@ehu.eus)

Staff and budget for energy transition

Maybe you have answered these questions before, but it is important that we have the most up-to-date information.

13. People working in energy issues (number of equivalent full-time municipal employees or subcontracted)
14. People working in energy transition issues (energy efficiency, promotion of RES, energy democracy, sustainable mobility, etc.,)
15. Annual budget for energy transition (Should exclude personal costs)

16. If you have any documents about the staff and budget for energy transition that you want to share, you can paste the link here or email name@ehu.eus

Plans for investment and citizen participation

In this section we are interested in the plans for energy transitions in the future, and the information about citizen participation in the energy transition of your municipality

17. Does your municipality already have published plans for renewable energy power development?

- Yes
- No

18. If the previous answer was yes, what is the amount of additional MW planned during the next tax year?
19. Number of municipality-led initiatives and campaigns for energy transition

- 0
- 1–5
- 6–10
- 15+

20. Number of citizenship/cooperative-led initiatives and campaigns for energy transition

- 0
- 1–5
- 6–10
- 15+

21. If you have any interesting documents that you want to share with us about the energy transition in your municipality, you can paste the link here or send an email to name@ehu.eus

Appendix B. Standardised Data of the Research Project

Table A1. Interpretation of some of the received RES data.

City	Data Type	Received Value	Considered Value	Reason
Metz	Installed RES electric (MW)	13,100	131.00	Received data is quite high and presents no proportionality with the energy generation indicated
Horst aan de Maas	Installed RES thermal (MW)	3.07 PJ/year	852,777 MWh	Unit change from International System to required (MWh) is applied. Data is allocated in the energy column
Horst aan de Maas	Installed RES electric (MW)	3.45 PJ/year	958,333 MWh	Unit change from International System to required (MWh) is applied. Data is allocated in the energy column
Manchester	Installed RES thermal (MW)	53.82017	53.8	The last 4 digits refer to the year of the data
G. Manchester	Installed RES electric (MW)	1,262,017	126	The last 4 digits refer to the year of the data
G. Manchester	Consumption Electricity (MWh/year)	139,322,016	13,932	The last 4 digits refer to the year of the data
G. Manchester	Consumption Gas (MWh/year)	216,720,002,016	21,672,000	The last 4 digits refer to the year of the data
G. Manchester	Consumption Coal (MWh/year)	5,162,016	516	The last 4 digits refer to the year of the data
Mizil	Installed RES electric (MW)	1735	1.735	Based on data given in a preliminary survey 1.735 MW PV
Mizil	Production RES electric (MWh)	0.67	670	Produced energy-power ratio is logical with this figure (value was introduced in GWh)
Nottingham	Production RES electric (MWh)	-	6	Based on data given in a preliminary survey: 6 MW PV
Pamplona	Production RES electric (MWh)	190	0.19	Produced energy-power ratio is logical with this figure (value was introduced in GWh)
Tampere	Production RES thermal (MW)	-	315	Based on data given in a preliminary survey: 83 MW Biomass, 232 CHP
Tampere	Production RES electric (MW)	-	16	Based on data given in a preliminary survey: 16 MW Hydro
Zenica	Produced RES electric (MWh)	0.9	900	Produced energy-power ratio is logical with this figure (value was introduced in GWh)
Zenica	Produced RES thermal (MWh)	0.2	200	Produced energy-power ratio is logical with this figure (value was introduced in GWh)

Table A2. GHG emission, energy consumption and RES installation and production data of all 27 municipalities, after the standardisation of the results.

| City | GHG (t CO$_2$ eq/Year) | Energy Consumption (MWh/Year) | | | | | RES Installation and Production | | | |
		Electricity	Gas	Liquid Fuels	Coal	Total	Thermal Power (MW)	Thermal Energy (MWh/Year)	Electric Power (MW)	Electric Energy (MWh/Year)
Amsterdam	4500	5,787,800	11,386,400	6,123,200	437,723	23,735,122	-	-	-	-
Aradippou	98,383	77,482	8737	94,480	2103	182,802	-	9675	1.08	1742
Barcelona	3,413,260	6,825,200	4,755,340	3,414,760	0	15,145,912	101.00	81,268	13.00	16,414
Burgas	1,192,800	1,041,600	558,600	1,146,600	136,416	2,883,216	-	-	-	-
Cadiz	611,660	374,036	84,169	921,060	0	1,379,264	-	-	1.07	1385
Dobrich	585,040	510,880	145,710	562,380	0	1,218,970	0.00	0.00	0.00	0.00
Frankfurt	9,467,655	4,699,832	2,708,405	6,045,000	745,125	14,198,362	64.44	10,697	31.00	25,181
Frederikshavn	458,000	420,277	326,944	697,222	0	1,444,443	418.30	-	42.30	330,408.56
Horst aan de Maas	695,050	286,111	1,269,444	486,111	0	2,041,666	-	852,777.78	-	958,333.33
Komotini	350,415	329,450	75,474	373,776	0	778,700	0.00	0.00	0.03	29.60
Krizevci	79,800	21,211	47,153	81,000	8	149,371	0.00	-	0.68	672
Litomerice	81,765	161,500	142,250	168,750	78,035	550,535	1.57	-	-	-
G. Manchester	13,500,000	13,581,000	21,671,998	19,521,000	516	54,774,514	53.80	-	126.00	179,347
Metz	869,712	953,885	1,1163,280	1,689,420	0	3,806,585	45.00	94,454	131.00	670
Mizil	49,376	38,499	45,655	47,945	5295	137,395	-	-	1.74	-
Nis	1,679,600	1,201,200	442,000	868,400	311,451	2,823,051	-	-	-	-
Nottingham	1,257,583	1,240,386	2,333,802	1,395,843	8713	4,978,744	-	-	-	-
Pamplona	1,028,000	667,975	1,223,742	2,747,484	14,394	4,653,595	0.20	350	0.19	225
Plymouth	1,053,000	904,000	1,557,000	1,879,800	17,000	4,357,800	1.80	-	7.30	-
Rijeka	486,400	508,160	524,800	753,920	0	1,786,880	0.00	0.00	0.11	86.43
San Sebastian	1,170,181	680,702	732,568	1,400,855	0	2,814,125	7.34	9159	1.63	1,630
Tampere	1,920,960	3,589,040	283,040	1,939,520	263,065	6,074,664	99.00	-	-	-
Vaxjo	268,000	670,000	0	718,000	100	1,388,100	-	670,000	-	235,000
Velika Gorica	241,365	252,162	257,800	374,115	0	884,077	-	-	0.15	-
Vienna	8,356,000	7,815,00	17,314,000	12,621,000	8,007	37,758,006	283.00	1,270,000	256.00	1,401,000
Vila Nova de Gaia	1,640,837	1,750,868	1,225,720	2,801,294	0	5,777,882	-	-	6.50	32,040
Zenica	253,085	132,156	0	379,489	124,534	636,179	3.00	200	1.44	900

Table A3. Number of campaigns led by the council or cooperatives/citizens, staff on energy, staff on transition/reducing energy use or RES, budget dedicated to energy transition and plans for RES investments.

City	Council Led Campaigns	Staff on Energy (# of FTE Staff)	Staff on Transition/Reducing Energy Use/RES (# of FTE Staff)	Annual Budget Dedicated to Energy Transition (€)	Plans for RES Investment (MW for 2020)
Amsterdam	>15	-	-	87,500,000	-
Aradippou	1–5	2	2	70,000	6.00
Barcelona	>15	15	55	-	1.50
Burgas	-	-	-	-	-
Cadiz	1–5	1	1	70,000	-
Dobrich	1–5	3	3	200,000	-
Frankfurt	>15	23	13	1,800,000	-
Frederikshavn	6–10	8	2	58,000	-
Horst aan de Maas	1–5	5,5	3,5	60,000	<1
Komotini	1–5	8	2	500,000	-
Krizevci	1–5	1	1	792,000	-
Litomerice	1–5	2	2	200,000	-
G. Manchester	6–10	15	15	7,020,000	10.00
Metz	>15	1	5	500,000	Yes
Mizil	1–5	4	4	1,000,000	-
Nis	-	6	3	20,000	1.00
Nottingham	-	-	-	-	Yes
Pamplona	1–5	3	1	100,000	-
Plymouth	6–10	16	16	589,000	Yes
Rijeka	0	1	1	-	-
San Sebastian	1–5	4	11	400,000	0.07
Tampere	-	-	-	-	-
Vaxjo	-	-	-	-	Yes
Velika Gorica	1–5	1	1	40,000	-
Vienna	>15	25	-	-	Yes
Vila Nova de Gaia	1–5	10	-	5,000,000	0.50
Zenica	1–5	1	0	250,000	-

Table A4. National average energy consumption data corresponding to each city. TPES data have been extracted from IEA, while TPEF and HEF data have been calculated by the authors using GMRIO methodology.

Country	City	Transportation	National Products and Services	Imported Products and Services (HEF)	Transformation and Losses	Residential	TOTAL (MWh/yr/Cap)
Netherlands	Amsterdam	7.12	14.40	8.91	22.68	6.74	59.85
Cyprus	Aradippou	8.88	6.25	23.92	9.82	4.58	53.46
Spain	Barcelona	7.74	7.29	7.68	11.17	3.81	37.69
Bulgaria	Burgas	5.46	6.38	6.87	14.07	3.74	22.79
Spain	Cadiz	7.74	7.29	7.68	11.17	3.81	37.69
Bulgaria	Dobrich	5.46	6.38	6.87	14.07	3.74	22.79
Germany	Frankfurt	8.06	12.86	5.99	14.98	7.94	49.84
Denmark	Frederikshavn	8.06	8.35	20.91	8.54	8.65	54.52
Netherlands	Horst aan de Maas	7.12	14.40	8.91	22.68	6.74	59.85
Greece	Komotini	6.24	5.35	14.49	8.30	4.53	38.91
Croatia	Grad Krizevci	5.89	5.77	5.65	5.00	6.95	29.26
Czech Republic	Litomerice	6.75	10.44	0.81	21.13	7.39	46.52
UK	G. Manchester	7.23	6.87	19.93	10.95	6.70	51.68
France	Metz	7.61	8.95	8.07	18.98	6.91	50.51
Romania	Mizil	3.35	4.65	1.95	6.42	4.31	20.67
Serbia	Nis	3.34	5.42	2.87	11.51	4.85	27.99
UK	Nottingham	7.23	6.87	19.93	10.95	6.70	51.68
Spain	Pamplona	7.74	7.29	7.68	11.17	3.81	37.69
UK	Plymouth	7.23	6.87	19.93	10.95	6.70	51.68
Croatia	Rijeka	5.89	5.77	5.65	5.00	6.95	29.26
Spain	San Sebastian	7.74	7.29	7.68	11.17	3.81	37.69
Finland	Tampere	8.36	26.63	3.74	26.75	10.25	68.25
Sweden	Vaxjo	9.50	17.45	5.56	22.06	8.68	63.24
Croatia	Velika Gorica	5.89	5.77	5.65	5.00	6.95	29.26
Austria	Vienna	11.06	13.38	14.57	11.69	8.18	58.88
Portugal	Vila Nova de Gaia	6.49	7.47	9.02	7.89	3.05	33.91
Bosnia and Herzegovina	Zenica	3.46	3.45	1.31	12.38	3.04	21.02

References

1. McGlade, C.; Ekins, P. The geographical distribution of fossil fuels unused when limiting global warming to 2 °C. *Nature* **2015**, *517*, 187–190. [CrossRef] [PubMed]
2. Albuerne, Y.L.; Velez, N.R.B. Beneficios económicos y ambientales con la implementación de una red eléctrica inteligente. *DYNA Energ. Sostenibilidad* **2019**, *8*.
3. Grayson, M. Energy transitions. *Nature* **2017**, *551*, S133. [CrossRef] [PubMed]
4. Akizu, O.; Urkidi, L.; Bueno, G.; Lago, R.; Barcena, I. Tracing the emerging energy transitions in the Global North and the Global South. *Int. J. Hydrog. Energy* **2017**, *42*, 18045–18063. [CrossRef]
5. Bridge, G.; Bouzarovski, S.; Bradshaw, M.; Eyre, N. Geographies of energy transition: Space, place and the low-carbon economy. *Energy Policy* **2013**, *53*, 331–340. [CrossRef]
6. Burke, M.J.; Stephens, J.C. Energy democracy: Goals and policy instruments for sociotechnical transitions. *Energy Res. Soc. Sci.* **2017**, *33*, 35–48. [CrossRef]
7. Van der Schoor, T.; van Lente, H.; Scholtens, B.; Peine, A. Challenging Obduracy: How Local Communities Transform the Energy System. *Energy Res. Soc. Sci.* **2016**, *13*, 94–105. [CrossRef]
8. Creupelandt, D.; Vansintjan, D. Deliverable2.3. REScoop—Mobilizing European Citizens to Invest in Sustainable Energy. H2020-EE-2014-4-PDA- 649767. 2014.
9. Vita, G.; Ivanova, D.; Dumitru, A.; García-Mira, R.; Carrus, G.; Stadler, K.; Hertwich, E.G. Happier with less? Members of European environmental grassroots initiatives reconcile lower carbon footprints with higher life satisfaction and income increases. *Energy Res. Soc. Sci.* **2020**, *60*, 101329. [CrossRef]
10. Arto, I.; Capellán-Pérez, I.; Lago, R.; Bueno, G.; Bermejo, R. The energy requirements of a developed world. *Energy Sustain. Dev.* **2016**, *33*, 1–13. [CrossRef]
11. Akizu-Gardoki, O.; Bueno, G.; Wiedmann, T.; Lopez-Guede, J.M.; Arto, I.; Hernandez, P.; Moran, D. Decoupling between human development and energy consumption within footprint accounts. *J. Clean. Prod.* **2018**, *202*, 1145–1157. [CrossRef]
12. Akenji, L. Consumer scapegoatism and limits to green consumerism. *J. Clean. Prod.* **2014**, *63*, 13–23. [CrossRef]
13. Grabs, J.; Langen, N.; Maschkowski, G.; Schäpke, N. Understanding role models for change: A multilevel analysis of success factors of grassroots initiatives for sustainable consumption. *J. Clean. Prod.* **2016**, *134*, 98–111. [CrossRef]
14. Kooij, H.J.; Oteman, M.; Veenman, S.; Sperling, K.; Magnusson, D.; Palm, J.; Hvelplund, F. Between grassroots and treetops: Community power and institutional dependence in the renewable energy sector in Denmark, Sweden and the Netherlands. *Energy Res. Soc. Sci.* **2018**, *37*, 52–64. [CrossRef]
15. U.N. Publications (Ed.) *Sustainable Development Goals Report 2016*; United Nations: New York, NY, USA, 2016.
16. Sperling, K.; Hvelplund, F.; Mathiesen, B.V. Centralisation and decentralisation in strategic municipal energy planning in Denmark. *Energy Policy* **2011**, *39*, 1338–1351. [CrossRef]
17. Pirgmaier, E.; Steinberger, J.K. Roots, Riots, and Radical Change—A Road Less Travelled for Ecological Economics. *Sustainability* **2019**, *11*, 2001. [CrossRef]
18. Zúñiga, A.R.; Eguino, M.G.; Arto, I. decarbonisation of the public administration by the electrification of urban buses. case study the city of vitoria. *DYNA* **2019**, *94*, 632–635.
19. Comodi, G.; Cioccolanti, L.; Polonara, F.; Brandoni, C. Local authorities in the context of energy and climate policy. *Energy Policy* **2012**, *51*, 737–748. [CrossRef]
20. Emelianoff, C. Local Energy Transition and Multilevel Climate Governance: The Contrasted Experiences of Two Pioneer Cities (Hannover, Germany, and Växjö, Sweden). *Urban Stud.* **2014**, *51*, 1378–1393. [CrossRef]
21. mPOWER—Municipal Power. Available online: https://municipalpower.org/ (accessed on 19 December 2019).
22. Tagliapietra, S.; Zachmann, G.; Edenhofer, O.; Glachant, J.-M.; Linares, P.; Loeschel, A. The European union energy transition: Key priorities for the next five years. *Energy Policy* **2019**, *132*, 950–954. [CrossRef]
23. Joas, F.; Pahle, M.; Flachsland, C.; Joas, A. Which goals are driving the Energiewende? Making sense of the German Energy Transformation. *Energy Policy* **2016**, *95*, 42–51. [CrossRef]
24. International Energy Agency. *World Energy Balances 2017*; International Energy Agency: Paris, France, 2019.
25. Fanning, A.L.; O'Neill, D.W. The Wellbeing–Consumption paradox: Happiness, health, income, and carbon emissions in growing versus non-growing economies. *J. Clean. Prod.* **2019**, *212*, 810–821. [CrossRef]

26. Mediavilla, M.; Miguel, L.J.; de Castro, C. Un modelo marco para la transición energética. In Proceedings of the 9th International Conference of the European Society of Ecological Economics, Istanbul, Turkey, 14–17 July 2011.

27. Rao, N.D.; van Ruijven, B.J.; Riahi, K.; Bosetti, V. Improving poverty and inequality modelling in climate research. *Nat. Clim. Chang.* **2017**, *7*, 857–862. [CrossRef]

28. Murakami, K.; Kaneko, S.; Dhakal, S.; Sharifi, A. Changes in per capita CO2 emissions of six large Japanese cities between 1980 and 2000: An analysis using 'The Four System Boundaries' approach. *Sustain. Cities Soc.* **2020**, *52*, 101784. [CrossRef]

29. Van den Dobbelsteen, A.; Roggema, R.; Tillie, N.; Broersma, S.; Fremouw, M.; Martin, C.L. 4.6—Urban Energy Masterplanning—Approaches, Strategies, and Methods for the Energy Transition in Cities. In *Urban Energy Transition*, 2nd ed.; Droege, P., Ed.; Elsevier: Amsterdam, The Netherlands, 2018; pp. 635–660.

30. Stulz, R.; Tanner, S.; Sigg, R. Chapter 16—Swiss 2000-Watt Society: A Sustainable Energy Vision for the Future. In *Energy, Sustainability and the Environment*; Sioshansi, F.P., Ed.; Butterworth-Heinemann: Boston, MA, USA, 2011; pp. 477–496.

31. European Commission. *Proposal for a Regulation of the European Parliament and of the Council on the Governance of the Energy Union, Amending Directive 94/22/EC, Directive 98/70/EC, Directive 2009/31/EC, Regulation (EC) No 663/2009, Regulation (EC) No 715/2009, Directive 2009/73/EC, Council Directive 2009/119/EC, Directive 2010/31/EU, Directive 2012/27/EU, Directive 2013/30/EU and Council Directive (EU) 2015/652 and Repealing Regulation (EU) No 525/2013: COM (2016) 759*; European Commission: Brussels, Belgium, 2016.

32. Veum, K.; Bauknecht, D. How to reach the EU renewables target by 2030? An analysis of the governance framework. *Energy Policy* **2019**, *127*, 299–307. [CrossRef]

33. Akerboom, S.; Botzen, W.; Buijze, A.; Michels, A.; van Rijswick, M. Meeting goals of sustainability policy: CO2 emission reduction, cost-effectiveness and societal acceptance. An analysis of the proposal to phase-out coal in the Netherlands. *Energy Policy* **2020**, *138*, 111210. [CrossRef]

34. Chang, K. Emissions reduction targets and wealth distribution effects through interprovincial emissions trading scheme in China. *Energy Procedia* **2019**, *159*, 539–544. [CrossRef]

35. EEA. European Energy Award Gold Municipalities – eea. 2020. Available online: https://www.european-energy-award.org/european-energy-award-gold-municipalities (accessed on 18 February 2020).

36. Covenant of Mayors. Available online: https://www.covenantofmayors.eu/ (accessed on 19 December 2019).

37. Taylor, N.G.; Szbó, S.; Kona, A.; Ossenbrink, H. Deployment Pathways for Photovoltaics in the EU Towards 2020: Comparing Economic Factors with Policies at Municipal Level. *31st Eur. Photovolt. Sol. Energy Conf. Exhib.* **2015**, 3034–3041. [CrossRef]

38. Donnerer, D.; Boyer, F. National Energy and Climate Plans. *Energy Cities* **2019**. Available online: https://energy-cities.eu/publication/national-energy-and-climate-plans-fail-to-acknowledge-cities-leading-role-in-the-european-energy-transition/ (accessed on 14 November 2019).

39. European Union. The European Green Deal Sets Out how to Make Europe the First Climate-Neutral Continent by 2050. EEAS—European External Action Service—European Commission. Available online: https://eeas.europa.eu/headquarters/headquarters-homepage/71922/european-green-deal-sets-out-how-make-europe-first-climate-neutral-continent-2050_ro (accessed on 19 December 2019).

40. Nieto, J.; Carpintero, Ó.; Miguel, L.J.; de Blas, I. Macroeconomic modelling under energy constraints: Global low carbon transition scenarios. *Energy Policy* **2019**, 111090. [CrossRef]

41. Bekebrede, G.; van Bueren, E.; Wenzler, I. Towards a Joint Local Energy Transition Process in Urban Districts: The GO2Zero Simulation Game. *Sustainability* **2018**, *10*, 2602. [CrossRef]

42. European Commission H2020. Municipal Action, Public Engagement and Routes Towards Energy Transition | mPOWER Project | CORDIS. 2018. Available online: https://cordis.europa.eu/project/rcn/213584/factsheet/en (accessed on 21 November 2019).

43. Energy Cities. We Are the European City Network that Defends a Locally Driven Energy Transition. *Energy Cities* **2019**. Available online: https://energy-cities.eu/ (accessed on 11 February 2020).

44. Neill, S.P.; Hashemi, M.R. *Fundamentals of Ocean Renewable Energy*; Elsevier: Amsterdam, The Netherlands, 2018.

45. IPCC. *IPCC—Task Force on National Greenhouse Gas Inventories*; Institute for Global Environmental Strategies (IGES): Hayama, Japan, 2006.

46. Steinberger, J.K.; Roberts, J.T. From constraint to sufficiency: The decoupling of energy and carbon from human needs, 1975–2005. *Ecol. Econ.* **2010**, *70*, 425–433. [CrossRef]
47. Gemeente Horst aan de Maas. Available online: https://www.horstaandemaas.nl/ (accessed on 19 December 2019).
48. Cazcarro, I.; Amores, A.F.; Arto, I.; Kratena, K. Bridge matrices for feeding macroeconomic models with consumption survey's profiles for the EU28 countries. In Proceedings of the 27th International Input-Output Conference (IIOA) Conference, Glasgow, Scotland, 30 June–5 July 2019.
49. Akizu-Gardoki, O.; Villamor, E.; Bueno, G.; Heinonen, J.; Lopez-Guede, J.M. Measuring energy footprint in bottom-up energy transitions in the Basque Country. In Proceedings of the 27th IIOA Conference, Glasgow, Scotland, 30 June–5 July 2019.
50. UNDP. Trends in the Human Development Index, 1990-2015. 2015. Available online: http://hdr.undp.org/en/composite/trends (accessed on 11 January 2020).
51. World Bank. *World Bank National Accounts. GDP Per Capita (Current US$)*; World Bank: Washington, DC, USA, 2019.
52. D'Amico, A.; Ciulla, G.; Panno, D.; Ferrari, S. Building energy demand assessment through heating degree days: The importance of a climatic dataset. *Appl. Energy* **2019**, *242*, 1285–1306. [CrossRef]
53. Prag, A.; Röttgers, D.; Scherrer, I. *State-Owned Enterprises and the Low-Carbon Transition*; International Energy Agency: Paris, France, 2018.
54. EHAA. *4/2019 LEGEA, Otsailaren 21ekoa, Euskal Autonomia Erkidegoko Jasangarritasun Energetikoari Buruzkoa*; EHAA: Basque Country, Spain, 2019; p. 1087.
55. Kunze, C.; Becker, S. Collective ownership in renewable energy and opportunities for sustainable degrowth. *Sustain. Sci.* **2015**, *10*, 425–437. [CrossRef]
56. Capellán-Pérez, I.; Campos-Celador, Á.; Terés-Zubiaga, J. Renewable Energy Cooperatives as an instrument towards the energy transition in Spain. *Energy Policy* **2018**, *123*, 215–229. [CrossRef]
57. Eichermüller, J.; Furlan, M.; Habersbrunner, K.; Kordić, Z.; Furlan, M.; Habersbrunner, K. *Potential of Energy Cooperatives to Meet Emission Targets and Supply Society with Affordable, Safe and Renewable Energy and Gender-Sensitive Participation Opportunities*; Women Engage for a Common Future: Utrecht, The Netherlands, 2017.
58. Lenzen, M.; Murray, J.; Sack, F.; Wiedmann, T. Shared producer and consumer responsibility — Theory and practice. *Ecol. Econ.* **2007**, *61*, 27–42. [CrossRef]

© 2020 by the authors. Licensee MDPI, Basel, Switzerland. This article is an open access article distributed under the terms and conditions of the Creative Commons Attribution (CC BY) license (http://creativecommons.org/licenses/by/4.0/).

Article

Energy Modelling as a Trigger for Energy Communities: A Joint Socio-Technical Perspective

Viktor Bukovszki [1], Ábel Magyari [1], Marina Kristina Braun [1], Kitti Párdi [1] and András Reith [1,2,*]

[1]   Advanced Building and Urban Design Ltd., 1139 Budapest, Hungary; bukovszki.viktor@abud.hu (V.B.); magyari.abel@abud.hu (Á.M.); marina.braun90@web.de (M.K.B.); pardi.kitti@abud.hu (K.P.)
[2]   Research Group 'Well Being Research Incubator', University of Pécs, 7624 Pécs, Hungary
*   Correspondence: reith.andras@abud.hu

Received: 16 March 2020; Accepted: 26 April 2020; Published: 5 May 2020

Abstract: Mainstreaming energy communities has been one of the main challenges in the low-carbon transition of cities. In this sense, urban building energy modelling (UBEM) has an untapped role in enabling energy communities, as simulations on urban models provide evidence-based decision support to reduce risks, engage, motivate and guide actors, assert wider policy goals and regulatory requirements. This accelerating role and the potential of UBEM is not sufficiently understood, as research into energy community focuses on its barriers and impacts, while the research of UBEM is mainly technologically oriented. This review takes a sociotechnical approach to explore whether UBEM is a technological trigger for energy communities, furthering the conceptual framework of transition management. factors influencing energy community progression in different use-cases and stages of their lifecycle are compiled to assess the affordances of distinct capabilities of prevalent UBEM tools. The study provides a guide for energy community planners to UBEM. It matches different tool capabilities to the various stages of the project lifecycle for the different use-cases, equipping them with the means to accelerate the low-carbon transition of cities from the bottom-up. Finally, the study defines a development trajectory oriented towards application in urban sustainability to a rather new UBEM field.

Keywords: energy community; urban building energy modelling; transition management; multi-level perspective; sustainable transition; energy modelling; urban scale energy modelling

1. Introduction

1.1. The Need for Energy Communities in Low Carbon Cities

Energy communities (EC) have been steadily gathering attention, as social innovations potentially driving the decarbonisation of energy systems through its democratization. Although they are widely researched from sociotechnical, socioeconomic, governance, psychosocial perspectives [1], the definition of energy communities is contested due to the term community being itself debated [2]. Energy communities, however, can be recognized as a collective of actors voluntarily mobilized around a shared objective relating to energy—either shared management of energy systems or collective purchasing of energy [3].

The significance of ECs is their potential role in driving the decarbonisation of cities, promoting investment in and access to clean, affordable energy, responding directly to at least goals 7 and 11 of the UN sustainable development goals [4]. By investing in decentralized renewable energy production assets in energy efficiency, they contribute directly to the energy system decarbonisation [2,5]. Even more profound value is seen in giving control to the ones who benefit from the outcomes, in the process of producing them [6]. Community energy projects aim to mobilize and empower consumers, previously on the fringe of a vertically integrated energy market. This decentralization is seen as a tool to democratize energy systems [7], granting voice, power and ownership to individuals, community groups and municipalities [2,8,9]. This arrangement has multiple benefits. First, it recruits grassroots human resource to drive decarbonisation, to identify and solve local problems through public innovations and to translate sectoral cooperation to multiplicative community benefits [10,11]. Second, behaviour change to more sustainable lifestyles is more likely to occur when also driven by intra-group solidarity and peer effects than global environmental problems [12]. Finally, energy communities may act as policy labs, niches for governments to pilot new regulatory frameworks [8].

In western countries, ECs are trending while legislation is catching up. There are currently around 3500 recognized renewable energy cooperatives in Europe, mostly in Germany and Denmark [13]. The European Commission released the 'Clean Energy for All Europeans' Package in December of 2018, which provides a legal 'enabling' framework for the participants of energy communities [14]. The Member States are due to adapt the regulations into their national legal system by 2021 [14]. This legal framework enables the members of energy communities to be the beneficiaries of activities, such as "generation, distribution, supply, aggregation, consumption, sharing, storage of energy and provision of energy-related services" [13]. Since there are differences between the aforementioned two types of energy communities, the Clean Energy Package includes the Internal Electricity Market Directive (EU) 2019/944, which states the definition of citizen energy communities (CEC), while the revised Renewable Energy Directive (EU) 2018/2001 defines the renewable energy communities (REC) [13]. Both directives emphasize the shift in the role of citizens from passive consumers to energy prosumers in the energy system, and both EC types as legal entities have common characteristics, like the goal of achieve social, economic and environmental benefits, and must be open and voluntary for all citizens without discrimination [15]. CEC however is a more general and REC is a more restrictive concept, with differences such as locality not being required for CECs [13], energy can be generated from fossil-fuels, as well as from renewable resources in CECs [15] and RECs exclude the participation of large enterprises [13].

In the US, regulatory barriers are more pronounced. The Federal Energy Regulatory Commission (FERC) has the authority at national level over interstate transmission and wholesale price [16]. However, FERC does not have the authority over power transactions for distributed generation (DG). There are entities therefore which fall under FERC jurisdiction, some fall under state jurisdiction and some under both [17]. Moreover, the crucial security regulations by the Security Exchange Commission does not disambiguate whether community energy counts as security [18].

Regarding policies, on the federal level, renewable investment is incentivized via tax credits, but without special provisions for community projects, while states have a variety policies towards community energy (e.g., Virtual Net Metering (VNM), Statewide shared energy programs, incentives) [19].

1.2. The Significance of Urban Building Energy Modelling

Energy modelling on the building scale is a mature and complete field, providing reliable decision-support for building energy design [20]. Urban building energy modelling (UBEM) seeks to upscale this field to better understand of new and existing neighbourhoods and assess urban energy systems described by Keirstead et al. [21] as "formal systems that represents the combined processes of acquiring and using energy to satisfy the energy service demands of a given urban area". While research in UBEM has surged [21], it is still yet considered "half-baked" [20] and has tremendous potential.

Sola et al. [22] describes Urban-scale Building Energy Modelling (UBEM) as part of Urban Scale Energy Modelling (USEM). According to them and Allegrini et al. [23] USEM is capable of modelling not just building related, but multisectoral energy flows including grid, mobility, microclimate, therefore accurately model district urban energy systems. Part of this is UBEM which can simulate energy demand of the building stock by combining energy models of standalone buildings into a summarized district-scale model. According to another definition form Reinhart and Davila [24] UBEM is a tool able to simulate energy demand on a city block, district, entire city or even on a bigger scale.

Goy and Finn [25] differentiate small- and large-scale energy modelling at five buildings/households in their review [25]. On small scale building energy modelling is where the aim is to obtain data for internal thermal control, or thermal loads, however at large scale energy modelling aim is to predict performance indicators like building energy consumption, CO_2 emission and new policy impacts [25]. It is a necessity when considering place-based ECs to have information about the building energy demand, since according to [3] these type of ECs gather on spatial basis and are based on shared ownership, typically in blocks, flats, building blocks or districts. While USEM, as described above vaguely refers to multisectoral energy flows in urban context and examples mentioned in [22,23] also incorporate tools which do not take building energy demand into consideration, for the purpose of this study we considered USEM as tools which can model building energy demand, and other energy flows as well.

UBEM's significance is multifaceted. Simulations promote market competitiveness, which in a liberalized market is strongly tied to the success of a new energy paradigm [26]. Urban scale simulations can provide a better understanding of the optimum combination of building and area specific measures and interchange of energy options [27]. Through benchmarking they can provide transparency [28] in energy efficiency markets, therefore growing trust and increasing investment appetite [29]. Analysing different scenarios can contribute in the development of consumption awareness and therefore raise consciousness for the sustainable environment [27], also capable of helping energy policy formulation since it frequently leans on the evaluation of overall building performance [30].

1.3. Gap in the Research Fields

The potential of energy communities remains theoretical, and communities themselves exist in niches of a few industrialized, developed nations [1]. Studies setting up the research agenda for energy communities point out an empirical gap in understanding "who the project is for [...] and how do they benefit" [6]. This is a common theme for energy communities, both their design and their research seem ill-equipped to fully map the distributional aspects of the multiple impacts of projects [6]. This is partly due to the convention to take buildings as isolated units of investigation for planning energy [31]. The influence of urban surroundings on their energy performance has not been properly incorporated as well as the interdependencies that may occur amongst them [31].

This means both community energy research and practice lack the tools to incorporate emergent properties on the urban scale such as microclimate, renewable potential or load-curve differences [32]. Regarding practice, this results in major barriers to progress community energy projects, because it means uncertainties are high, participant and supporting networks cannot be established on a performance-basis, regulations, policymakers and financers are more difficult to be convinced [2]. Regarding research, this is evident in calls for more empirical knowledge on the changes community energy delivers [6]. This means that the gap in research—lack of evidence in the distributional multiple impacts of energy communities—can be traced to missing means to produce such evidence, which would also be a trigger for the practice of energy communities. Hypothetically, urban-scale energy modelling could be such a tool, but the two research fields have not yet met, there are no reviews on the potential of UBEM in advancing ECs (see Section 2). Studies of UBEM are technically focused, lacking application-oriented classifications to assess potential in energy communities, while studies on EC do not explore technological triggers to overcome barriers (see Section 2).

1.4. Theoretical Background

The following two subsections justify the research gap by summarizing recent reviews in both EC and UBEM, showcasing a lack of intersections in previous studies. Subsequently, a new conceptual framework rooted in transition theory is defined in which the research gap will be filled.

Previous reviews concerning EC can be grouped according to their subject of focus: one group studies community energy in general, while others specialize in a specific type of energy community—characterised by their core activity. Schoor et al. [1] made a review of community energy research identifying that most studies come from developed countries and that there are different networks building up the discourse—however, these networks rarely interact. Brummer [2] collects definitions of community energy, its benefits provided for society and the barriers of EC projects. Berka et al. [12] and Roby et al. [33] investigate community energy impacts with different approaches. Nolden et al. [34] move on to business models, particularly in the UK, and how they evolved over time. Ceglia et al. [35] propose a standard for smart energy communities. Drivers and barriers feature in most previous studies, Lehtonen et al. [36] explore the role of trust more deeply. Moroni et al. [3] use a transition theory approach to classify energy communities, introducing the distinction between place-based and non-place-based communities.

Most of the specialized studies focus on renewable energy communities. Creamer et al. [6] have developed a conceptual framework and sets the focus of research on impacts, while others studied impacts [37,38] and monitored adoption [39]. Hess et al. [40] and Joshi et al. [41] made comparative reviews of multiple case studies, with the former focusing on country-level differences, and the latter exploring how justice is addressed. Bauwens [42] collects factors determining investment. Regarding institutional drivers, Heldeweg et al. [43] outlines and argues for a distinct legal form for renewable energy communities in a separate institutional context, while Petersen [44] analyses municipal energy plans as instruments.

Out of the remaining specialised studies, Gorroño-Albizu et al. compares community ownership models for renewable energy production and microgrid ownership [45]. Others [46–48] focus on community energy storage, its potential role, challenges, social, environmental, economic impacts, with an extended description of applied technologies. Warneryd et al. [49] explores institutional frameworks that drive microgrids, while two reviews [50,51] collects general microgrid drivers and challenges. Van Cutsem et al. [52] is a study on demand-response communities and the process of decentralization. Peer-to-peer electricity markets are the focus for Sousa et al. [53], classifying market designs, motivations and challenges. One review conceptualizes energy cooperation in industrial parks [54]. Finally, three reviews focus on broader "green neighbourhoods", community projects with more complex sustainability profiles, where energy is one component [32,55,56].

Review articles are considerably scarcer with technological factors of EC progression. While there is extensive literature on drivers, barriers and challenges of multiple EC types, and they are linked to institutional, social or economic interventions, this review will continue by investigating how technologies relate to these drivers, barriers and challenges.

In case of UBEM, numerous reviews have been done, however only outside the field of energy communities. In most cases the reviews differentiate the UBEM tools regarding their approaches. Swan and Ugursal [57] and many others [58,59] differentiated 2 mainly different building energy modelling methods: Top-down and Bottom up. Some of the reviews like [60,61] are focusing on classifying UBEM tools by this methodology. Li et al. [60] in their review classified the UBEM models in the aforementioned way, and emphasized the advances and still existing discrepancies in geospatial techniques. Abbasabadi et al. [61] described strengths and limitations by each method and extended their research further on urban scale energy simulation.

Sola et al. [22] expressed the need for a new hybrid tool for properly model energy use at urban scale incorporating other urban scale energy uses. [22] with the same approach reviewed not only UBEM tools, but holistic USEM tools They used a decomposition framework, where tools are decomposed into sub-models and their sub-models are reviewed as well. In addition, further explored how integrated and co-simulation platforms can work individually and together.

Allegrini et al. [23] reviewed 20 tools which can model neighbourhood level energy systems. In their review they created a comprehensive matrix where the capabilities of the twenty reviewed tools can be compared and screened easily. Reinhart et al. [24] reviewed models which are based on a bottom-up methodology. They provided a comprehensive review about the existing workflows and challenges in modelling in such a way due to the lack of data.

Ferrari et al. [62] reviewed 17 tools where these tools were classified based on their most useful features [62]. Their goal was to identify user friendly tools with hourly or sub-hourly outputs. Six of them were identified in the paper. Manfren et al. [26] assessed tools for distributed generation projects. They decomposed the distributed generation adoption into work phases and paired them with tools according to their inherent features. It is clearly visible that most reviews are presenting UBEM as a technological niche itself, hence this review will reposition UBEM and USEM tools as part of a socio-technological framework.

Given the divergence of previous studies, a discourse to conceptualize the research gap must be defined. While multiple research fields engage in the investigation of energy communities [1], this study is positioned in the field of transition management due to its core tenet being built upon the entanglement of social and technical practices [63]. At the heart of its conceptual framework is the socio-technical system, in which the multi-level perspective (MLP), helps to visualize how the energy communities as the social niche with the contribution of a technological novelty (as UBEM) can make a shift in the prevailing regime of the energy sector Figure 1.

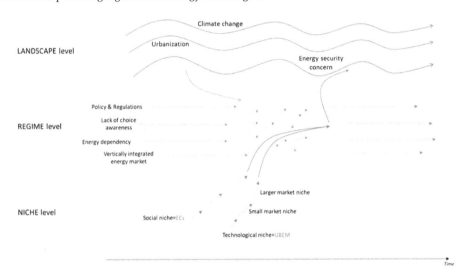

Figure 1. Positioning research subject in the multi-level perspective—adapted figure of Geels [64].

The regime is the meso-level comprising of the dominant socio-technical system [65]. The regime defining the energy sector is influenced by the relation between social interests, like policies and regulations (from municipal, national, supranational levels), user preferences, which is characterized by a lack of choice awareness, energy dependency and the passive demand side in the energy system in a centralized, vertically integrated energy market [66]. MLP states that transitioning this regime towards decarbonisation is dependent on the novel technologies entangled with social change [63,67]. On the one hand, this is pushed from the micro-level, in niches, where technological innovations are sheltered from the selection of mainstream market [65] (Figure 2). On the other hand, the external factors are also essential in order to transform the regime, which in the context of MLP is the landscape (macro-level). The landscape can include extreme events, such as climate change, but it can also be less conspicuous events, like urbanization, or energy security concerns [65].

Figure 2. Positioning of research subject in niche development—adapted figure of Geels [65].

In this context, ECs are social innovations existing on niche level that need to progress from the protected environment into small market niche and eventually larger market niche. The strategic niche management (SNM) discourse explores the factors and process of niche progression [63,67]. A bottom-up initiative, like the energy communities as social niche can affect the regime, in this process the ECs become nodes in the decentralized energy sector, which can include the energy production, consumption as well as management. The members of community turn into prosumers from consumers [2]. This transition decreases their dependency on the vertically integrated energy market. Moreover, the change in regime can also occur as the involvement of users into the energy system, which raises awareness on the energy related issues, as well as on sustainability, thus increases their choice awareness. This, in combination with landscape pressures that provide a window of opportunity is the precursor for regime transition.

While the SNM emphasizes the dominant role of the niches in the replacement of regime, the transition does not depend on a single factor, rather different dynamics must reinforce each other on multiple dimensions. In that regard SNM usually focuses on the technological novelties as the dominant forces to make a shift in the current regime arguing for complementary social, institutional, behavioural change [63,67]. In other words, it focuses on technological niches, and how they can be enriched by a social perspective, but not the other way around. However, in case of ECs, it is the social novelty—with enabling technologies—that would eventually replace both the prevailing technology and social, political as well as cultural practices (the regime), ultimately feeding back to the landscape level [64,65].

By shifting the focus to a social innovation at the niche force driving change, and the technical innovation as the support, the conceptual framework of transition theory must be expanded to characterise this support. The theory of affordances is applied as an approach to link technological characteristics to the psychosocial, socioeconomic and governance factors describing EC drivers and barriers. Originally a concept describing complementarity between animals and their environment [68], affordance refers to the range of interactions possible between an environment and an agent operating within it [69]. In the field of design, the notion is used to sort the behaviour not only made possible, but also suggested by specific design features, in other words, the perceived affordances [70]. In this case, affordances are inherent in the object, technology, artefact, and more importantly, are influenced by design choices [71]. However, affordances are differentiated from capabilities or functionalities, as the same capability can have different affordances in different goal-oriented actions [72,73]. In the context of UBEM for example, the capability to predict energy demand affords evidence-basis for planning for consumers, but also affords risk elimination for a potential investor. Affordances that are intended by a product or technology, affordances that are suggested by its design features and actual observed behaviour are expected to deviate—the size of the gap is usually an indicator of good user-experience design. It is also important to note that by affording a set of interactions over others, features of technologies or environments do not only influence individual behaviour, but indirectly afford organizational models, routines, social practices in general, [74,75]. Thus, the notion of affordances fits the discourse of sociotechnical transitions well and is a useful method to articulate what exactly is in technology that breaks down a non-technical barrier, and how. This review offers a methodological contribution to transition theory by expanding its conceptual framework with affordances, which will allow investigations in the role of technology in accelerating social innovations, social niches.

1.5. Research Aim

The primary, practical objective is to explore whether a social niche—energy communities—can be cross-fertilized by a technological one—urban building energy modelling. The main research question is built around the phrase "technological trigger", which in this context describes multiple ways a technology enables or supports the penetration of an innovative social concept. This, in the context of energy communities means three things: it can either trigger the creation of new energy communities, it can accelerate the growth or diversification of energy communities and it can push the social niche of energy communities towards becoming absorbed by the regime. On that premise, the main research question and its decomposition is as follows:

Main research question (MRQ): Is urban building energy modelling a technological trigger for energy communities?

RQ1: Which factors trigger energy community progression in different use-cases?

RQ2: Which factors trigger energy community progression at their different lifecycle phases?

RQ3: Is it possible to identify different utilities of UBEM tool-types during the lifecycle of energy communities?

The main research question refers to matching UBEM against specific factors that influence the progression of ECs from social niches. Therefore, the answer will provide a set of these factors and argue how UBEM interacts with them. Subsequent research questions disaggregate this answer in three ways: by use-cases of ECs (RQ1), by EC lifecycle phases (RQ2), by UBEM tool types (RQ3). Investigating them are justified by three hypotheses that express such disaggregation will be meaningful (see H1, H2, H3 below).

RQ1 is required as the common classification of ECs differentiate them by their functional diversity (single-purpose, and multi-purpose) or by location specificity (place-based, non-place-based) [3]. On the one-hand UBEM tools themselves are place-based, narrowing the scope of the study. On the other hand, it is expected that the core activity of the energy community, for example whether it is providing flexibility services, invest in renewable energy production, will have different challenges, development processes and different potential entry points for UBEM or other technological innovations. This expectation is expressed in hypothesis H1, where EC use-case is defined as the core energy management activity, which is being shared:

Hypothesis (H1). *Different use-cases of energy communities have different factors to progress from niches to which UBEM tools respond differently.*

Second, it is reasonable to expect that different challenges burden ECs during different phases of their lifecycle. It is also a possibility that similar challenges in different stages respond to UBEM features differently. RQ2 thus disaggregates the MRQ to lifecycle, and the expectation is expressed as hypothesis H2:

Hypothesis (H2). *Energy communities in different lifecycle phases have different factors to progress from niches to which UBEM tools respond differently.*

Finally, it is reasonable to expect that UBEM itself has the variety to offer different strengths either per use-case or per lifecycle phase. This means, again, a disaggregation of the main research question to an UBEM tool classification (RQ3), to which a third hypothesis is formulated:

Hypothesis (H3). *Different types of UBEM tools accelerate energy community progression from niches differently.*

In the light of previous reviews and the theories, answering the main research question also carries over to practical objectives in providing a manual for EC planners to the world of UBEM and in raising awareness for future R&D trajectories for UBEM. Literacy in UBEM is hypothesised to give means to justify EC potential in low-carbon transition of cities and communities. On the other hand, application-oriented analyses of UBEM tools, such as this study, will provide criteria for UBEM development as it seeks its appropriate market. Finally, with the introduction of affordances to the conceptual framework of the multi-level perspective, a third practical objective of the study is to expand the scope of the SNM literature to technologically enabled social (sociotechnical) niche management. This is done so through demonstrating the conceptual framework based on affordances on the case of UBEM enabling ECs.

The remainder of the article is structured as follows: Section 2 presents the methodology of a two-tiered systematic literature review and builds an analytic framework by expanding a strategic niche management approach with the concept of affordances. In Section 3, results are presented as follows: Sections 3.1–3.3 contain the results of the EC meta-review, and Section 3.4 is an analysis of UBEM tools in the EC context. In Section 4, the known limitations of this paper are discussed followed by the reflections on the original research questions and pointing out possible trajectories for future work. Finally, the last section completes the paper with the conclusion in Section 5.

2. Materials and Methods

2.1. Research Design

To answer the research question, a new analytic framework was first designed that decomposes both energy communities and UBEM tools to information entities relatable to each other, namely: EC progression factors and capabilities of UBEM tools. Then, a two-tiered systematic literature was conducted into the research of EC and UBEM, respectively, to collect these information entities. EC use-cases and lifecycle phases were identified to answer research sub-questions. Finally, the results were matched to see the potential interactions between UBEM and EC as the EC-specific affordances of UBEM (Figure 3).

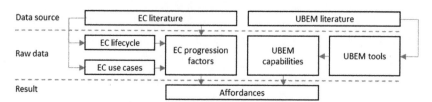

Figure 3. Overview of research process.

To meet the research objective of providing a manual for EC practitioners, the EC analytic framework must consist of features corresponding to disaggregation requirements of the main research question, namely: different use-cases, a breakdown of typical life-cycles, and a collection of progression factors. In the framework, the features for the analysis of UBEM are the progression factors, while use-cases and lifecycle phases are structural metadata assigned to the factors. The working definition for progression factor in this study is any condition that is indicative for the progression of energy communities through their lifecycle. Progression factors were extracted from the reviewed articles and labelled by which lifecycle phase and which use-case they are relevant for. This labelling was essential to answer research questions 2 and 3. Apart from essential structural metadata, supplementary labelling schemes describing the importance of each factor and the discipline with highest authority in them were added. The supplementary metadata were chosen to support the practical objective of providing a manual for EC planners, and were selected due to availability of information, based on a preliminary review of the literature. All categories in essential and supplementary metadata were defined from the literature, and not top-down—meaning alternative categorizations are valid. With four distinct categorizations, the factors were analysed on their relationships to each other by inspecting pairwise correlations among categories and by agglomerative hierarchical clustering using the UPGMA algorithm [76] (Supplementary Materials). The reason for inspecting this relationship is to validate whether the categories are redundant, and to see how factors can be bundled together for communication to EC practitioners.

The UBEM analytic framework was an amalgamation of the frameworks of four most prevalent UBEM tool reviews [22,61,62,77]. The features used to describe and classify UBEM tools in these four articles were taken as UBEM capabilities for coupling against EC progression factors. However, not all UBEM approaches were considered relevant for the research question. Generally, UBEM can be classified into two distinct approaches: top-down and bottom-up [57–59], complemented by hybrid approaches which combine the two [59,60,78]. Top-down modelling was excluded from this study, as they are incapable of modelling complex scenarios in energy transitions due to their reliance on aggregated historical statistical data and they are not able to consider different energy saving measures in different spatiotemporal situations, or occupancy types. [78,79].

Categorisation of UBEM tools evolved naturally as they became more mature and acquired more functions. Analysis of frameworks from four [22,61,62,77] of the collected review articles were used to define a comprehensive analytic framework.

For the analytic framework of this study, all features of bottom-up and hybrid modelling tools that were present in more than one article were automatically retained; the rest went under a systematic preselection process (see Table 1 for list of selected and filtered features). Features were excluded if: (1) they were duplicates, or included in the other features (e.g., exo- or endogenous demand modelling, Impact of user behaviour, Time horizon); (2) does not correspond to the working UBEM definition (e.g., building stock location, building characterization); (3) there is not sufficient information in the reviews and the original articles of the tools (e.g., non-residential type of building, input type).

Table 1. List of selected and filtered urban building energy modelling (UBEM) tool features.

Features	Hong et al. [77]	Ferrari et al. [62]	Abbasabadi et al. [61]	Sola et al. [22]	Filtered
Output types (as described in Abbasabadi et al. [61])		×	×	×	
Optimal Spatial scale (as described in Ferrari et al. [62])	×	×	×		
Approach (As described in Hong et al. [77])	×		×	×	
Time step (As described in Ferrari et al. [62])		×		×	
Energy service (As described in Ferrari et al. [62])		×		×	
Licence (As described in Ferrari et al. [62])		×		×	
Energy generation modelling (As described in Sola et al. [22])			×	×	
Urban climatology model				×	
Time Horizon		×			1
Target users	×				
Input type	×				3
Web-based vs. Standalone desktop	×				
Building stock location				×	2
Building Characterization				×	2
Exo-or Endogenous demand modelling				×	1
Impact of user behaviour on Building energy demand				×	1
Non-residential type of building				×	3
Integrated vs. Co-sim tool				×	

1 duplicates, or included in the other features, 2 not correspond to the working UBEM definition, 3 insufficient information in the reviews and the original articles of the tools.

However, not all analysed tools were present in all four reviews. The original articles of the included tools were used to fill in missing features to avoid information gaps. All, but 12 feature-tool couplings were filled this way. As in the case of EC progression factors, a typology of tools based on these features was produced via agglomerative hierarchical clustering, using the UPGMA algorithm [76], and a pairwise correlation matrix was produced. Again, this exercise was used to see whether there is a useful categorisation of tools, and to test whether the UBEM capabilities (the final list of features) are all necessary.

Finally, the relationship between EC and UBEM was justified through the concept of affordances, using EC progression factors as key performance indicators for the UBEM capabilities. Constructing an affordance is not defining a single feature but is discussing the way a certain user appropriate features for goal-oriented actions [80]. At its core, an affordance is the dynamic between features and actions, that is: the feature, a set of actions made possible by that feature, and the way the feature facilitates those actions [81]. This also means that an affordance is situational, as facilitation would occur for certain users, in certain contexts, which must be specified to justify an affordance [82]. Finally, the actions afforded must relate to the goal of the user [73,74].

Therefore, these six components, features, actions, facilitation, user, context and goal must be present to define an affordance (Figure 4).

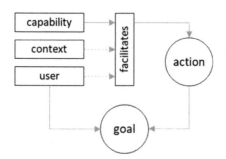

Figure 4. Components defining technological affordances.

In this study, the EC progression factors, and their metadata define the context and goals, while UBEM capabilities refer to features. Taking the EC planner as the user, an affordance can be specified by describing facilitation, and actions that are linked to user goals. Thus, an affordance exists if (1) in the context defined by EC use-case and lifecycle, (2) for an EC planner or project manager as a user, there is a (3) set of UBEM capabilities that (4) facilitate (5) a set of actions to (6) reach the goal of the user defined by meeting one or more progression factors. If the six components are justifiably present, the affordance exists. As progression factors were already classified by use-case and lifecycle phase, affordances could also be examined against both. This provides the necessary disaggregation for the research sub-questions, while a collection of justified affordances is the answer to the main research question.

2.2. Data Extraction

To extract information for analysis, two secondary data sources are investigated: review articles and case studies of energy communities. Thus, the feature extraction phase consists of an overview of reviews with the scope of review articles and meta-analyses and a systematic review with a scope of case studies. This distinction is chosen as recent reviews will not cover recent case studies, and because case studies are expected to yield more information on project lifecycle, while reviews are expected to give a better overview of EC use-cases. Both data sources are expected to return progression factors. The review of UBEM tools will rely on the secondary data source of UBEM proof of concept studies. The second phase of the research is also a systematic review, with the scope of UBEM tools.

The Scopus database was chosen for publication selection for its larger share of unique citations in both social science and engineering citations [83]. For the overview of reviews, the search term ("energy community" OR "community energy" OR "energy cooperative" OR "citizen energy") AND "review" was used for review. The time period for search was set to 2018-2020 at first, with annual extensions planned if insufficient information would have been generated—however, database was saturated with the first batch, see paragraphs below. For the review of case studies, ("energy community" OR "community energy") AND "case study" was used for the same years. For the review of UBEM tools, "urban" AND "energy" AND "model" was used for years between 2015 and 2020.

In all cases, the articles went through a preselection process (Figure 5). Titles were checked for overall domain relevance, while the abstracts were read for a relevance of the narrower topic. For example, an article on nutrition [84] was filtered out in the first step, while another [85] was filtered out in the second step, as it was a study on energy, however not on community energy as per definition. In addition to relevance check, articles had to be reviews, case studies and original articles introducing new UBEM tools, respectively. Finally, the following exclusion criteria were defined: the geographical scope is limited to the EU/US and cases where EC is the only viable alternative for energy distribution due to various constraints such as remote communities. These criteria were applied to meet the practical objectives of the study.

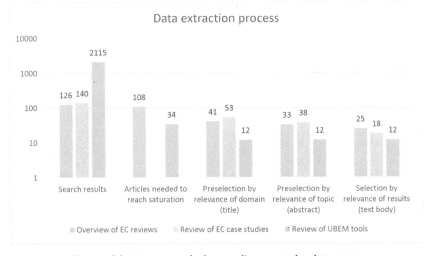

Figure 5. Selection process of references disaggregated to data sources.

The final articles, after confirmation in the text, that they contribute to study results, were selected in a bottom-up manner, by defining a threshold for data saturation. The data saturation threshold is a way of determining after how much articles does the research become redundant [86]. In studies, where the task of the observations is to provide new labels or classes, there is a characteristic saturation curve, plotted as the number of observations against the quantity of new labels accumulated with each observation. This curve is steep for the first "n" observations and flattens out afterwards. A flat curve means that repeated observations will likely not yield new labels, the database is saturated. Data saturation curves were used for the overview of reviews and the review of UBEM tools (Figure 6). The observations were the articles read, and the labels were the progression factors and the UBEM tools respectively. The threshold conditions for saturation were set as the difference quotient for observations $O_n - O_{n-3}$; $O_n - O_{n-5}$; and $O_n - O_{n-10}$. The three ranges were chosen to decrease sensitivity to small-scale disturbances, and to set a minimum number of articles to be read.

The actionable set of articles included 25 EC reviews, 18 EC use-cases and 12 UBEM articles. Saturation for UBEM tools was reached at 12 articles and 43 tools. A total of 34 out of 2115 search hits were assessed before saturation, out of which 12 was preselected. Due to lack of information or failure to meet UBEM/USEM definitions, 21 tools were excluded. The 22 remaining tools were further analysed. For the progression factors, saturation was reached at 20 articles, with 49 progression factors. Including preselection, this meant that 108 of the 126 articles were processed, out of which 41 was preselected by domain relevance and 33 by topical relevance. A total of 8 unique use-cases were identified, supplemented by hybrid use-cases as one category. However, 5 use-cases were considered for use-case-specific progression factors, due to lack of data, or conflict with the definition (see Section 3.1). Three use-cases, community choice aggregation, microgrids and green neighbourhoods were not considered for unique progression factor extraction.

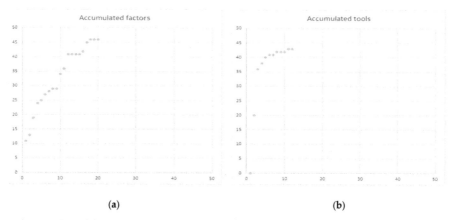

(a) (b)

Figure 6. Log of data saturation: (**a**) Number of accumulated progression factors plotted against number of energy community (EC) reviews on the left; (**b**) number of accumulated UBEM tools plotted against number of UBEM reviews on the right.

3. Results

The results are presented following the logic of affordances: Section 3.1 introduces the different identified use-cases for ECs (corresponding to affordance context), Section 3.2 describes phases of a generalized EC project lifecycle (affordance context), Section 3.3 collects EC progression factors (affordance goal) and examines according to the selected structural metadata, Section 3.4 constructs affordances from UBEM features (affordance capabilities), and disaggregates them as per the research questions.

3.1. Energy Community Use-Cases

The following use-cases were identified during the study: renewable energy production, peer-to-peer energy market, demand-response providing community, bulk investment in energy conservation measures, community choice aggregation, collective grid ownership and community energy storage. Additionally, the green neighbourhood is a special case not strictly an EC, and three hybrid use-cases were also identified.

Three use-cases, community choice aggregation, microgrids and green neighbourhoods were not considered for unique progression factor extraction. Community choice aggregation (CGO) allows cities or other local government units to aggregate customers within their jurisdictions and to procure energy for them, either through contracts or through ownership of generation [40]. Although the subject of the article was a comparison between community choice model and renewable energy community, the former is not in fact an energy community, but a pooling of consumers under a single trusted intermediary to bargain on their behalf. Collective grid ownership is a valid EC, however it never appeared on its own in the literature but integrated to one of the other use-cases [45,49]. Finally, green neighbourhoods are unique models targeting complex sustainability goals on the neighbourhood scale [32,55,56]. These ambitious projects are often government-funded flagship projects or experimental niches, or unique market niches of bottom-up initiatives. They operate partially or fully on a combined waste-water-energy nexus, seeking to leverage all three circulations to close loop, essentially leaving behind no waste, wastewater and taking in no energy from external sources [55,87]. Green neighbourhoods can be models for energy communities on the long-term, but the multiplicative impacts of such projects scale at the cost of scaling their complexity, operational and investment costs. Given that green neighbourhoods fit the definition of multi-purpose energy communities, any universal EC progression factor will also be valid for them as well.

From the core investigated use-cases, the energy conservation investment community (ECC) pools resources to bulk invest in interventions reducing their energy consumption, such as purchasing energy-efficient appliances, retrofitting the building envelope, replacing windows or multiple of the above in deep retrofit projects (Figure 7). The reduction of operational costs makes energy conservation communities relevant for ESCO financing, and the contribution to decarbonisation by demand reduction are measurable contributions to government sustainability policy [33].

Figure 7. Energy conservation investment community use-case. Dashed line denotes the community.

Peer-to-peer energy markets (P2PM) rely on community microgrids to sell and buy electricity produced locally in distributed plants, and externally if the microgrid is connected (Figure 8). Regarding market structure, the model can either be a full market, a decentralized market or a hybrid solution in between. The main difference between full and decentralized markets is the lack/presence of a community representative, who acts as intermediary for both internal market governance and as a medium between the decentralized community and the energy market. In hybrid models, members may join individually, or through the representative [53].

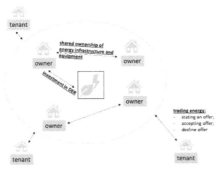

Figure 8. Peer-to-peer energy market use-case. Dashed line denotes the community.

Renewable energy communities (REC) are the most well-researched use-cases. Historically, decentralized renewable energy communities kicked of the social innovation niche, buy pooling resources to invest in energy production (Figure 9). In a decentralized model, there is a single or several power plants for the entire community, which can both be utilized to meet the demands of the community itself, but also to sell excess energy if they have access to wholesale markets. In a distributed model, the community functions more akin to energy conservation communities, to bulk invest in renewable production on household level [42]. Distributed production, alongside with microgrid ownership, are constituent use-cases for peer-to-peer energy markets.

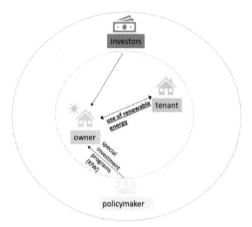

Figure 9. Renewable energy community use-case. Dashed line denotes the community.

Demand-response energy communities (DRC) are one of the more novel, experimental use-cases that stem from the mainstreaming of renewable production and distributed energy production. Since both trends have threats to maintaining grid balance, a community offering to harmonize load curves en masse is a viable service for grid operators (Figure 10). This involves consumers in the management of stable grids, therefore such interventions are labelled demand-side responses. The key strategies for managing load curves is through changing consumption habit, with load shaving meaning changing consumption amounts at certain times of a days, while load shifting is offsetting supply to other uses.

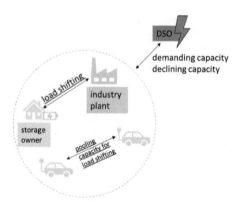

Figure 10. Demand-response community use-case. Dashed line denotes the community.

Community energy storage (CSE) is a modular, scalable, virtual energy storage built up from a grid of distributed storage units owned by community members (Figure 11). On their own, virtual storage communities can offer flexibility services like demand-response communities, while in combination with local production, they may serve as buffers to locally produced surplus. Community storage, if place-based is its own category in terms of scale (tens to hundreds of kWh) and is not a substitution for large storage with capacity levels in the MWh-GWh scale. Most common technologies include lithium-ion batteries, lead-acid batteries, flow batteries and more recently hydrogen for electricity, and water tanks and phase-change materials for thermic energy.

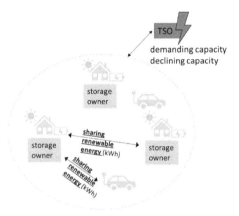

Figure 11. Community energy storage use-case. Dashed line denotes the community.

Hybrid use-cases are trending due to the associative nature of the use-cases and the potential of stacking services [88]. We have seen before that renewable energy communities can evolve into peer-to-peer markets, but it is also possible for prosumers to build a diverse grid stabilisation portfolio, by having both demand and supply side options (Figure 12). Renewable production can mitigate or eliminate undersupply, while community energy storage can act as a buffer in case of oversupply. Energy conservation measures are supplementary to all other use-cases, expanding external markets of any local production use-case by decreasing internal demand [46]. It is also an option for renewable energy communities to distribute some production and assets, and keep others at community level, while also acquiring energy storage to provide full stack energy services internally [14,89,90].

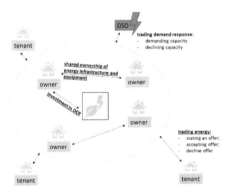

Figure 12. Hybrid renewable-demand response community use-case. Dashed line denotes the community.

3.2. The Energy Community Lifecycle

Based on the case studies and reviews, the EC lifecycle can be broadly split into five phases: initiation, design and implementation, operation and further development meaning either social, or technological scaling (Figure 13) [14,35,49,52,87,89–100].

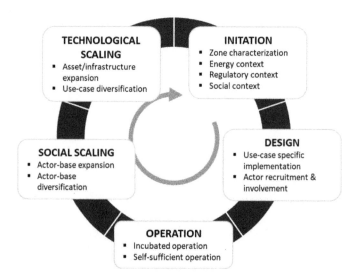

Figure 13. Overview of the generalized energy community project lifecycle.

EC initiation involves defining the overall strategy for the EC, namely an analysis of the characteristics of the area, the local energy sources, the users and of the community itself [35]. As for the energy context, the strategy of the EC is mostly defined by the varying energy load curves for prosumer types as well as the production and conversion system technology are based on the available energy resources. During initiation, the regulatory context, the compliance to regulatory requirements, synergies or counter-synergies with policy targets are also investigated. The initiation phase ends with the social approach, where the social impacts, the project's positive and negative implications, and potential integrations with other community-driven projects such as car-sharing, co-housing are assessed. The depth of transition delivered by ECs depend on who is involved and who leads the process during initiation. Most can be classified as government-driven or bottom-up, grassroots initiatives [101], however, there are existing ECs that were initiated by organised institutional entrepreneurs as intermediaries, like banks, public bodies, consultants [100].

The complexity of the design phase of each EC is heavily influenced by the use-case. For RECs, the community is on its own by using the right set of tools and expert help [87,96,97]. Whereas, the number of actors involved in P2PM necessitate a trading platform to handle all interactions between the different stakeholders and the network operator [98]. In case of demand response (DRC), the DSO and an aggregator need to have access to the EC's devices [99]. CGO use-cases involve local utilities, state and federal actors and research institutes [49].

In the operation phase ECs is split up into two parts: the incubated operation of ECs, meaning the operation with a supportive agency e.g., government, and the self-sufficient operating ECs. Most case studies reported of self-sufficient operation of RECs [95,100], whereas CGO and P2PM cases run almost exclusively through facilitators [49,102].

Beyond operation, there are multiple pathways for further development of ECs: they can scale technically or socially. Technical upscaling can mean the improvement of current use-cases, such as introducing distributed ledger technologies [52], or by better network performance and reliability [98]. It can also mean diversifying the use-case, involving new services, leading to EC hybrids. Similarly, social upscaling can mean both increasing memberships, or diversifying membership, such as by involving industrial or mobility sector actors [93].

3.3. Progression Factors

Based on the EC reviews progression factors are grouped into seven new categories: "interactions with regulation and governance", "information and knowledge", "economic influencers", "technological infrastructure", "requirements for justice", "actor-bound drivers and criteria" and "network drivers and criteria" groups. This section begins with the description of progression factors by group, followed by their analysis via the metadata designated in Section 3.3. See Appendix A for all progression factors.

3.3.1. Interactions with Governance and Regulation

Most reviews discussed relationships with public authorities either as regulatory conditions and challenges or the difficulty of securing long-term, reliable political support (Table 2). At the heart of this is the requirement for the normative alignment of energy communities, meaning their format must be recognizable in terms of legal definitions [43]. In countries, where legislation does not yet recognize energy communities, tend to categorize them as a cooperative or a company. Such labels lead to unfair comparisons, as the same regulatory standards could apply to an EC as to a conventional energy provider [87,90]. Normative alignment is shown to erect insurmountable entry barriers to community initiatives that fail to navigate through convoluted legal requirements [2]. Moreover, even municipalities that initiate energy communities, face challenges when ensuring compliance to national strategies and laws [44]. This is due to change in the EU for RECs, as nation states committed to their normative alignment [103]. While this challenge is most prevalent during initiation phase, regulatory barriers influence the whole lifecycle, for example by cutting off community microgrids from energy markets, due to unsatisfactory interoperability standards [50]. Changing regulations would require political commitment, but for many countries, community energy is simply not on the agenda [35] or is subjected to inconsistent policies [2].

Table 2. Progression factors tied to interactions with governance and regulation.

Interactions with Governance and Regulation		
Multi-bilateral contracting	The existence of standardised, yet flexible peer-to-peer templates for rapid application.	[3,53]
Multi-bilateral trading	A trading model harmonizing concurrent bilateral transactions on a shared infrastructure.	[87]
Legal and regulatory compliance	The ease of alignment between the energy community (or the facilitation thereof) and the regulatory regime.	[2,35,43–45,50,51,53,87,90,104]
Land-use and building code regulation	Land-use and building codification responsive to community-energy potentials.	[3,39]
Unfavourable taxation	Taxation policy fit-for a more decentralised energy market, level playing field for large and small actors.	[33]
Political landscape: inconsistency, engagement, support	The policies affecting community energy are volatile, hindering the planning of projects.	[2,35,38,44,46]

3.3.2. Information and Knowledge

It is crucial for the fitness of energy communities, that the relevant actors acquire the necessary knowledge to make decisions [46]. Many of the more practical barriers or failure scenarios can be traced back to lack of knowledge, and given the horizontal nature of energy communities, this knowledge is highly heterogeneous (Table 3). Proposals often overshoot natural or physical possibilities, factors such as sun, biomass, wind availability or proximity to sea, impacts of climate change, building conditions, settlement layout may contradict expectations if not thoroughly understood [44]. It is generally an obstacle that the multiple impacts and broader societal implications of energy communities are only conceptualized, but not sufficiently specified, quantified, measured [33], hindering not only recruitment, but also normative alignment (ref former [2]). Support from policymakers is an essential enabler, but only if communities can convince how their projects fit to relevant targets [40]. Research on the impacts of CRE projects are based on interviews, surveys in costly and highly specific case studies, model-based assessments are limited to regional-scale econometric analyses [12]. Apart from the public sector, prospective members themselves are rarely aware of how local energy systems work, what are the potentials for community energy, or the necessity of sustainable transition [3]. Community energy is simply not in the general discourse well enough to support the assimilation of project proposals [48], and even existing communities miss out on involving support by not understanding and communicating the distributional aspects of their projects, and how a certain stakeholder is specifically affected by it [46]. It is also important to plan for how EC initiatives interact with other projects, when calculating impacts, as certain synergistic co-benefits might greenlight some otherwise unfeasible projects [55], and if other pre-existing societal problems force EC off the agenda [12,35]. Finally, information provision is linked to data scarcity, the fragmentation of data ownership, its fitness-for-purpose is often questionable, imposing significant work for data acquisition and pre-processing [44,87].

Table 3. Information and knowledge related progression factors.

Information and Knowledge		
Ambiguity in network operation	Methodology for co-simulation of distribution networks and P2P energy trading.	[87]
Information barrier	Discourse among the relevant actors supporting the diffusion and assimilation of community-energy.	[38,44–46,90]
Community problem field	Knowledge of pre-existing complex, socioeconomic, structural challenges in the focus of the community.	[12,35]
Natural preconditions	Knowledge of potential natural resources and limitations due to environmental factors and scenarios (such as solar availability).	[44]
Physical preconditions	Knowledge of physical possibilities and constraints (such as building conditions).	[44]
Data quality	Feasible availability of timely, accurate, reasonable, relevant, actionable data on the appropriate scale.	[44,47,87]
Awareness	The general understanding of the local energy transmission systems, production opportunities and sustainability challenges.	[3,39,51]
Broader societal impact/benefit	Knowledge of the multiple impacts of projects.	[6,12,35,39,40]
Specificity	Knowledge of the distributional impacts of projects.	[39,46]
Synergies	Knowledge of co-impacts of the project aggregate of the energy community.	[47,55]
Granularity	Data generated of marketable performance on the scale of viable products and services	[47]

3.3.3. Economic Influencers

Financing community energy projects is a recurring challenge in the literature (Table 4). Energy communities usually require both a heavy upfront investment for infrastructural interventions, and significant costs for operation [3,45,49]. Much of this is traceable back to high transaction costs, comprising of searching for stakeholders and supporters, bargaining and negotiation with actors, acquiring and disseminating relevant information, dispute settlement, monitoring and opportunity costs [34]. Meeting the legal entry barriers, connecting to the grid and entering wholesale market, and knowledge production in general are factors discussed earlier, but they are with financial implications [33]. On the other hand, financial benefits stem from the local production and trade of energy at a lower price, the pooled investment on energy conservation and efficiency measures, and selling flexibility services [42]. Many projects do not scale to the point to produce enough economic surplus to cover operational expenditures, and there is always a danger of growing "too big", losing the social cohesion that came from the direct relationships of the community [2]. There is much reliance on external incentives, the availability of favourable taxation, feed-in-tariff rates, subsidies, commercial investments and loans support projects directly [3,33,49], while providing a level playing field for market actors, and easing access to information and crucial indirect tools to make community energy economically more viable [46,49].

Table 4. Economic influencer progression factors.

Economic Influencers		
Internal financial incentives	Monetizable benefits from the actions of the energy community.	[42]
External financial incentives	Policies, instruments, subsidies supporting funding investment and operation.	[2,3,45,46,49,51,105]
Cost	Handling of high transaction costs and upfront investment costs.	[2,3,12,34,39,44,45,47,49,87,105]
Access to wholesale markets	Opportunity to sell community-based services on the larger energy market.	[2,33,104]
Optimal size	Appropriate community size balancing (dis)economies of scale and social cohesion.	[2]

3.3.4. Technological Infrastructure

Known technological progression factors are conditions for either the energy or the information infrastructure (Table 5). There is a disparity among use-cases: while renewable EC factors are mostly regulatory, economic or social, peer-to-peer markets and demand-response communities pose unique technical criteria. It is crucial for markets, to operate on a low-voltage distribution grid—microgrid—that can function both in island mode and connected to the wider grid [49,53]. When infrastructure exists, distributing production in an energy market introduces three technical challenges: (1) upscaling multi-directional energy flows, (2) the diversification of energy supply and (3) upscaling of market actors [53]. The latter is also true for demand-response communities, as it essentially creates a market for flexibility services [35]. Scaling energy flows is a concern for grid operation, necessitating some mechanism to predict and to handle grid congestion, maintain grid balance and assure the supply of adequate quality energy.

Table 5. Progression factors stemming from technological infrastructure.

Technological Infrastructure		
Microgrid	Low-voltage distribution grid that can be operated as island as well as connected to the wider grid.	[39,47,49,53]
Market transaction cost optimization	Optimal markets need to minimize the total transaction costs by regulating energy flows based on the dynamism of demand and supply.	[53]
Privacy	Secure, anonymized individual inputs, including needs signalling, and assertion of rights.	[53]
Peer preferences optimization	Management of peer preferences, expectations and behaviour.	[35,53]
Scalability of negotiations	Computational capacity to handle negotiation and consensus as the community scales.	[53]
Quality assurance	Guarantees for meeting reliability, quality, security standards of energy sources.	[53]
Grid congestion	Stable, secure grid operation as the community, and thus energy flows scale.	[53]

Apart from the grid itself, EC use-cases such as P2P energy markets have unique challenges regarding ICT infrastructure to enable intra- and inter-EC transactions [106]. Scaling market size in terms of actors is on the one hand a—currently unresolved—computational challenge of handling negotiations and consensus mechanisms, but on the other hand it is also an optimization problem of multiple peer preferences and the market as a whole [35,53]. Most importantly, this includes minimization of the total transaction costs by regulating energy flows based on the dynamism of demand and supply, and integrating system-level optimum with the optimum of individual behaviour, expectations, preferences. Peer level input, including the assertion of their rights must also be extracted and processed, and in a way that it does not compromise their privacy.

3.3.5. Requirements for Justice

Justice, especially procedural justice is heavily featured in the discourse of transition management (Table 6). Sound institutional design, providing democratic legitimacy within energy communities is still a challenge [49]. As a result of the phrase "community", it is easy to believe the model is inherently positive, and more involvement is socially empowering, but there must be safeguards to assess and enforce legitimacy. Input legitimacy is measured on who is included in decision-making—or the community itself—which is where governance network models can be misleading: they might report high participation, but might exclude certain actors simply because they were out of reach from the social networks used for recruitment [12]. Failures in input legitimacy might lead to already powerful actors driving community energy, deepening existing conflicts and demotivating people not just from participating in community energy, but other governance network-based initiatives [35]. Throughput legitimacy, on the other hand, refers to the role each actor has in decision-making, and governance network negotiations do tend to give asymmetrical powers to those with more resources [42]. In case of peer-to-peer markets, this could lead to exacerbating energy poverty among the economically disadvantaged [53]. However it is the strength of networked governance that it provides an arena for discussions on issues of relevance, a core value incentivising membership, which must supplemented by instruments to monitor and supress exploitative conduct both within the communities, and on the markets [40]. Finally, output legitimacy in energy communities is expected to be sound, due to broad decision-ownership, however the way decisions are reached can be opaque under layers of negotiations, and any measure of transparency improves the community output legitimacy [42].

Table 6. Justice-related progression factors.

Justice		
Energy poverty threat	P2P markets may result in the energy poverty of economically disadvantaged groups.	[53]
Procedural justice	Institutional design and practices ensuring fair processes of decision-making, resource allocation, arbitration.	[6,12,42,49]
Transparency of energy market	Monitoring restructuring energy markets to recognize and supress exploitative conduct.	[40]
Input legitimacy	Measures against the uneven access to the community, exclusion of vulnerable groups, (e.g., women).	[12]

3.3.6. Actor-Bound Drivers and Criteria

Actor-bound drivers and criteria are factors describing the people who support, oppose or disengage from EC projects (Table 7). All three groups can influence the success of projects. Opponents are those who actively resists community energy, whether because of legitimate concerns, such as unwillingness to pay the opportunity cost, or through bounded rationality, which may surface as resistance towards either environmentalism, community ownership, or collective actions [35,105]. It is a matter of providing input legitimacy to give voice to concerns, provide mutually agreeable evidence to negate unwarranted opposition, and a just consensus and compensation mechanism for legitimate opposition. Other actors, who are passive, but should be supportive, might also be driven by bounded rationality, by inertia—disengagement despite the known benefits due to perceived discomfort of change [2,53], by lack of interest in energy-related issues [43], or by a wait-and-see attitude [2]. While opponents and bystanders influence mainly the initiation of projects, rebound effects are threats post interventions. Physical interventions without behaviour change results in net increase of energy consumption, hindering wider societal impacts of the EC [12]. In all cases, having community energy up on the agenda in both the political and in social discourse and placing it in the specific reality and value models are key conditions in overcoming passive, rebound and resistant behaviour.

Table 7. Actor-bound progression factors.

Actors		
Inertia, passivity	Inhibition of transition without active opposition, due to disengagement.	[2,35,43,105]
Opposition, scepticism	Unhandled active opposition and concerns to transition.	[2,35,43,105]
Self-identity	Supportive attitude, motivations, identity congruent with the mission of the project.	[38,42,44,105]
Reliance on volunteers/lack of time	Single or multiple committed change-agents driving the process voluntarily.	[2,12]
Pre-existing knowledge and skills	Actor-level understanding of regulation, technologies, markets through existing knowledge or intermediaries.	[2,12,34,44,46, 90]
Active involvement	High degree of ownership, community leadership and meaningful individual roles.	[12,38,39,45, 105]
Rebound effect	Adverse behavioural adjustment to technological improvements.	[12]
Place attachment	Acceptance and support of locally bound or originated products and services.	[105]

The self-identity of actors, attitudes and individual motivations, such as concern for environment, or grassroots enthusiasm may promote membership [42]. In multiple cases support for renewables and for divesting from coal, nuclear produces more engaged change-agents than individual economic benefits [105]. These change-agents, single or multiple committed evangelists for the cause, have been critical for most energy communities, as they usually mobilize their social networks, seek out professional expertise and lobby for political and financial support voluntarily in their free times [2,12]. This however bars potential energy communities that do not have change-agents, or they do not have the time or social capital to succeed. There is also great potential in intermediaries who may trigger knowledge diffusion, improve the accessibility of the community to supportive networks and resources, but is an additional cost in an already strained business model [12]. However, community-led projects, with more opportunities to distribute responsibilities, and assign roles to individuals fare better in terms of multiple benefits capturing than outsourced, or commercial-led projects [12,45,105].

3.3.7. Network Drivers and Criteria

Networks shape knowledge diffusion, resource, procedural flows among EC actors, and may provide platforms for social cohesion and grassroots empowerment [42,49,105] (Table 8). In terms of the internal network of the community itself, there must be a clarity of the objectives and purposes of the community: whether it serves a public task or brings profit or provides community service, all needs to be specified [43] and be consistent among members [3]. It is a common barrier to adequately communicate the project scope, conditions and benefits to prospective members [2]. This hinges on the bridging, or linking capital in EC actor networks—the efficiency of interactions cascading through them [12]. Mirroring self-identity, it is also beneficial to develop a group-identity, or to base the EC on an existing social group, with which members associate with [42]. However, it is necessary for EC mobilization to go beyond social networks to exploit multiple benefits [2]. Broad coalition of stakeholders are required to make many projects feasible, and it is difficult to identify and engage all of them [44]. Connecting to external, established interests may also prompt cross-fertilization and support, such as relationships to social movements or similar projects [43], and favourable network conditions improve access to relevant competences, resources, implementers, change-agents [44]. This does not undervalue social networks. Frequency and emergent saturation of community energy in social network clusters accelerates total saturation in said cluster due to peer effects [42]. However, there are certain actors who cannot be neglected in the decentralization of the energy market: providers of technical infrastructure. The partnership, or lack of partnership from local utilities provider can make or break community microgrid projects [49], while ICT providers of services, platforms and infrastructure are crucial for the operation of energy markets [106].

Table 8. Network-bound progression factors.

	Networks	
Articulate shared mission	Expected impacts and mission specified, and communicated in a measurable, achievable, specific, time-based, realistic manner.	[2,3,43,87]
Embeddedness, robust, resilient network	Connectedness to relevant actors, established networks with cross-fertilization potential.	[3,38,40,43,44]
Group identity	Shared sense of belonging to the social group constituting the energy community.	[12,42,49]
Relational goods, social value, empowerment	Perceived social value of networked cooperation through interactions and participation.	[38,42,49,105]
Peer effect	Frequency and emergent saturation in social network clusters accelerates total saturation in said cluster.	[42]
Market concentration	Engagement or resistance of actors and gatekeepers involved in centralized energy markets.	[2,39,40,47,49,50]
Identifying and engaging the appropriate network	Recruitment beyond social networks, on an outcomes/performance basis.	[2,39,44,46,90,93,106]
Bridging capital	Efficiency of knowledge transfer and negotiations through upscaling networks.	[12,38]
Trust	Trust eases transaction costs associated with negotiations in networked organizations.	[3,12,33,38]

3.3.8. Classification of Progression Factors

There is no consistent classification of progression factors in the literature, although many take an attempt to classify by relevant discipline [2,42,55,105]. The identified factors display an interdisciplinary scope of energy communities, with a slight skew towards social sciences and humanities (Figure 14). However, a sizeable proportion of factors (18 out of 49) had implications from multiple perspectives—one notable example is the optimal size of energy communities, which influences social acceptance and cohesion [42], economies of scale [2] and the complexity of computations [53].

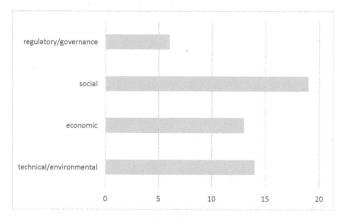

Figure 14. Progression factor distribution by discipline.

Factors were also classified by relative importance: conditions, which are necessary requirements for EC progression, barriers/challenges, which are definitive for successful progression, and enablers, which accelerate/hinder project progression. For example, the existence of a microgrid for peer-to-peer markets [53], or the compliance of the grid operator in case of renewable energy communities [49], are preconditions, with no possibilities of initiating the project without them in place. Internal incentives are challenges, as financially unsustainable ECs might still exist through subsidization [42]. Finally, access to other, community-based networks is an enabler for recruitment of support and diffusion of knowledge, for example [43]. The distribution of factors in the three categories is even, with slight skew towards barriers (Figure 15).

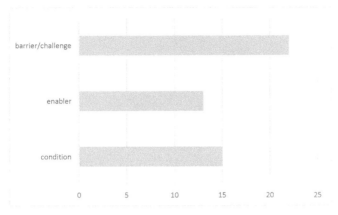

Figure 15. Progression factor distribution by role.

Based on relevant use-case, the distribution of factors reflects the distribution of literature (Figure 16). As the largest, single-use-case group of articles focus on renewable energy communities, most of the progression factors describe them. This does not mean that these factors are not applicable to other use-cases, however, there is insufficient evidence to confirm that they do or do not (see discussion).

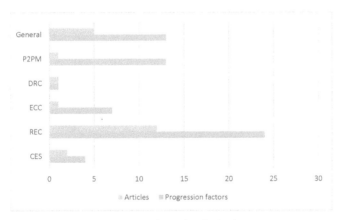

Figure 16. Progression factor distribution by use-case.

Finally, the classification by lifecycle phase heavily skews towards the earlier stages of energy communities. However, this does not mean that most barriers are overcome by the time operational phase kicks in, due to overlaps among the categories. A total of 19 factors are relevant in more than one phase, and 7 factors are relevant for all phases. The largest overlap (12) is between initiation and both technical and social upscaling phases, while the overlap between operation and initiation is only 1 (Figure 17). This displays a polarization of progression factors between operating the community and setting up the community—whether this "setting up" is the one that launches the project, or one that develops it further either technically or socially.

If all classification rationales are taken into consideration, with equal weight, hierarchical clustering returns the dendrogram shown on Figure 18. It is notable that none of the clusters are tight: even the most distant clusters can be reached with less than 3 steps, and over two-thirds of the factors would not be paired with any other, when setting cut-off for clustering to the average distance.

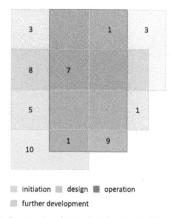

initiation   design   operation
further development

Figure 17. Progression factor distribution by lifecycle phase.

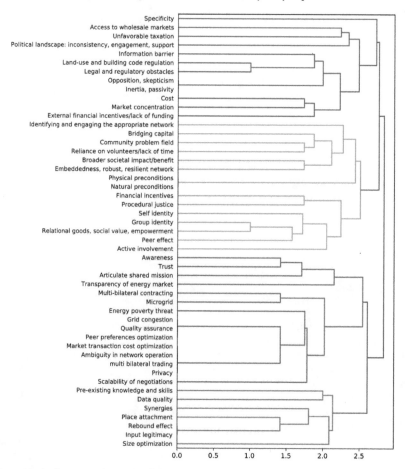

Figure 18. Agglomerative hierarchical clustering of progression factors by discipline, role, use-case, lifecycle phase.

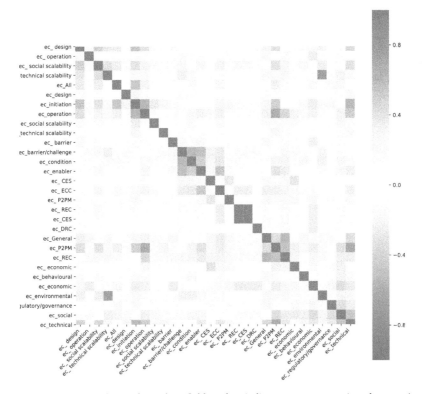

Figure 19. Pairwise correlation of metadata. Colder colour indicates a category consistently appearing together for progression factors.

The clusters themselves are heterogeneous both in terms of discipline and in terms of lifecycle, meaning it would be difficult to bundle interventions and responses even if the use-case is known. This is because there are very few classes that share the same factors, as shown on the correlation matrix of features (Figure 19). The top five positive correlates are shown on Table 9.

Table 9. Top 5 pairwise correlates of metadata.

Feature_1	Feature_2	Correlation
enabler	ECC	0.547
initiation	design	0.575
P2PM	operation	0.698
P2PM	technical	0.717
environmental	technical scalability	0.808

3.4. The Analysis of UBEM Tools

In this section, the results are presented as follows: first the choice of UBEM capabilities from the features listed in the four reviews are justified, then the individual affordances are constructed in the context of EC lifecycle phases, for goals of meeting progression factors, for EC planners as users and from UBEM capabilities as the affording agents. Due to inconclusive matching of progression factors to use-cases, the use-case as a context was not used (see Section 3.3). The section concludes with the disaggregation of results to EC phases.

The choice of UBEM capabilities is justified by the sparseness of agglomerative hierarchical clustering and the correlation matrix of capabilities. Clustering shows that the tools are generally distinct, as clusters only start to form at around 2.0 average distance, while all tools can be covered at 4.0 average distance (Figure 20). If four groups were to be generated—as shown in the figure—the threshold average distance would have to be set for 3.5, and this would still yield 6 unique tools (UrbanOPT [107], COFFEE [108], UrbanFootprint [109], CoBAM [110], SEMANCO [111] and OpenIDEAS [112]). The most similar tools at 2.0 average distance are UMEM [113] to MESCOS [114] and Georgia University [115] to Simstadt [79].

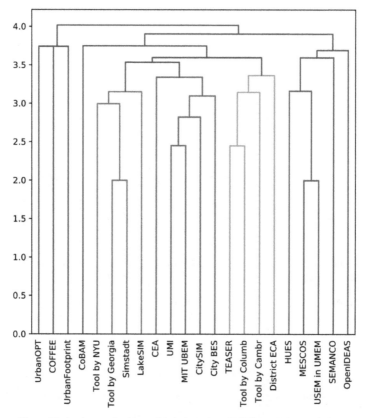

Figure 20. Agglomerative hierarchical clustering of UBEM tools by capabilities.

This result is also supported by the pairwise correlation of capabilities that show how often two capabilities share the same tool (Figure 21). It is notable that the correlation matrix is sparse and the only strongly correlated (coefficient higher than 0.7) pair is target groups: urban planner, and target groups: policymaker. They appear together in 81.67% of the tools.

In this framework, the capabilities for the 22 tools which remained after the data extraction were filled in (Appendix B), and affordances were constructed accordingly. A total of 5 affordances were generated, responding to 45 of the 49 progression factors (Table 10). The individual affordances are described below.

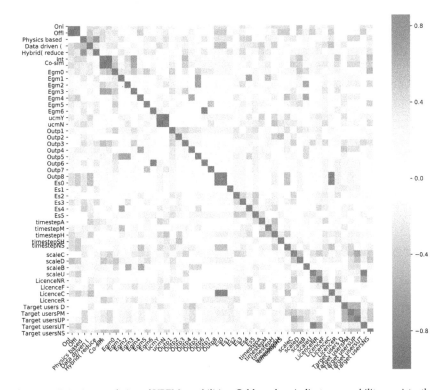

Figure 21. Pairwise correlation of UBEM capabilities. Colder colour indicates a capability consistently appearing together for tools.

Table 10. Identified affordances in relation to constituent capabilities and related goals (progression factors).

Affordances	UBEM Capability	Progression Factor
Accessible transparent and relevant early-stage spatiotemporal predictions.	Free, Web-based	Awareness
		Trust
		Transparency
		Bridging capital
		Informational barrier
		Inertia, passivity
		Opposition, scepticism
		Relational goods social value, empowerment
		Reliance on volunteers/lack of time
	Hybrid or reduced order bottom-up, Over-hourly resolution.	Transparency
		Pre-existing knowledge and skills,
		Specificity,
		Active involvement,
		Helps with finding synergies
		Natural pre-conditions
		Physical pre-conditions
		Opposition, scepticism
		Relational goods social value, empowerment
		Data quality
		Self-identity
	Diverse range of energy services	Energy poverty threat
		Social scalability
		Input legitimacy
		Active involvement.

Table 10. *Cont.*

Affordances	UBEM Capability	Progression Factor
Coupling impacts to heterogenous needs	Economic outputs	Market transaction cost optimization Quality assurance Financial incentives External financial incentives/lack of funding Broader social impact/benefit Market concentration Political landscape: inconsistency, engagement, support Community problem field Cost
	Bottom-up approach, Co-simulation, Sub-hourly output, District scale, Diverse range of energy services	Rebound effect Social scalability Broader social impacts/benefits Market transaction cost optimization Physical preconditions Natural preconditions Articulate shared mission Market concentration Input legitimacy Cost Specificity Identifying and engaging the appropriate networks Peer preferences optimization
Quick feedback from coarse data	Desktop based	Privacy
	Top down, over hourly, City scale	Land use and building code regulation Reliance of volunteers/lack of time Cost
Multi-scale detailed analysis	Bottom up stochastic, Sub-hourly output resolution, District scale	Multi-bilateral contracting Ambiguity of network
	Economic outputs	Legal and regulatory obstacles
Grid simulation	Co-simulation, Sub-hourly output, Diverse range of energy services, Energy generation modelling,	Microgrid Grid congestion Market concentration

3.4.1. Accessible Transparent and Relevant Early-Stage Spatiotemporal Predictions

An UBEM tool with web-based interface can afford to provide more accessibility, to its users than its standalone desktop-based counterparts and therefore helps in achieving awareness, trust, transparency, avoiding opposition, scepticism, helps in bridging capital and solving the information barrier, inertia and passivity and the reliance on volunteers. UBEM tools with hybrid or reduced order bottom up approaches are the most capable to calculate and iterate quickly and to work in data scarce environments. Calculating outputs in over-hourly resolution fosters the time- and computational efficiency further. With these capabilities UBEM tools can afford to provide transparency, existing knowledge and skills, specificity to the market, self-identity, active involvement, embeddedness and robust network, helps with finding synergies, natural and physical pre-conditions, data quality and provide quick granular data against opposition and scepticism.

Co-simulation platform architecture provides modularity and scalability for the platform. This modularity and the modelling of different energy services, on both supply and demand side with visualization capabilities can solve energy poverty threat, find synergies, define social scalability and input legitimacy and foster active involvement, embeddedness and robust resilient network by representing relevant spatiotemporal data. Since modelling of different energy services on supply side and other energy fluxes is an inherent capability, and modular software architecture is also more characteristic by USEM tools, therefore an USEM tool can satisfy the needs described at this affordance.

3.4.2. Coupling Impacts to Heterogeneous Needs

When it comes to modelling behavioural and technological changes in an energy community bottom-up approaches are far superior than top-down approaches. Bottom-up approaches with sub-hourly outputs on neighbourhood level can model multiple energy services both demand and supply side and generate wide range of output types. With this a wide range of granular data can be generated which provides specificity and allows actors to understand the causes of rebound effect, helps in the technological side of social scalability, market transaction and cost optimization, defining physical and natural preconditions, articulate share missions, mapping broader social impacts/benefits, costs, identifying and engaging the appropriate networks and helps with input legitimacy. An econometric model coupled with UBEM can immediately valorise the generated data, and analyse the results in line with the economic macro-environment or community problem field, and this way affords to give help with financial incentives, external financial incentives/lack of funding, analysing the inconsistencies, engagement and support in the political landscape, costs, provide quality assurance for prices, optimize market transaction costs, identify broader social impacts/benefits. Co-simulational tool architecture can afford modularity and scalability, which suggests that tools built this way could afford the transition into a real-time decision support system during operational phase with a higher probability. Since modelling of different energy services on supply side and other energy fluxes is an inherent capability, and modular software architecture is also more characteristic by USEM tools, therefore an USEM tool can satisfy the needs described at this affordance.

3.4.3. Quick Feedback from Coarse Data

As bottom-up models are better at generating detailed data, top-down models usually create outputs quicker and can work with coarse statistical data. With over-hourly outputs on a city scale this method can afford to inform land use and building code regulations, provide data to help with the present reliance of volunteers, and can analyse cost efficiencies. Desktop based tools are able to provide data offline, and therefore they can offer a highest level of privacy than web-based ones. An UBEM tool can satisfy the defined progression factors at this affordance.

3.4.4. Multi-Scale Detailed Analysis

Bottom-up approaches are generally better at scenario analysis. With sub-hourly or hourly output resolution bottom-up models which are capable of taking occupant behaviour into consideration can afford with the help of econometric model to provide an analysis of the network ambiguity and fundamental boundary conditions for multi-bilateral contracting also able to help removing legal and regulatory obstacles with price analysis of different energy vectors, and therefore helping economic standardization. An UBEM tool can satisfy the defined progression factors at this affordance.

3.4.5. Grid Simulation

Co-simulational scalable, and modular software architecture allows higher flexibility, while sub-hourly output resolution, heterogeneous energy generation and energy services modelling means detailed energy supply and demand results. With these capabilities, tools can afford microgrid simulations, grid congestion analysis and therefore attracting DSOs and end market concentration. Grid-simulation can be part of an USEM tool, therefore here an USEM tool is able to satisfy the needs defined at this affordance.

3.4.6. The Analysis of UBEM Tools by EC Lifecycle

Pairing UBEM capabilities with EC life-cycle stages results in the following table (Table 11). In every column, the highest amount of progression factors is highlighted with bold and in every row the highest amount of progression factors is highlighted with shading. The results show that accessible transparent and relevant early-stage spatiotemporal predictions respond to the highest amount of progression factors. This is followed by coupling impacts to heterogeneous needs. Other combinations respond to between 1–3 factor each lifecycle phase. It also shows that initiation phase is most well responded to by UBEM capabilities, followed by design and social upscaling, while operation and technical upscaling are least represented.

Table 11. Impact of affordances by energy community lifecycle phase. Shaded cells indicate highest value in row, italic text indicates highest value in column.

Affordances	Initiation	Design	Social Upscaling	Technical Upscaling	Operation
Accessible transparent and relevant early-stage spatiotemporal predictions.	*14 factors*	*11 factors*	*10 factors*	*7 factors*	*7 factors*
Coupling impacts to heterogeneous needs	*14 factors*	*11 factors*	8 factors	6 factors	6 factors
Quick feedback from coarse data	3 factors	2 factors	-	-	2 factors
Multi-scale detailed analysis	2 factors	1 factor	-	-	1 factor
Grid simulation	2 factors	1 factor	-	-	1 factor

4. Discussion

4.1. Limitations

Known limitations must be considered when reading the results. First, new knowledge given in this study is based on secondary information (reviews). While the progression factors, EC lifecycle, and main use-cases were empirically grounded, the corresponding affordances of UBEM capabilities—and thus the answer to the research question—still needs to be proven through case studies. Second, the development of UBEM tools compared to their original papers are not always comprehensively documented, therefore some information may be outdated and actual UBEM platforms may have more capabilities than described here. In addition, the utility of clustering progression factors by use-case is limited, due to lack of literature on the more unconventional use-cases beyond renewable energy communities. Additionally, limiting the research to western countries introduce a bias for both the progression factors themselves, and their metadata. Further studies, investigating Asian, Latin American and African initiatives could uncover different challenges and enablers, identifying context-specific progression factors for EC development. It must also be noted that the regulatory conditions for the normative alignment of RECs is about to change in the EU, as Member States commitments stated in their National Energy and Climate Plans [103]. This translates to both regulatory/policy factors and economic factors, as there is a recent, clear political statement in support of RECs, which will likely carry over to incentives. However, it is unclear whether and how this translates to other and hybrid use-cases of ECs. While there is a more general CEC and a more restrictive REC definition in EU legislation, if policy goals do not mention for instance community storage, then government subsidies will not be designed for them, their legal entry barriers will still exist, which hinders CES initiation. Therefore, the results (progression factors) must be read per use-case, as not all apply with equal weight. This amplifies the significance of not being able to group progression factors by use-case properly. It is advised for further case studies of novel EC use-cases to document their unique progression factors. Regarding policy, it is recommended that EC definition, and thus related policy instruments are differentiated by use-case. Additionally, the concept of CECs could be appropriated to support experimental, proto-ECs with a legislative pathway to evolve them into more specialized EC categories as their use-cases mature.

4.2. Reflection on Research Questions

The first research question referred to the common use-cases of energy communities, which are described in Section 3.1. While a majority of ECs are renewable energy communities, there is an abundance of ways actors can cooperate on energy-related matters. There are also obvious synergies among use-cases for hybrid, or multi-purpose energy communities to be developed. Some ECs already diversify their services, such as acquiring storage after saving up from energy sales revenues [14,89,90]. On the one hand, this trend points to a potential for existing ECs to pilot new unique or hybrid use-cases, leapfrogging some of the initiation-exclusive progression factors and accelerating EC uptake. On the other hand, more research into the development, drivers and barriers of novel use-cases are needed. Especially when it comes to hybrid use-cases and multi-purpose ECs, both the progression factors influencing the projects and the impacts will be a result of multiple interacting core activities.

It has been noted in previous reviews that such assessment is a research gap [2,6], and this study has found only one article discussing co-impacts [55].

The second research question referred to the various progression factors of ECs, collected and compiled in Section 3.3. A full classification of progression factors is presented in Appendix A. Due to limitations mentioned above, only one essential classification can be considered conclusive: by lifecycle phase. While the case studies and reviews identified four distinct phases (see Section 3.2), the analysis of progression factors revealed a clear distinction between operation and all other phases. This is reasonable, considering operation refers to the continuity of some form of status-quo, while initiation, design, early implementation, and various further developments are changes in the status quo. Most progression factors refer to initiation either exclusively or together with other phases. In reflection to the practical objective of supporting EC planners and policymakers, the EC progression factors by lifecycle phase are summarized on a project lifecycle wheel, reflecting the weight of each phase (Figure 22).

The third research question referred to the utility of UBEM tools in the various lifecycle phases of ECs, which is described in Section 3.4. It was shown that free, web-based hybrid or reduced order bottom-up models with over-hourly output resolution and heterogeneous output types and energy service modelling are most suitable for social upscaling; while bottom-up co-simulation model with an econometric model, sub-hourly output and diverse range of energy services modelling on district scale and the aforementioned tool are equally the best suited for initiation. There is only one existing tool for the former CityBES [116], and several for the latter HUES [117], UMEM [113], MESCOS [114]. In general, most UBEM capabilities deliver affordances for initiation and design stages, where most progression factors are. This also feeds into the main research question, whether UBEM is a technological trigger. The potential of UBEM, and UBEM-based simulation pipelines lie in the fact that they offer flexible decision-support in the earlier stages of projects, and whenever they are further developed. While decision-support for the operation of energy communities would require short term dynamic predictions on high resolutions to optimize the operation of energy communities, UBEM is a far more cost-efficient, early-stage alternative, requiring less input data and returning easy-to-understand outputs. To provide a quick tool for EC planners, the UBEM capabilities to look for based on progression factors, is summarized on a bipartite graph (Figure 23).

Reflecting on the second practical objective, recommending a development direction for UBEM, the trends in EC use-cases (see discussion above, based on section) make a good argument to invest in UBEM tool agility. The most impactful modelling capabilities were output resolution, output diversity, modularity and web deployment. Resolution on sub-hourly levels is necessary to forecast interactions on P2P energy markets, as trading usually occurs with 15-min frequency [27]. Output diversity and modularity becomes important with the diversification of energy community use-cases, and the growing prevalence of multi-purpose communities, such as green neighbourhoods. The value of UBEM tools is likely going to be determined by how many intertwined inputs and impacts do they handle, whom can be convinced with the evidence simulations provide. In other words, UBEM needs to respond well to in- and output diversification. This is why all affordances are met by USEM tools, whereas only two out of five are met by UBEM-only tools. Tools that either integrate UBEM with other models, such as City Energy Analyst [118], LakeSIM [119], CitySIM [120] and UrbanFootprint [109] with in-built transportation models, or tools that are modular and technically scalable, such as SEMANCO [111], UMEM [113], will be better suited to deliver diverse outputs reflecting EC use-case diversification. However, scalability to diverse, often uncertain and low-quality input data, which necessitates robust modules for data ingestion and pre-processing, is still something UBEM pipelines struggle with [121]. Finally, apart from architecture and functionalities, accessibility to users is also crucial, as seen by the performance of web-based tools versus desktop tools. While this was not explored as modelling tools are designed for engineers, user friendliness could be a pivotal improvement in the EC context. Given that laypeople gain formal powers and responsibilities in the EC model, tools in the future could support simple functionalities for users outside a niche of experts.

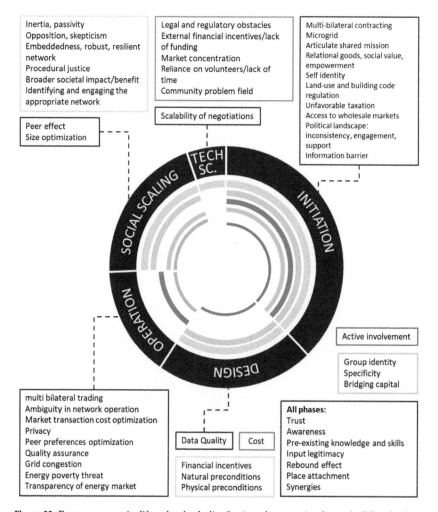

Inertia, passivity
Opposition, skepticism
Embeddedness, robust, resilient network
Procedural justice
Broader societal impact/benefit
Identifying and engaging the appropriate network

Peer effect
Size optimization

Legal and regulatory obstacles
External financial incentives/lack of funding
Market concentration
Reliance on volunteers/lack of time
Community problem field

Scalability of negotiations

Multi-bilateral contracting
Microgrid
Articulate shared mission
Relational goods, social value, empowerment
Self identity
Land-use and building code regulation
Unfavorable taxation
Access to wholesale markets
Political landscape: inconsistency, engagement, support
Information barrier

TECH SC.

SOCIAL SCALING

INITIATION

OPERATION

DESIGN

Active involvement

Group identity
Specificity
Bridging capital

multi bilateral trading
Ambiguity in network operation
Market transaction cost optimization
Privacy
Peer preferences optimization
Quality assurance
Grid congestion
Energy poverty threat
Transparency of energy market

Data Quality | Cost

Financial incentives
Natural preconditions
Physical preconditions

All phases:
Trust
Awareness
Pre-existing knowledge and skills
Input legitimacy
Rebound effect
Place attachment
Synergies

Figure 22. Energy community lifecycle wheel: distribution of progression factors by lifecycle phase.

Finally, reflecting on the research of energy communities, affordances have been a seamless addition to the conceptual frameworks of transition theory, multi-level perspective (MLP) and strategic niche management, as a missing link between the capabilities of enabling technologies, and the challenges posed by socio-technical transitions. We argue that technological affordances deserve an equal footing with institutional design and behaviour change, among factors that enrich any niche concept, be it a fundamentally technical, or a fundamentally social niche. Furthermore, the concept of MLP substantiates the influence of energy communities and UBEM tools on the user behaviour and preferences, which can gradually change the extraneous forces of the landscape, such as climate change. More articles need to be written on the role of technological affordances in fostering sustainable socio-technical transitions, with a special attention to disruptive technologies.

Figure 23. UBEM-EC matchmaker: bipartite graph pairing UBEM capabilities to progression factors by colour.

5. Conclusions

The study explored the potential role of urban building energy modelling in enabling the research and planning of energy communities. The conceptual framework of strategic niche management in the transition theory discourse was amended by the notion of affordances, to provide the missing link for studying technology as a trigger for social innovations. The literature on energy community was probed to reveal the diverse use-cases, general lifecycle and progression factors encompassing enablers, conditions and barriers of energy communities. The literature on urban building energy modelling was investigated to identify tool capabilities that afford specific progression factors. The study revealed that as an early-stage decision- and design-support tool, UBEM is a potential technological trigger to support kickstarting energy communities.

Energy communities are promising social instruments to invest in accessible, clean energy sources, system-level energy efficiency and offer a bottom-up path to low-carbon urban energy systems. This study unveiled UBEM as technological instruments for energy communities. As a step in the convergence of engineering and socio-technical discourses, it contributes to the task of transition studies of bridging social and technological innovations for a low-carbon future.

Supplementary Materials: Python-based in-house data science module "padron" was used for agglomerative hierarchical clustering and visualizations. The specific code used is available online at https://github.com/bvabud/Project_Ence, Agglomerative clustering notebook for progression factors: ec_progression_factor_classification_CODE, Agglomerative clustering notebook for UBEM tools: ubem_tool_classification_CODE.

Author Contributions: Conceptualization, V.B., Á.M. and A.R.; methodology, V.B.; formal analysis, V.B., Á.M. and M.K.B.; investigation, V.B., Á.M., M.K.B. and K.P.; data curation, V.B., Á.M. and M.K.B.; writing—original draft preparation, V.B., Á.M., M.K.B. and K.P.; writing—review and editing, V.B., Á.M. and A.R.; visualization, V.B.; supervision, A.R.; All authors have read and agreed to the published version of the manuscript.

Funding: This research received no external funding.

Acknowledgments: The authors would like to acknowledge the support to facilitate the research provided by the University of Pécs, Faculty of Engineering and Information Technology within the framework of the Biomedical Engineering Project of the Thematic Excellence Programme 2019 (TUDFO/51757-1/2019-ITM and the Advanced Building and Urban Design.

Conflicts of Interest: The authors declare no conflict of interest.

Appendix A

Table A1. Energy community progression factors.

Progression Factors	Use-Case	Lifecycle	Type	Classification	Reference
Access to wholesale markets	REC, P2PM	initiation	condition	economic	[2,3,58,89]
Active involvement	REC	operation, social scalability	enabler	social	[2,48,107]
Ambiguity in network operation	P2PM	operation	condition	technical	[12,53,54,60,108]
Articulate shared mission	General	initiation	condition	social	[89]
Awareness	General	All	enabler	social	[3,54,68]
Bridging capital	REC	initiation, social scalability	condition	social	[12,53]
Broader societal impact/benefit	REC	initiation, design, social scalability	enabler	social, economic	[6,12,50,54,55]
Community problem field	REC	initiation, design	condition	social, economic	[12,50]
Cost	General	initiation, design, operation	barrier/challenge	economic	[2,3,12,49,54,59,61,62,64,89, 108]
Data quality	REC	design	barrier/challenge	technical	[59,62,89]
Embeddedness, robust, resilient network	General	initiation, design, social scalability	enabler	social	[3,53,55,58,59]
Energy poverty threat	P2PM	operation	barrier/challenge	social	[68]
External financial incentives/lack of funding	General	initiation, design	enabler, barrier	economic	[2,3,60,61,64,86,108]
Financial incentives	REC, ECC	initiation, design, technical scalability, social scalability	enabler	economic	[62]
Granularity	P2PM, DRC	initiation, social scalability	barrier/challenge	economic	[68]
Grid congestion	P2PM	operation	barrier/challenge	technical	[12,57,64]
Group identity	REC, ECC	initiation, social scalability	enabler	social	[2,54,59,61,93,96,109]
Identifying and engaging the appropriate network	REC, CES, P2PM	initiation, design, social scalability	barrier/challenge	social, economic	[2,50,58,108]
Inertia, passivity	General	initiation, design, social scalability	barrier/challenge	behavioural	[53,54—61,93]
Information barrier	General	initiation	barrier/challenge	social, economic	[12]
Input legitimacy	REC	All	barrier/challenge	social	[57]
Land-use and building code regulation	General	initiation	barrier/challenge	regulatory/governance	[3,54]
Legal and regulatory obstacles	General	initiation, design	barrier/challenge	regulatory/governance	[2,50,58—60,65,66,88,89,93,107]
Market concentration	General	initiation, design	condition	economic	[2,54,55,62,64,65]
Market transaction cost optimization	P2PM	operation	condition	technical	[68]
Microgrid	P2PM	initiation	condition	technical	[54,62,64,68]
multi bilateral trading	P2PM	operation	condition	technical	[3,68]
Multi-bilateral contracting	P2PM	initiation	condition	regulatory/governance	[89]
Natural preconditions	REC	initiation, design, technical scalability, social scalability	condition	environmental	[59]
Opposition, scepticism	General	initiation, design, social scalability	barrier/challenge	behavioural	[2,50,58,108]
Optimal size	REC	social scalability	barrier/challenge	social, economic	[1]
Peer effect	REC, ECC	social scalability	enabler	social	[57]
Peer preferences optimization	P2PM	operation	barrier/challenge	technical	[50,68]

Table A1. *Cont.*

Progression Factors	Use-Case	Lifecycle	Type	Classification	Reference
Physical preconditions	REC	initiation, design, technical scalability, social scalability	condition	environmental	[59]
Place attachment	REC	All	enabler	social	[108]
Political landscape: inconsistency, engagement, support	REC, CES	initiation	barrier/challenge	regulatory/governance	[2,50,53,59,61]
Pre-existing knowledge and skills	REC, CES	All	barrier/challenge	technical, economic	[2,12,49,59,61,93]
Privacy	P2PM	operation	condition	technical	[68]
Procedural justice	REC, ECC	initiation, design, social scalability	enabler	regulatory/governance	[6,12,57,64]
Quality assurance	P2PM	operation	barrier/challenge	technical	[68]
Rebound effect	REC	All	barrier/challenge	social	[12]
Relational goods, social value, empowerment	REC, ECC	initiation	enabler	social	[53,57,64,108]
Reliance on volunteers/lack of time	REC	initiation, design	barrier/challenge	social	[2,12]
Scalability of negotiations	P2PM	technical scalability	barrier/challenge	technical	[68]
Self identity	REC, ECC	initiation	enabler	behavioural	[53,57,59,108]
Specificity	CES, REC, ECC	initiation, social scalability	barrier/challenge	economic	[54,61]
Synergies	REC	All	enabler	technical	[62,70]
Transparency of energy market	General	operation	condition	regulatory/governance	[55]
Trust	General	All	condition	social	[3,12,48,53]
Unfavourable taxation	DRC	initiation	barrier/challenge	economic	[48]

Appendix B

Table A2. Summary of UBEM and USEM tools.

Tools/Features	Online vs. Offline	Approach	Int or Cosim	Time Step	Energy Service	Output Types	Urban Climatology Model	Energy Generation Modelling	Optimal Spatial Scale	Licence	Target Users
MIT UBEM [78]	Standalone desk based	Physics based dynamic	Integrated	Hourly	Heating, Cooling, Lighting	Building operational energy demand	Yes	None	City scale	Free	Urban planners, policy makers
City BES [116]	Web-based	Physics based dynamic	Integrated	Sub-hourly	Heating, Cooling, Electricity, Lighting, Domestic Hot Water	Operational energy use; retrofit strategies	Yes	None	City scale	Free	Urban planners, policy makers
UMI [122]	Standalone desk based	Physics based dynamic	Integrated	Hourly	Heating, Cooling, Lighting	Building operational and embodied energy use; walkability score; daylighting	Yes	None	City scale City/District	Free	District energy managers
Tool by Columbia [123]	Standalone desk based	Physics based dynamic	Integrated	Hourly	Electricity, Space heating, DHW	Building operational energy demand	No	None	City scale	Research	District energy managers
Tool by Cambridge [124]	Standalone desk based	Physics based dynamic	Co-simulational	Yearly	Electricity, Gas	Building operational energy demand	No	None	District Scale	Research	District energy managers
UrbanOPT [107]	Web-based	Physics based dynamic	Integrated	Not sufficient inf.	Heating, Cooling	Strategies, District heating and cooling, and electricity network	Not sufficient inf.	PV, CHP, heat pumps, community energy storage	Building level	Research	District energy managers
COFFEE [108]	Web-based	Physics based dynamic	Integrated	Hourly	Heating, Lighting, Appliances, Cooling, Ventilation	Building operational energy demand, Optimization, Strategies. Operational energy use; r generation, transport choice, and other energy efficiency standards,	Not sufficient inf.	Not sufficient info	Utility scale	Not sufficient information	Utility program
CitySIM [120]	Standalone desk based	Physics based dynamic	Integrated	Hourly	Heating, Cooling, Ventilation, Appliances, Lighting	District heating, Electricity Network, Optimization analysis, Mobility characterization	Yes	Storage, CHP, r thermal, PV, wind	District scale	Free	Urban planners, policy makers
SEMANCO [111]	Standalone desk based	Physics based dynamic	Co-simulational	Yearly	Heating, Cooling, Appliances,	Building operational energy demand, Economic model, Maintenance costs	Not sufficient inf.	Heat pumps, PV system, district heating	City scale	Research	Urban planners, policy makers
Simstadt [79]	Standalone desk based	Reduced order method	Integrated	Monthly	Heating, Cooling, Domestic Hot Water, Electricity	Thermal energy demand	Yes	None	City scale	Research	Urban planners, policy makers
LakeSIM [119]	Standalone desk based	Reduced order method	Integrated	Monthly	Heating, Cooling, Appliances, Lighting	Mobility characterization, Transport energy demand modelling, Electricity network modelling, Optimization analysis.	No	Yes	City scale	Research	Urban planners, policy makers

Table A2. *Cont.*

Tools/Features	Online vs. Offline	Approach	Int or Cosim	Time Step	Energy Service	Output Types	Urban Climatology Model	Energy Generation Modelling	Optimal Spatial Scale	Licence	Target Users
Tool by Georgia [115]	Standalone desk based	Reduced order method	Integrated	Hourly	Space heating, Cooling,	Building operational energy demand	Yes	None	City scale	Research	Urban planners, policy makers
OpenIDEAS [112]	Standalone desk based	Reduced order method	Co-simulational	Not sufficient info	Space heating, Cooling, DHW, Lighting, appliances	Electricity Network, Optimization analysis	No	Storage BIPV, heat pumps	District scale	Research	District energy managers
CEA [118]	Standalone desk based	Engineering & Statistical/Reduced order method	Integrated	Hourly	Electricity, Space heating Space cooling Heating, Cooling, Lighting appliances, DHW,	Energy system simulation, Mobility characterization, Transport energy demand modelling, District heating, District cooling, Optimization	No	Storage, HP, CHP, PV, r thermal, Chiller	City/District District scale	Free-Free	Urban planners, policy makers
TEASER [125]	Standalone desk based	Reduced order method	Integrated	Hourly	Heating	Operational energy demand	No	None	City scale	Free	District energy managers
Tool by NYU [126]	Web-based	Data driven	Integrated	Annual	Gas, electricity	Building operational energy demand Emission, Land consumption,	No	None	City scale	Research	Urban planners, policy makers
UrbanFootprint [109]	Web-based	Data driven	Integrated	Not sufficient inf.	Not sufficient info	Conservation, Water use, Energy Use, Walk accessibility, Transit accessibility, Transportation, Costs,	No	None	City scale	Commercial	Urban planners, policy makers
CoBAM [110]	Standalone desk based	Data driven	Integrated	Annual	Heating, Cooling, Lighting, DHW	Building energy consumption, Emission	Yes	None	District	Not sufficient information	Policy makers
DistrictECA [127]	Standalone desk based	Bottom-up deterministic	Integrated	Monthly	Electricity, Space heating	Energy system simulation	Not sufficient inf.	Heating, cooling, Local and external storage CHP, Heat pumps	District	Free	Not sufficient information
HUES [117]	Standalone desk based	Simulation/Engineering	Co-simulational	Hourly	Electricity, Space heating, Space cooling, Heating, Electricity	Operational energy demand, District heating, Electricity network, Optimization analysis, Energy system optimisation	Yes	Storage, thermal	District/Building	free	Not sufficient information
UMEM [113]	Standalone desk based	Engineering	Co-simulational	Hourly	Heating, Cooling, Ventilation, Appliances, Lighting	District heating, Electricity network, Optimization analysis	Yes	Storage, CHP, thermal, PV, wind	District	Research	Not sufficient information
MESCOS [114]	Standalone desk based	Engineering	Co-simulational	Hourly	Heating, Electricity	District heating, Electricity network, Optimization analysis	Yes	Electrical storage, PV	District	Research	Not sufficient information

Energies **2020**, *13*, 2274

References

1. Van Der Schoor, T.; Scholtens, B. The power of friends and neighbors: A review of community energy research. *Curr. Opin. Environ. Sustain.* **2019**, *39*, 71–80. [CrossRef]
2. Brummer, V. Community energy—Benefits and barriers: A comparative literature review of Community ENERGY in the UK, Germany and the USA, the benefits it provides for society and the barriers it faces. *Renew. Sustain. Energy Rev.* **2018**, *94*, 187–196. [CrossRef]
3. Moroni, S.; Alberti, V.; Antoniucci, V.; Bisello, A. Energy communities in the transition to a low-carbon future: A taxonomical approach and some policy dilemmas. *J. Environ. Manag.* **2019**, *236*, 45–53. [CrossRef] [PubMed]
4. Ferri, N. United Nations general assembly. *Int. J. Mar. Coast. Law* **2010**, *25*, 271–287. [CrossRef]
5. Oteman, M.; Wiering, M.; Helderman, J.K. The institutional space of community initiatives for renewable energy: A comparative case study of the Netherlands, Germany and Denmark. *Energy. Sustain. Soc.* **2014**, *4*, 1–17. [CrossRef]
6. Creamer, E.; Taylor Aiken, G.; Van Veelen, B.; Walker, G.; Devine-Wright, P. Community renewable energy: What does it do? Walker and Devine-Wright (2008) ten years on. *Energy Res. Soc. Sci.* **2019**, *57*, 101223. [CrossRef]
7. Alanne, K.; Saari, A. Distributed energy generation and sustainable development. *Renew. Sustain. Energy Rev.* **2006**, *10*, 539–558. [CrossRef]
8. Tomain, J.P. The Democratization of Energy. *Vand. J. Transnatl. Law* **2015**, *48*, 1125–1145.
9. Walker, G.; Devine-Wright, P. Community renewable energy: What should it mean? *Energy Policy* **2008**, *36*, 497–500. [CrossRef]
10. Romero-Rubio, C.; De Andrés Díaz, J.R. Sustainable energy communities: A study contrasting Spain and Germany. *Energy Policy* **2015**, *85*, 397–409. [CrossRef]
11. Hoppe, T.; Graf, A.; Warbroek, B.; Lammers, I.; Lepping, I. Local governments supporting local energy initiatives: Lessons from the best practices of Saerbeck (Germany) and Lochem (The Netherlands). *Sustainability* **2015**, *7*, 1900–1931. [CrossRef]
12. Berka, A.L.; Creamer, E. Taking stock of the local impacts of community owned renewable energy: A review and research agenda. *Renew. Sustain. Energy Rev.* **2018**, *82*, 3400–3419. [CrossRef]
13. Caramizaru, A.; Uihlein, A. *Energy Communities: An Overview of Energy and Social Innovation*; Publications Office of the European Union: Luxembourg, 2020.
14. Lowitzsch, J.; Hoicka, C.E.; Van Tulder, F.J. Renewable energy communities under the 2019 European Clean Energy Package—Governance model for the energy clusters of the future? *Renew. Sustain. Energy Rev.* **2020**, *122*, 109489. [CrossRef]
15. RES-Scoop. What Are 'Citizen' and 'Renewable' Energy Communities? Available online: https://uploads.strikinglycdn.com/files/b8d598e0-52c2-480c-b0bc-1953228c3bce/Q%26A%20Briefing%20-%20what%20are%20citizens%20energy%20communities%20%26%20renewable%20energy%20communities%20in%20the%20CEP%20-%20final.pdf (accessed on 15 February 2020).
16. Fink, S.; Porter, K.; Rogers, J. *The Relevance of Generation Interconnection Procedures to Feed-in Tariffs in the United States*; National Renewable Energy Laboratory: Golden, CO, USA, 2010.
17. Chernyakhovskiy, I.; Tian, T.; Mclaren, J.; Miller, M.; Geller, N.; Chernyakhovskiy, I.; Tian, T.; Mclaren, J.; Miller, M.; Geller, N. *U.S. Laws and Regulations for Renewable Energy Grid Interconnections*; National Renewable Energy Laboratory: Golden, CO, USA, 2016; pp. 1–29.
18. Klein, S.J.W.; Coffey, S. Building a sustainable energy future, one community at a time. *Renew. Sustain. Energy Rev.* **2016**, *60*, 867–880. [CrossRef]
19. Feldman, D.; Brockway, A.M.; Ulrich, E.; Margolis, R. *Shared Solar: Current Landscape, Market Potential, and the Impact of Federal Securities Regulation*; National Renewable Energy Laboratory: Golden, CO, USA, 2015; p. 70.
20. Thomas, D.; Miller, C.; Kämpf, J.; Schlueter, A. Multiscale Co-simulation of EnergyPlus and CitySim models derived from a Building Information Model. In *Bausim 2014: Fifth German-Austrian IBPSA Conference*; RWTH Aachen University: Aachen, Germany, 2014; pp. 469–476.
21. Keirstead, J.; Jennings, M.; Sivakumar, A. A review of urban energy system models: Approaches, challenges and opportunities. *Renew. Sustain. Energy Rev.* **2012**, *16*, 3847–3866. [CrossRef]

22. Sola, A.; Corchero, C.; Salom, J.; Sanmarti, M. Multi-domain urban-scale energy modelling tools: A review. *Sustain. Cities Soc.* **2019**, *54*, 101872. [CrossRef]

23. Allegrini, J.; Orehounig, K.; Mavromatidis, G.; Ruesch, F.; Dorer, V.; Evins, R. A review of modelling approaches and tools for the simulation of district-scale energy systems. *Renew. Sustain. Energy Rev.* **2015**, *52*, 1391–1404. [CrossRef]

24. Reinhart, C.F.; Cerezo Davila, C. Urban building energy modeling—A review of a nascent field. *Build. Environ.* **2016**, *97*. [CrossRef]

25. Goy, S.; Finn, D. Estimating demand response potential in building clusters. *Energy Procedia* **2015**, *78*, 3391–3396. [CrossRef]

26. Manfren, M.; Caputo, P.; Costa, G. Paradigm shift in urban energy systems through distributed generation: Methods and models. *Appl. Energy* **2011**, *88*, 1032–1048. [CrossRef]

27. Monti, A. *Energy Positive Neighborhoods and Smart Energy Districts Methods, Tools, and Experiences from the Field*; Academic Press: Cambridge, MA, USA, 2016; ISBN 9780128099513.

28. Perez-Lombard, L.; Ortiz, J.; González, R.; Maestre, I.R. A review of benchmarking, rating and labelling concepts within the framework of building energy certification schemes. *Energy Build.* **2009**, *41*, 272–278. [CrossRef]

29. Kanagaretnam, K.; Mestelman, S.; Nainar, S.M.K.; Shehata, M. Transparency and empowerment in an investment environment. *J. Bus. Res.* **2014**, *67*, 2030–2038. [CrossRef]

30. Tardioli, G.; Kerrigan, R.; Oates, M.; O'Donnell, J.; Finn, D.P. Identification of representative buildings and building groups in urban datasets using a novel pre-processing, classification, clustering and predictive modelling approach. *Build. Environ.* **2018**, *140*, 90–106. [CrossRef]

31. Ratti, C.; Baker, N.; Steemers, K. Energy consumption and urban texture. *Energy Build.* **2005**, *37*, 762–776. [CrossRef]

32. Amaral, A.R.; Rodrigues, E.; Rodrigues Gaspar, A.; Gomes, Á. Review on performance aspects of nearly zero-energy districts. *Sustain. Cities Soc.* **2018**, *43*, 406–420. [CrossRef]

33. Roby, H.; Dibb, S. Future pathways to mainstreaming community energy. *Energy Policy* **2019**, *135*, 111020. [CrossRef]

34. Nolden, C.; Barnes, J.; Nicholls, J. Community energy business model evolution: A review of solar photovoltaic developments in England. *Renew. Sustain. Energy Rev.* **2020**, *122*, 109722. [CrossRef]

35. Ceglia, F.; Esposito, P.; Marrasso, E.; Sasso, M. From smart energy community to smart energy municipalities: Literature review, agendas and pathways. *J. Clean. Prod.* **2020**, *254*, 120118. [CrossRef]

36. Lehtonen, M.; De Carlo, L. Community energy and the virtues of mistrust and distrust: Lessons from Brighton and Hove energy cooperatives. *Ecol. Econ.* **2019**, *164*, 106367. [CrossRef]

37. Van der Waal, E.C. Local impact of community renewable energy: A case study of an Orcadian community-led wind scheme. *Energy Policy* **2019**, *138*, 111193. [CrossRef]

38. Pellicer-Sifres, V.; Belda-Miquel, S.; Cuesta-Fernandez, I.; Boni, A. Learning, transformative action, and grassroots innovation: Insights from the Spanish energy cooperative Som Energia. *Energy Res. Soc. Sci.* **2018**, *42*, 100–111. [CrossRef]

39. Von Wirth, T.; Gislason, L.; Seidl, R. Distributed energy systems on a neighborhood scale: Reviewing drivers of and barriers to social acceptance. *Renew. Sustain. Energy Rev.* **2018**, *82*, 2618–2628. [CrossRef]

40. Hess, D.J.; Lee, D. Energy decentralization in California and New York: Conflicts in the politics of shared solar and community choice. *Renew. Sustain. Energy Rev.* **2020**, *121*, 109716. [CrossRef]

41. Joshi, G.; Yenneti, K. Community solar energy initiatives in India: A pathway for addressing energy poverty and sustainability? *Energy Build.* **2020**, *210*, 109736. [CrossRef]

42. Bauwens, T. Analyzing the determinants of the size of investments by community renewable energy members: Findings and policy implications from Flanders. *Energy Policy* **2019**, *129*, 841–852. [CrossRef]

43. Heldeweg, M.A.; Saintier, S. Renewable energy communities as 'socio-legal institutions': A normative frame for energy decentralization? *Renew. Sustain. Energy Rev.* **2020**, *119*, 109518. [CrossRef]

44. Petersen, J.P. The application of municipal renewable energy policies at community level in Denmark: A taxonomy of implementation challenges. *Sustain. Cities Soc.* **2018**, *38*, 205–218. [CrossRef]

45. Gorroño-Albizu, L.; Sperling, K.; Djørup, S. The past, present and uncertain future of community energy in Denmark: Critically reviewing and conceptualising citizen ownership. *Energy Res. Soc. Sci.* **2019**, *57*, 101231. [CrossRef]

46.   Parra, D.; Swierczynski, M.; Stroe, D.I.; Norman, S.A.; Abdon, A.; Worlitschek, J.; O'Doherty, T.; Rodrigues, L.; Gillott, M.; Zhang, X.; et al. An interdisciplinary review of energy storage for communities: Challenges and perspectives. *Renew. Sustain. Energy Rev.* **2017**, *79*, 730–749. [CrossRef]

47.   Freitas Gomes, I.S.; Perez, Y.; Suomalainen, E. Coupling small batteries and PV generation: A review. *Renew. Sustain. Energy Rev.* **2020**, *126*, 109835. [CrossRef]

48.   Van Summeren, L.F.M.; Wieczorek, A.J.; Bombaerts, G.J.T.; Verbong, G.P.J. Community energy meets smart grids: Reviewing goals, structure, and roles in Virtual Power Plants in Ireland, Belgium and the Netherlands. *Energy Res. Soc. Sci.* **2020**, *63*, 101415. [CrossRef]

49.   Warneryd, M.; Håkansson, M.; Karltorp, K. Unpacking the complexity of community microgrids: A review of institutions' roles for development of microgrids. *Renew. Sustain. Energy Rev.* **2020**, *121*, 109690. [CrossRef]

50.   Hirsch, A.; Parag, Y.; Guerrero, J. Microgrids: A review of technologies, key drivers, and outstanding issues. *Renew. Sustain. Energy Rev.* **2018**, *90*, 402–411. [CrossRef]

51.   Biresselioglu, M.E.; Nilsen, M.; Demir, M.H.; Røyrvik, J.; Koksvik, G. Examining the barriers and motivators affecting European decision-makers in the development of smart and green energy technologies. *J. Clean. Prod.* **2018**, *198*, 417–429. [CrossRef]

52.   Van Cutsem, O.; Ho Dac, D.; Boudou, P.; Kayal, M. Cooperative energy management of a community of smart-buildings: A Blockchain approach. *Int. J. Electr. Power Energy Syst.* **2020**, *117*, 105643. [CrossRef]

53.   Sousa, T.; Soares, T.; Pinson, P.; Moret, F.; Baroche, T.; Sorin, E. Peer-to-peer and community-based markets: A comprehensive review. *Renew. Sustain. Energy Rev.* **2019**, *104*, 367–378. [CrossRef]

54.   Butturi, M.A.; Lolli, F.; Sellitto, M.A.; Balugani, E.; Gamberini, R.; Rimini, B. Renewable energy in eco-industrial parks and urban-industrial symbiosis: A literature review and a conceptual synthesis. *Appl. Energy* **2019**, *255*, 113825. [CrossRef]

55.   Saheb, Y.; Shnapp, S.; Johnson, C. The Zero Energy concept: Making the whole greater than the sum of the parts to meet the Paris Climate Agreement's objectives. *Curr. Opin. Environ. Sustain.* **2018**, *30*, 138–150. [CrossRef]

56.   Tam, V.W.Y.; Karimipour, H.; Le, K.N.; Wang, J. Green neighbourhood: Review on the international assessment systems. *Renew. Sustain. Energy Rev.* **2018**, *82*, 689–699. [CrossRef]

57.   Swan, L.G.; Ugursal, V.I. Modeling of end-use energy consumption in the residential sector: A review of modeling techniques. *Renew. Sustain. Energy Rev.* **2009**, *13*, 1819–1835. [CrossRef]

58.   Johnston, D. A Physically-Based Energy and Carbon Dioxide Emissions Model of the UK Housing Stock. Ph.D. Thesis, Leeds Metropolitan University, Leeds, UK, 2003; p. 280.

59.   Kavgic, M.; Mavrogianni, A.; Mumovic, D.; Summerfield, A.; Stevanovic, Z.; Djurovic-Petrovic, M. A review of bottom-up building stock models for energy consumption in the residential sector. *Build. Environ.* **2010**, *45*, 1683–1697. [CrossRef]

60.   Li, W.; Zhou, Y.; Cetin, K.; Eom, J.; Wang, Y.; Chen, G. Modeling urban building energy use: A review of modeling approaches and procedures. *Energy* **2017**, *141*, 2445–2457. [CrossRef]

61.   Abbasabadi, N.; Ashayeri, J.K.M. Urban energy use modeling methods and tools: A review and an outlook. *Build. Environ.* **2019**, *161*, 106270. [CrossRef]

62.   Ferrari, S.; Zagarella, F.; Caputo, P.; Bonomolo, M. Assessment of tools for urban energy planning. *Energy* **2019**, *176*, 544–551. [CrossRef]

63.   Hegger, D.L.T.; Van Vliet, J.; Van Vliet, B.J.M. Niche management and its contribution to regime change: The case of innovation in sanitation. *Technol. Anal. Strateg. Manag.* **2007**, *19*, 729–746. [CrossRef]

64.   Geels, F.W. Analysing the breakthrough of rock "n" roll (1930–1970) Multi-regime interaction and reconfiguration in the multi-level perspective. *Technol. Forecast. Soc. Change* **2007**, *74*, 1411–1431. [CrossRef]

65.   Geels, F.W. Technology Analysis & Strategic Management The dynamics of transitions in socio-technical systems: A multi-level analysis of the transition pathway from horse-drawn carriages to The Dynamics of Transitions in Socio-technical Systems: A Multi-level Analy. *Technol. Anal. Strateg. Manag.* **2005**, *17*, 445–476.

66.   Hodson, M.; Marvin, S. Can cities shape socio-technical transitions and how would we know if they were? *Res. Policy* **2010**, *39*, 477–485. [CrossRef]

67.   Schot, J.; Geels, F.W. Strategic niche management and sustainable innovation journeys: Theory, findings, research agenda, and policy. *Technol. Anal. Strateg. Manag.* **2008**, *20*, 537–554. [CrossRef]

68.   Gibson, J.J. The Theory of Affordances. In *Perceiving, Acting, Knowing. Toward an Ecological Psychology*; Lawrence Erlbaum Associates: Mahwah, NJ, USA, 1977; pp. 67–82.

69. Norman, D.A. Affordance, conventions, and design. *Interactions* **1999**, *6*, 38–43. [CrossRef]
70. Markus, M.L.; Silver, M. A Foundation for the Study of IT Effects: A New Look at DeSanctis and Poole's Concepts of Structural Features and Spirit. *J. Assoc. Inf. Syst.* **2008**, *9*, 609–632. [CrossRef]
71. Sadler, E.; Given, L.M. Affordance theory: A framework for graduate students' information behavior. *J. Doc.* **2007**, *63*, 115–141. [CrossRef]
72. Carlo, J.L.; Lyytinen, K.; Boland, R.J. Dialectics of collective minding: Contradictory appropriations of information technology in a high-risk project. *MIS Q. Manag. Inf. Syst.* **2012**, *36*. [CrossRef]
73. Chatterjee, S.; Moody, G.; Lowry, P.B.; Chakraborty, S.; Hardin, A. Information Technology and organizational innovation: Harmonious information technology affordance and courage-based actualization. *J. Strateg. Inf. Syst.* **2020**, 101596. [CrossRef]
74. Durugbo, C.M. Affordance-based problem structuring for workplace innovation. *Eur. J. Oper. Res.* **2020**. [CrossRef]
75. Volkoff, O.; Strong, D.M. Critical Realism and Affordances: Theorizing It-Associated Organizational Change Processes. *MIS Q.* **2013**, *37*, 819–834. [CrossRef]
76. Sokal, R.R. *A Statistical Method for Evaluating Systematic Relationships*; University of Kansas: Lawrence, KS, USA, 1958; Volume 38, ISBN 0001948000237.
77. Hong, T.; Chen, Y.; Luo, X.; Luo, N.; Lee, S.H. Ten questions on urban building energy modeling. *Build. Environ.* **2020**, *168*, 106508. [CrossRef]
78. Davila, C.C.; Reinhart, C.F.; Bemis, J.L. Modeling Boston: A work flow for the efficient generation and maintenance of urban building energy models from existing geospatial datasets. *Energy* **2016**, *117*, 237–250. [CrossRef]
79. Nouvel, R.; Duminil, E.; Coors, V.; Eicker, U. *Simstadt, A New Workflow-Driven Urban Energy Simulation Platform for Citygml City Models*; CISBAT: Lausanne, Switzerland, 2015.
80. Chatterjee, S.; Moody, G.; Lowry, P.B.; Chakraborty, S.; Hardin, A. Strategic Relevance of Organizational Virtues Enabled by Information Technology in Organizational Innovation. *J. Manag. Inf. Syst.* **2015**, *32*, 158–196. [CrossRef]
81. Zammuto, R.F.; Griffith, T.L.; Majchrzak, A.; Dougherty, D.J.; Faraj, S. Information Technology and the Changing Fabric of Organization. *Organ. Sci.* **2007**, *18*, 749–762. [CrossRef]
82. Gal, U.; Jensen, T.B.; Lyytinen, K. Identity orientation, social exchange, and information technology use in interorganizational collaborations. *Organ. Sci.* **2014**, *25*, 1372–1390. [CrossRef]
83. Martín-Martín, A.; Orduña-Malea, E.; Thelwall, M.; Delgado-López-Cózar, E.; Orduna-Malea, E.; Thelwall, M.; Delgado-López-Cózar, E.; Delgado López-Cózar, E. Scopus: A systematic comparison of citations in 252 subject categories. *J. Informetr.* **2018**, *12*, 1160–1177. [CrossRef]
84. Marshall, S.; Craven, D.; Kelly, J.; Isenring, E. A systematic review and meta-analysis of the criterion validity of nutrition assessment tools for diagnosing protein-energy malnutrition in the older community setting (the MACRo study). *Clin. Nutr.* **2018**, *37*, 1902–1912. [CrossRef] [PubMed]
85. Francisco, A.; Taylor, J.E. Designing community-scale energy feedback. *Energy Procedia* **2019**, *158*, 4178–4183. [CrossRef]
86. Tran, V.T.; Porcher, R.; Tran, V.C.; Ravaud, P. Predicting data saturation in qualitative surveys with mathematical models from ecological research. *J. Clin. Epidemiol.* **2017**, *82*, 71–78.e2. [CrossRef]
87. Karunathilake, H.; Hewage, K.; Prabatha, T.; Ruparathna, R.; Sadiq, R. Project deployment strategies for community renewable energy: A dynamic multi-period planning approach. *Renew. Energy* **2020**, *152*, 237–258. [CrossRef]
88. Renaissance-h2020.eu. Available online: https://www.renaissance-h2020.eu/ (accessed on 15 February 2020).
89. Kim, M.H.; Kim, D.; Heo, J.; Lee, D.W. Energy performance investigation of net plus energy town: Energy balance of the Jincheon Eco-Friendly energy town. *Renew. Energy* **2020**, *147*, 1784–1800. [CrossRef]
90. Hansen, P.; Morrison, G.M.; Zaman, A.; Liu, X. Smart technology needs smarter management: Disentangling the dynamics of digitalism in the governance of shared solar energy in Australia. *Energy Res. Soc. Sci.* **2020**, *60*, 101322. [CrossRef]
91. Hasanov, M.; Zuidema, C. The transformative power of self-organization: Towards a conceptual framework for understanding local energy initiatives in The Netherlands. *Energy Res. Soc. Sci.* **2018**, *37*, 85–93. [CrossRef]
92. Ruggiero, S.; Martiskainen, M.; Onkila, T. Understanding the scaling-up of community energy niches through strategic niche management theory: Insights from Finland. *J. Clean. Prod.* **2018**, *170*, 581–590. [CrossRef]

93. Capellán-Pérez, I.; Campos-Celador, Á.; Terés-Zubiaga, J. Renewable Energy Cooperatives as an instrument towards the energy transition in Spain. *Energy Policy* **2018**, *123*, 215–229. [CrossRef]
94. Freitas, S.; Reinhart, C.; Brito, M.C. Minimizing storage needs for large scale photovoltaics in the urban environment. *Sol. Energy* **2018**, *159*, 375–389. [CrossRef]
95. Mundaca, L.; Busch, H.; Schwer, S. 'Successful' low-carbon energy transitions at the community level? An energy justice perspective. *Appl. Energy* **2018**, *218*, 292–303. [CrossRef]
96. Heaslip, E.; Fahy, F. Developing transdisciplinary approaches to community energy transitions: An island case study. *Energy Res. Soc. Sci.* **2018**, *45*, 153–163. [CrossRef]
97. Rafique, M.M.; Rehman, S.; Alhems, L.M. Developing zero energy and sustainable villages—A case study for communities of the future. *Renew. Energy* **2018**, *127*, 565–574. [CrossRef]
98. Hayes, B.P.; Thakur, S.; Breslin, J.G. Co-simulation of electricity distribution networks and peer to peer energy trading platforms. *Int. J. Electr. Power Energy Syst.* **2020**, *115*, 105419. [CrossRef]
99. Lezama, F.; Soares, J.; Canizes, B.; Vale, Z. Flexibility management model of home appliances to support DSO requests in smart grids. *Sustain. Cities Soc.* **2020**, *55*, 102048. [CrossRef]
100. Mahzouni, A. The role of institutional entrepreneurship in emerging energy communities: The town of St. Peter in Germany. *Renew. Sustain. Energy Rev.* **2019**, *107*, 297–308. [CrossRef]
101. Mah, D.N. yin Community solar energy initiatives in urban energy transitions: A comparative study of Foshan, China and Seoul, South Korea. *Energy Res. Soc. Sci.* **2019**, *50*, 129–142. [CrossRef]
102. Buth, M.A.; Wieczorek, A.A.; Verbong, G.G. The promise of peer-to-peer trading? The potential impact of blockchain on the actor configuration in the Dutch electricity system. *Energy Res. Soc. Sci.* **2019**, *53*, 194–205. [CrossRef]
103. Commission, E.-E. National energy and climate plans (NECPs)-Energy European Commission. Available online: https://ec.europa.eu/energy/topics/energy-strategy/national-energy-climate-plans_en (accessed on 8 February 2020).
104. Heras-Saizarbitoria, I.; Sáez, L.; Allur, E.; Morandeira, J. The emergence of renewable energy cooperatives in Spain: A review. *Renew. Sustain. Energy Rev.* **2018**, *94*, 1036–1043. [CrossRef]
105. Koch, J.; Christ, O. Household participation in an urban photovoltaic project in Switzerland: Exploration of triggers and barriers. *Sustain. Cities Soc.* **2018**, *37*, 420–426. [CrossRef]
106. Ilieva, I.; Bremdal, B.; Ottesen, S.; Rajasekharan, J.; Olivella-Rosell, P. *Design Characteristics of a Smart Grid Dominated Local Market*; CIRED Workshop: Helsinki, Finland, 2016.
107. Polly, B.; Kutscher, C.; Macumber, D.; Schott, M.; Pless, S.; Livingood, B.; Geet, O. *From Zero Energy Buildings to Zero Energy Districts*; Publications Office of the European Union: Luxembourg, 2016.
108. Brackney, L.J. *NREL Portfolio-Scale Optimization of Customer Energy Efficiency Incentive and Marketing Cooperative Research and Development Final Report*; National Renewable Energy Laboratory: Golden, CO, USA, 2016.
109. UrbanFootprint. *The Ultimate Technical Guide: Guide to UrbanFootprint*; Calthorpe Analytics: Berkley, CA, USA, 2017; p. 62.
110. Lee, S.H.; Berkeley, L.; Zhao, F.; Augenbroe, G. The use of normative energy calculation beyond building performance rating. *J. Build. Perform. Simul.* **2013**, *6*, 282–290. [CrossRef]
111. FUNITEC. *SEMANCO: Prototype of the Integrated Platform*; FUNITEC: Barcelona, Spain, 2013.
112. Baetens, R.; De Coninck, R.; Van Roy, J.; Verbruggen, B.; Driesen, J.; Helsen, L.; Saelens, D. Assessing electrical bottlenecks at feeder level for residential net zero-energy buildings by integrated system simulation. *Appl. Energy* **2020**, *96*, 74–83. [CrossRef]
113. CCEM. Urban Multiscale Energy Modelling. Sustainable Cities and Urban Energy Systems of the Future. In *Heat & Buildings*; CCEM: Zurich, Switzerland, 2014; pp. 66–68.
114. Molitor, C.; Member, G.S.; Groß, S.; Zeitz, J.; Member, S.; Monti, A.; Member, S. MESCOS—A Multienergy System Cosimulator for City District Energy Systems. *IEEE Trans. Ind.* **2014**, *10*, 2247–2256. [CrossRef]
115. Li, Q.; Quan, S.J.; Augenbroe, G.; Yang, P.P.; Brown, J. Building energy modelling at urban scale: Integration of reduced order energy model with geographical information. In Proceedings of the 14th Conference of International Building Performance Simulation Association, Hyderabad, India, 7–9 December 2015; pp. 190–199.
116. Hong, T.; Chen, Y.; Lee, S.H.; Piette, M.P.; Chen, Y.; Piette, M.P. CityBES: A web-based platform to support city-scale building energy efficiency. *Urban Comput. Work. San Fr.* **2016**. [CrossRef]

117. Bollinger, L.A.; Evins, R. *Hues: A Holistic Urban Energy Simulation Platform for Effective Model Integration*; CISBAT: Lausanne, Switzerland, 2015; pp. 841–846.
118. Fonseca, J.A.; Nguyen, T.A.; Schlueter, A.; Marechal, F. City Energy Analyst (CEA): Integrated framework for analysis and optimization of building energy systems in neighborhoods and city districts. *Energy Build.* **2016**, *113*, 202–226. [CrossRef]
119. Bergerson, J.; Muehleisen, R.T.; Rodda, B.O.; Auld, J.A.; Guzowski, L.B.; Ozik, J.; Collier, N. Designing Future Cities: LakeSIM Integrated Design Tool for Assessing Short- And Long-Term Impacts of Urban Scale Conceptual Designs. *ISOCARP Rev.* **2015**, *11*, 48–63.
120. Robinson, D.; Haldi, F.; Kämpf, J.; Leroux, P.; Perez, D.; Rasheed, A.; Wilke, U. CITYSIM: Comprehensive Micro-Simulation of Resource Flows for Sustainable Urban Planning Citysim: Comprehensive Micro-Simulation of Resource Flows for Sustainable Urban Planning Solar Energy and Building Physics Laboratory (LESO-PB). In Proceedings of the Eleventh International IBPSA Conference, Glasgow, Scotland, 27–30 July 2009.
121. Schiefelbein, J.; Rudnick, J.; Scholl, A.; Remmen, P.; Fuchs, M.; Müller, D. Automated urban energy system modeling and thermal building simulation based on OpenStreetMap data sets. *Build. Environ.* **2019**, *149*, 630–639. [CrossRef]
122. Reinhart, C.F.; Dogan, T.; Jakubiec, J.A.; Rakha, T.; Sang, A. Umi-an Urban Simulation Environment for Building Energy Use, Daylighting and Walkability. In Proceedings of the BS2013: 13th Conference of International Building Performance Simulation Association, Chambéry, France, 26–28 August 2013.
123. Waite, M.; Modi, V. *Calibrated Building Energy Models for Community-Scale Sustainability Analyses*; ASME: Boston, MA, USA, 2014.
124. Tian, W.; Rysanek, A.; Choudhary, R.; Heo, Y. High Resolution Energy Simulations at City Scale. In Proceedings of the 14th Conference of International Building Performance Simulation Association, Hyderabad, India, 7–9 December 2015.
125. Remmen, P.; Lauster, M.; Mans, M.; Fuchs, M.; Müller, D.; Remmen, P.; Lauster, M.; Mans, M.; Fuchs, M. TEASER: An open tool for urban energy modelling of building stocks. *J. Build. Perform. Simul.* **2018**, *11*, 84–98. [CrossRef]
126. Kontokosta, C.; Marulli, D.; Tull, C.; Pingerra, R. *Web-Based Visualization and Prediction of Urban Energy Use from Building Web-Based Visualization and Prediction of Urban Energy Use from Building Benchmarking Data*; Bloomberg Data for Good Exchange: New York, NY, USA, 2015.
127. Erhorn-kluttig, H.; Erhorn, H.; Weber, J.; Wössner, S.; Budde, E. The District Energy Concept Adviser: A software tool to support urban decision makers in planning district energy supply schemes. In Proceedings of the Sustainable Building Conference sb13 Munich, Munich, Germany, 10–12 April 2013; pp. 721–727.

 © 2020 by the authors. Licensee MDPI, Basel, Switzerland. This article is an open access article distributed under the terms and conditions of the Creative Commons Attribution (CC BY) license (http://creativecommons.org/licenses/by/4.0/).

Article

Synthesising Residential Electricity Load Profiles at the City Level Using a Weighted Proportion (Wepro) Model

Angreine Kewo [1,2,*], Pinrolinvic D. K. Manembu [3] and Per Sieverts Nielsen [1]

[1] DTU Management, Technical University of Denmark, 2800 Kongens Lyngby, Denmark; pernn@dtu.dk
[2] Informatics Engineering Department, De La Salle Catholic University, Manado 95253, Indonesia
[3] Electrical Engineering Department, Sam Ratulangi University, Manado 95115, Indonesia; pmanembu@unsrat.ac.id
*   Correspondence: ankewo@dtu.dk

Received: 3 April 2020; Accepted: 6 July 2020; Published: 9 July 2020

Abstract: It is important to understand residential energy use as it is a large energy consumption sector and the potential for change is of great importance for global energy sustainability. A large energy-saving potential and emission reduction potential can be achieved, among others, by understanding energy consumption patterns in more detail. However, existing studies show that it requires many input parameters or disaggregated individual end-uses input data to generate the load profiles. Therefore, we have developed a simplified approach, called weighted proportion (Wepro) model, to synthesise the residential electricity load profile by proportionally matching the city's main characteristics: Age group, labour force and gender structure with the representative households profiles provided in the load profile generator. The findings indicate that the synthetic load profiles can represent the local electricity consumption characteristics in the case city of amsterdam based on time variation analyses. The approach is in particular advantageous to tackle the drawbacks of the existing studies and the standard load model used by the utilities. Furthermore, the model is found to be more efficient in the computational process of the residential sector's load profiles, given the number of households in the city that is represented in the local profile.

Keywords: modelling; Wepro model; residential; household; electricity; load profiles; LPG; ALPG

---

1. Introduction

The residential energy sector plays a crucial role in achieving greater energy efficiency and emissions reduction goals. Studies have suggested that residential energy use is of great importance in ensuring global energy sustainability, given its energy-saving potential [1,2]. The International Energy Agency (IEA) has calculated that the residential sector contributes about 25% of energy consumption and 17% of carbon dioxide (CO_2) emissions globally. It is therefore, essential to understand the residential energy consumption patterns locally to allow for an assessment of the energy-saving potential in the sector. However, lack of accessibility to measured high-resolution electricity consumption data at the city level such as smart-meter data and time use survey (TUS) data makes it difficult to understand the characteristics of electricity consumption locally. Research into this aspect will improve our understanding of residential electricity load profiles, which can be used to achieve improvements in energy efficiency as the residential sector has a major potential for energy savings [3]; to reduce CO_2 emissions as extensive studies have identified that household behaviour has a significant impact on consumption and emission [3,4]; and to optimise energy management [5] as these types of studies have supported transmission grid planning for better energy management [5,6]. This suggests that energy policy should vary depending on local characteristics. Trends towards small scale renewable electricity generation and introduction of heat pumps and electric cars are changing the local energy system. Furthermore, policies towards developing Positive Energy Districts (PEDs) support the relevance of studying electricity load profiles at the district level [7]. Therefore, a computational method is required to handle a large number of population datasets and handle the granularity of the data. To scope the focus on end-user consumption, it is important to measure residential electricity consumption per unit accurately with respect to time, or so-called 'temporal resolution'. 'Temporal resolution' refers to the granularity of the data-sampling rate, which may be more or less equal to the acquisition rate by meter [8]. The key in temporal-resolution load-profile models of residential electricity consumption is to emphasise identification of the resolution that represents the essential local characteristics and consumption behaviour [8,9]. The importance of temporal resolution load profiles is that they ensure the accuracy of calculations of self-consumption and are able to optimise short-term fluctuations of electricity supply and demand [10]. The temporal-resolution load-profile method is the focus of our work.

We propose a simplified approach which uses a weighted proportion (Wepro) model to synthesise the residential electricity load profile at the city level, by utilising existing household load profile generators such as load profile generator (LPG) and artificial load profile generator (ALPG). The model requires some limited input parameters at the city level: the citizens's age groups (AG), gender (GD) structure, and labour force (LF) composition. This weighted method is widely used across many sectors to proportionately reweight values especially in relation with population statistics. This model can be applied for synthesising a residential electricity load profile by proportionally matching the city's main characteristics with the representative household profiles provided in the load profile generators. This simplified method can tackle the drawbacks of the existing studies that require many input parameters or disaggregated individual end-use smart meter data to generate the load profiles and the drawbacks of the standard load model used by the utilities. It is also mentioned in [11] that distribution system operators (DSOs) use rough estimations with respect to the worst-case situations for modelling the residential load models which are important in their network planning processes and in defining a standard daily load profile. Although in practice, it is challenging to validate our results with measured data, since the measured data at the city level are mostly unavailable.

1.1. Load Profile Modelling Methods

There are different methods for modelling load profiles with top-down [12,13] or bottom-up [3,14–22] approaches. As mentioned, extensive studies have shown that the data availability is the main drawback of the approaches as they both require many input parameters or detailed aggregated input data of homogeneous activities. Our work applies a different approach where it presents a combination of a top-down approach with a few input parameters, which use general statistics information of a city and a bottom-up load model with high temporal resolution data. It simply utilises the existing household load profile generators that have covered the detailed disaggregated input data in relation with behaviour, occupancy, time-use appliances and other related variables. The fixed input parameters of the city will be matched and adjusted with the representative household profiles proportionally.

Many load profile studies [3,14–17,19–21] have applied the occupancy model, behavioural aspect and time-use of electrical appliance in their methods, where certain studies [14,15] emphasize more the psychology model of individual behaviour, which makes the pre-defined household profile more detailed and provides vary profiles. Some models are simulated based on stochastic models [18–20]. Besides focusing on the household load profiles, some studies aim at generating the load profiles at the city level or a higher level than household level [12,20,21]. In this context, the load profiles researches can be expanded from the temporal analysis to the spatial analysis such as performed in these studies [12,21], which could be one of our future interests. In addition, another approach of modelling residential electricity demand is to use a microsimulation method. In this case, the shifting from aggregate distributions to decision making units at the individual level is the main core of microsimulation modelling (MSM) [23]. MSM is characterised by a large-scale simulation, spatial behaviour in relation to energy consumption and interaction is the main feature of spatial environment. In consequence, the dynamic migration of the population will be simplified by the model [3]. While in our work, we model the population's variables: age group, labour force and gender structure. However, spatial interaction is not the main concern of our work.

The load profiles outputs are presented as high-resolution data. Existing energy studies were generating 60-min output data [6,21,22,24–29] and one-minute resolution data [14,16–20,30]. Some works [14,15] have provided a more detailed output in one-minute resolution at once generated 60-min report data. In our work, hourly temporal resolution data are provided to compare residential electricity consumption profiles based on seasonal variation, monthly variation and days variation. Seasonal variation in this case refers to the cycles of the season: Winter, Spring, Summer and Autumn. While the typical seasonal days are the selected days to be modelled in each season both weekdays and weekend. For example, we will select to model the one weekday and one weekend in Winter, Spring, Summer and Autumn seasons.

In generating the synthetic household load profile, extensive studies have proposed and demonstrated the models, and some of them [14–18,20,21] have also developed a simulator or generator. In this work, we focused on two household profile generators that have developed based on the closest dwelling profile to our case study: amsterdam (The Netherlands). The main reasons we selected to use LPG and ALPG in our model, because both of them are developed based on behavioural model, and having one detailed model as LPG and one simpler model as ALPG may represent the different variation.

Moreover, validating the accuracy of the generated load profiles is a challenging work due to the limited available measured data to compare with. ALPG compared it's synthesised load profiles data with measurement data over a year from transformers and households of 81 connected households located in Lochem (The Netherlands) [16,17]. Twenty two measured dwellings in United Kingdom were also used to validate a study of domestic electricity use [18]. LPG validated the generated load profiles data on different criteria: Plausibility check, yearly energy consumption and duration load curve value in comparison with smart meter data rollout in Germany by Institut für Zukunfts Energie Systeme (IZES). Some studies [19,20,30] used TUS data or other independent datasets as a measurement to validate the synthesised data. Most of the studies [14,16–18] presented matched results between the generated load profiles and the measured data.

Unfortunately, as our work is focused on the city level, it is more challenging to validate the synthesised data with the measured data because the measured data should be a comprehensive dataset that represents the city's data. Finding the available measured data of the case study is challenging, mostly due to the privacy issues, cost and the measured data should represent a city's residential sector by the households' amount in the city and to make sure that the residential dwellings are located inside the selected city. It easier to find the measured data of some households or residential data at the neighbourhood level as used in the validation of the mentioned studies [14–16,18], or if the TUS data at the city level has existed. As an overview, there are three available measured electricity consumption data at the national level or obtained from various locations in The Netherlands. A measured smart-meter data of 80-households in The Netherlands is available with hourly resolution at https://www.liander.nl/partners/datadiensten/open-data/data. In fact, these data are not considerable enough to represent a real measured data for the amsterdam residential load profile. These 80 households' locations are also undefined and require a pre-processing task since missing values exist in the dataset. Moreover, the year we modelled is 2015 and in 2015, a large section of amsterdam still used traditional meters, therefore hourly data was not available. Besides the strict privacy laws in The Netherlands, time and cost are the main considerations in obtaining smart-meter data if they are not open data. The requires time and resources to approach every customer or household, which make the cost to obtain the city's measured data relatively high. A national time-series electricity consumption data is also available at Open Power System Data [31]. The source of the data is provided by ENTSO-E

Transparency platform [32]. The European Network of Transmission System Operators (ENTSO-E) represents most of the electricity Transmission System Operators (TSOs) across Europe. In fact, the data consists of all sectors: residential, industrial and others which is also required to be synthesised if we want to take the residential part of this national load profile. In fact, amsterdam might have a different residential profile load profile than the national's residential profile. The third dataset is the residential electricity load profiles dataset provided by NEDU [33], which will be presented in the Section 4. Therefore, a future study would be followed to improve current work when there is more data available. In addition, Table 1 provides an initial overview of the important categories in the load profiles studies based on the discussion in the related works.

Table 1. Overview of the detail load profile modelling methods based on the discussion provided in the related works'.

Category	References
Approach	
▪ Bottom-up	[3,14–22,28]
▪ Top-down	[12,13]
Methods	
▪ Stochastics model	[18–20]
▪ Machine learning techniques	[4,8,34,35]
▪ Others	
Load profile's aspect	
▪ Behavioural	[3,14–17,19–21]
▪ Behavioural-psychology	[14,15]
▪ Time-use	[3,14–17,19–21]
▪ Occupancy	[3,14–17,19–21]
Load profile's output	
▪ Model	[3,14–17,19–21]
▪ Both: Model and simulator or generator	[14–18,20,21]
Output's resolution	
▪ One-minute	[14–20,30]
▪ Hourly	[6,11,14,15,21,22,24–29]
Validation	
▪ Measured data: Smart-meter data, utilities data	[14–18]
▪ TUS	[19,20,30]
▪ Specific validation method or algorithm	[14,15]
Scope	
▪ Household level	[3,14–17,19–21]
▪ Local level	[12,16,17,20,21]
▪ Both: Household and local level	[12,16,17,20,21]
Load profile's type	
▪ Temporal profile	[3,14–17,19–21]
▪ Temporal profile and spatial profile	[12,21]
Country	
▪ The Netherlands	[11,16,17,36]
▪ United Kingdom	[18,20]
▪ Germany	[14,15]
▪ Others	[12,34,35,37]

Furthermore, some case studies have employed data-mining techniques to identify residential electricity load profiles [4,8,34,35]. Recent studies have proposed data-mining-based methods such as K-means [4,29,34], hierarchical [29,35] and fuzzy algorithms for purposes of electricity load profile modelling [29]. A clustering-based framework to analyse household electricity consumption patterns using a k-means algorithm has been proposed for a study conducted in China. The clustering method was selected since the electricity consumption patterns in the data were relatively smooth. A k-means algorithm was applied because it works considerably faster than other cluster algorithms, and it was easier to interpret the clustering results. The analysis was conducted in three consecutive stages: holidays, seasonal and shifting phenomena [34]. Similarly, our study also clusters the load-profile analysis into three stages: seasonal, monthly and typical seasonal days. Another case study in China employed hierarchical clustering, which is widely recognised in the context of pattern recognition, because it is easy to operate, efficient and practical [35]. A quantitative analysis approach based on association rule mining (ARM) was proposed in [4] in order to identify the impacts of household characteristics (HCs) on residential electricity consumption patterns. In any case it is assumed that the load profile data on weekdays are somehow more typical and significant than those on weekend days, while our work has covered both the weekday load profiles and weekend day load profiles through selected typical days [4].

A range of statistical analysis methods have also been applied in order to model residential electricity load profiles [6,28,37–39], including determination of the key drivers of residential peak electricity demand. Some studies provided panel datasets including data from smart-meters [24,26,40]. A model was developed using Australian data for the greater Sydney region to analyse and model residential peak demand by providing both daily and seasonal patterns [37]. The analysis was in line with the results of multiple studies showing that peak residential electricity consumption was significantly influenced by the climate and the demand for cooling. In another study, hourly residential electricity consumption was used to estimate the Monte Carlo stochastic building-stock energy model of the dwellings in the sample and the climate data sources [28]. An error analysis was performed using normalised root mean square error (NRMSE), normalised mean absolute error (NMAE), maximum absolute difference (MAXAD) and maximum relative difference (MAXRD). The results from the modelling were validated using the hourly energy equations and electricity consumption data and the uncertainty of the Monte Carlo model was calculated using multiple runs as a sample. When combined with knowledge of user behaviour, this bottom-up building-stock approach, which uses energy performance certificate (EPC) databases, can be used to estimate aggregate mean hourly electricity consumption. In this case, calibration was required to develop urban energy models. This also indicated that the outdoor air temperature had a significant influence on the model [28].

1.2. Electricity Consumption Studies in The Netherlands

As an overview, some studies in relation with the electricity consumption in the case study's country are provided. The household electricity consumption constitutes approximately twenty percent of the total energy consumption in The Netherlands [41]. Behavioural profiles of electricity consumption can be determined according to Dutch household and dwelling characteristics [16,17,42]. A study based on collected questionnaires relating to the dwellings above in winter 2008 showed that household size, dwelling type, use of dryers, washing cycles and number of showers influence electricity consumption significantly [43]. Furthermore, a model-based analysis [41] has been performed to explore the effects of smart-meter adoption, occupant behaviour and appliance efficiency on reducing electricity consumption in relation to CO_2 emissions in The Netherlands. The paper looked at electricity consumption by end-users, projecting the best- and worst-case scenarios for carbon intensity annually. All cases assumed that carbon intensity would not increase in the future under current Dutch and European policies [41]. A real-life assessment of the effect of smart electrical appliances was conducted among Dutch households with a dynamic electricity tariff, an energy management system and a smart washing machine [29]. The results showed changes in laundry behaviour and thus electricity usage. The households regularly used the automation that came with smart washing machines [44]. The results of the study are interesting and could be a focus in our future work.

In relation to the residential Dutch load profiles, a recent study includes the local impact of an increasing penetration of photovoltaic (PV) panels and heat pumps (HPs) using the load measurements from three Dutch areas. It shows that the average daily load profile, without photovoltaics (PVs) and heatpumps (HPs) in all areas resembles the standard residential load profile. However, because of a shift from gas to electric stoves the time of peak load occurs earlier in the day [11]. We have also mentioned another profile generator ALPG [16,17] in our review, which is applied in our model. It is an open source load profile generator developed based on Dutch dwelling setting. The generated load profile is compared with measured data in Lochem (The Netherlands) over one year. It indicates a similar statistical trend, although some minor differences were identified, for instance the static stand-by power usage from the ALPG is too flat [16].

In brief, our contributions in this paper are the following: (1) We have developed a simplified method for modelling residential electricity load profiles in cities using Weighted proportion (Wepro) model that reflects local characteristics. (2) We introduce a practical and efficient approach to synthesize electricity load profiles, which does not require many input parameters or disaggregated individual end-uses input data to generate the load profiles. (3) We assess residential electricity load profiles based on time-division concepts: seasonal variation, monthly variation, typical seasonal days and hourly variation. The approach adopted here is illustrated the application in the case study with simple examples of the proportion adjustments of the city's profiles and household's profiles.

The rest of the paper is structured as follows: Section 2 describes the research design; Section 3 presents the results, which is the application of the method for the amsterdam case; Section 4 evaluates and discusses the results; and Section 5 concludes the paper and present the research implications for future work.

2. Materials and Methods

The proposed method consists of four phases: data collection, data pre-processing, data-modelling and load-profile analyses. Data collection can be challenging, frustrating and time-consuming, especially when we want to acquire high- resolution time series data. In order to generate the hourly profile of residential electricity consumption in cities, it is required to provide city's main input data on population information such as on gender, age groups and labour force. Furthermore, it is essential to identify the required dataset or information such as national holidays per year, solar irradiation dataset and outdoor temperature dataset. All these data should cover the same periods of time. In this work, the proposed model is validated by the case-study city of the H2020 ClairCity project presented here, namely amsterdam (The Netherlands). ClairCity is a research project modelling air pollution and carbon emissions. The project identifies current air emissions or pollutant concentrations by technology and citizens' activities, behaviour and practices in six pilot cities or regions: amsterdam, Bristol, Aveiro, Liguaria, Ljubljana and Sosnowiec. The aim is to develop locally specific policy packages in which clean-air, low-carbon, healthy futures are quantified, modelled and analysed [45–51].

In data collection and pre-processing phases, it is important to study the latter comprehensively, as it can improve data quality and the accuracy of the result [52]. Data corruption, missing values and outliers are the commonest problems in data-processing [52,53]. In general, there are four tasks in data pre-processing: cleaning, transformation, integration and reduction [52,54,55]. Table 2 summarises the common problems of data pre-processing tasks and their solutions:

In this work, the data collected from amsterdam (The Netherlands), are in the form of a panel dataset, which is a cross-sectional data sample at specific point in time [52]. The panel dataset consists of information on age groups, the gender structure of each age group, the labour force, national holidays, solar irradiation and temperature datasets. The information on age groups, gender and the labour force are obtained indirectly [56–58] from Central Bureau Statistics (CBS, The Netherlands). In this case, we have elected to model the load profile for 2015. The population age is grouped into three groups: 0–17 years old, 18–64 years old and above 64 years old. The unemployment rate is recorded as 6.7% [56]. The labour force and age groups data are not in the form of datasets. Both of them provide information on the share of employment and unemployment, and the share of population's age groups and gender structure in the city, during the selected period. Therefore, there is no pre-processing technique is required in this case as well as for the solar irradiation dataset provided in ALPG. Data on public holidays are integrated into LPG's model as one of the independent inputs, like the temperature dataset. The temperature dataset and solar irradiation dataset are retrieved from the Royal Netherlands Meteorological Institute (KNMI), the official Dutch national weather service. More specifically for temperature, we selected the data from the 240 Schiphol weather station, which is the nearest station to amsterdam and is in the same region of Noord-Holland. In this dataset, there is no missing values, noisy or inconsistent data. A reduction technique is applied, since the station code variable is not required in the modelling tool. Furthermore, due to the different standards between the data source and LPG's format. We transformed the dataset from .txt to .csv by reducing the first variable, station code, and normalising the temperature value. As mentioned, we have done data pre-processing tasks and documenting our specific work in relation to the data pre-processing steps in more details is in preparation.

Table 2. Data pre-processing: The tasks perform in data pre-processing include their common problems and solutions of these problems [52,55].

Task	Problem/Issue	Solution/Technique
Cleaning	Missing data	Ignore the record
		Determine and fill in the missing values manually
		Use an expected value
	Noisy data	Binning methods
		Clustering
		Machine-learning
	Inconsistent data	External reference
		Knowledge engineering tools
Transformation	Different format, scale or unit	Normalisation
		Aggregation
		Generalisation
Integration	Different standards among data sources	Combine data into a consistent database
Reduction	Complex analysis or unfeasible	Reduce unnecessary observations, variables or values

2.1. Data Modelling

In the data modelling we will apply the Wepro model to synthesise the residential electricity load profile at the city level through the household profile generators namely LPG and ALPG.

2.1.1. Weighted Proportion (Wepro) Model

The Wepro model is a simplified approach to model residential electricity load profiles in cities by adjusting and matching the proportion of city's weighted profiles with the households' profiles through the existing household profile generators. First, it is necessary to collect information on the citizens' age groups (AG), gender (GD) and labour force (LF). In this case, a figure for annual electricity consumption is not required, since we only focus on providing the share of hourly electricity load profiles. Second, we coupled the share of age groups and labour force and applied this share to proportionally fit the total population. The population is categorised into three groups by age: 0–17 years old, 18–64 years old and over 64 years old. Thus, the sum of the composition of these age groups represents the city's population by age group is expressed in Equation (1):

$$Tag = AG_1\% + AG_2\% + AG_3\% \tag{1}$$

where Tag is the total share of the age groups' share in the city. AG_1 is the age group for people aged 0 to 17, and AG_2 for people aged 18 to 64 and AG_3 for people over the age of 64. In more detail, each age group has gender information, although we can also identify gender information at the higher level of the age groups, giving totals for each gender in the city. In this model, more details on the gender composition of each age group is required as expressed in Equation (2):

$$Tmf = Ml\% + Fm\% \tag{2}$$

where *Tmf* is the total share of male's share and female's share in the city. *Ml* is Male and *Fm* is Female. We also need to identify the city's labour force composition. The shares of employment and unemployment represent the city's labour force is formed in Equation (3):

$$Tlf = Em\% + Un\% \tag{3}$$

where *Tlf* is the total share of employment's share and unemployment's share in the city. *Em* is Employment and *Un* = Unemployment. The labour force data are measured on the basis of the labour force population, which is only derived from one of the age groups. In this case, the labour force is included in AG_2 = 18–64 years old. Here the labour force is the proper set of age groups, labour force being an aspect of the age groups but not equal to age groups as shown in Equation (4):

$$AG = \{AG_1, AG_2, AG_3\} \text{ and } LF = \{AG_2\}$$

$$LF \subset AG \tag{4}$$

As mentioned, we employ the household profile generators in this case LPG and ALPG to generate the household load profiles. The first step is to select the household profiles to be modelled by the profile generators. The fundamental consideration is that the selected household profiles in the profile generators should represent the city's characteristics in term of age groups, gender structure and labour force, this being the focus of our study. This means that the selected household profiles should represent the city's profiles proportionally as depicted in Figure 1.

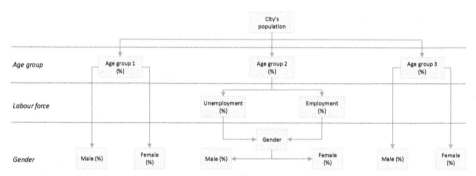

Figure 1. Weighted proportion structure of the city's main parameters: age group, labour force composition and gender structure.

- Capacity, fairness of allocation and rounding number

We apply the capacity model based on the amsterdam's age groups share in Figure 1 for selecting which household profiles to be modelled. The main goal is to determine the number of the occupants's profiles to be modelled as shown in the following expression of Equation (5):

$$Tamt = AG1wt + AG2wt + AG3wt \tag{5}$$

where *Tamt* is the total number of the occupants' profiles. *AG1wt* is the number in age group 1 based on it's weight. *AG2wt* is the number in age group 2 based on it's weight and *AG3wt* is the number in age group 3 based on it's weight. The share of the occupants for each group are converted to decimal form to provide the results of the total number of occupant-profiles from each age group.

Furthermore, the capacity model can also be extended to determine the gender of the selected profiles as expressed in Equation (6) if it is supported by the profile generators. In this case, it is applicable to LPG, since LPG provides detail characters of the occupants' gender information:

$$Tg = (AG1m * AG1wt) + (AG1f * AG1wt) + (AG2m * AG2wt) + (AG2f * AG2wt) + (AG3m * \\ AG3wt) + (AG3f * AG3wt) \quad (6)$$

Here Tg is the total number of combinations of the occupants' gender. AG1m is the share of males in age group 1. AG1f is the share of females in age group 1. AG2m is the share of males in age group 2. AG2f is the share of females in age group 2. AG3m is the share of males in age group 3 and AG3f is the share of females in age group 3. In this case a widely used fairness sharing technique called max-min fairness can be applied in sharing the allocations if it is required.

Therefore, the application of the Wepro model to the case-study city namely amsterdam is as follows: First, the city's population is represented by the sum of the composition of age groups in amsterdam. We grouped the city's age groups into three categories: 0–17 years old = 17.5%; 18–64 years old = 70.3%; and above 64 years old = 12.2% [57,58] using the formula in Equation (1):

$$Tag = 17.5\% + 70.3\% + 12.2\%$$

$$Tag = 100\%$$

In more detail, the gender structure is classified into three age groups. For the age group of 0 to 17-year-olds, 51.58% are male and 48.42% female. In the age group of 18- to 64-year-olds, 50.24% are male and 49.75% female. Finally, for the age group above 65, we identified 46.24% male and 53.75% female [57,58]. Therefore, Equation (2) is presented to identify the gender at the city level:

$$Tmf = 49.5\% + 50.5\%$$

$$Tmf = 100\%$$

Furthermore, the labour force data are measured on the basis of the labour force population, which is only derived from age group among 18- to 64-year-olds. The unemployment rate is recorded as 6.7% [56]. In this case, Equation (3) is used to identify the employment and unemployment shares.

$$Tlf = 93.3\% + 6.7\%$$

$$Tlf = 100\%$$

Here, Equation (4) is used where the labour force is the proper set of age groups, labour force being an aspect of the age groups but not equal to age groups:

$$AG = \{0\text{--}17 \text{ years old, } 18\text{--}64 \text{ years old, } 64+\} \text{ and } LF = \{15\text{--}64 \text{ years old}\}$$

$$70.3\% \text{ aged } 18 - 64 \subset 100\% \text{ aged } 0\text{--}17, 18\text{--}64, \text{ over } 64$$

We coupled the share of age groups and labour force and applied the Proportional matched profile to the total population as the city's main characteristics. Therefore, as displayed in Figure 2, the Amsterdam's main profile should reflect: The age groups, labour force and gender classes.

This means that from the age group percentage: The aged 0–17 group is nearly 20%, aged 18–64 is 70% and the rest 10% is for aged over 64. From this 70% where the aged 18–64, there is about 93% of this age group are people with work and the rest are not working. Furthermore, each age group illustrates a slight difference in the share of gender information, except for the aged over 64, where the female populations are slightly more dominant than the male populations.

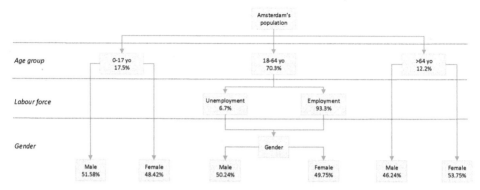

Figure 2. The application of the Weighted proportion (Wepro) model's structure to the case-study city, namely amsterdam, The Netherlands. It consists of the amsterdam's age group share, labour force composition share and gender share of each age group.

- Capacity, fairness of allocation and rounding number

Furthermore, Equation (5) is presented, where the weighted city's age group values are applied into a simple capacity model, in order to determine the capacity of the allocation. Therefore, based on the weighted values, we have ten capacity of the households profiles. It means, we can only select maximum ten occupants from the household profiles generators:

$$Tamt = 17.5\% + 70.3\% + 12.2\%$$

$$Tamt = 1.75 + 7.03 + 1.2$$

$$Tamt = 2 + 7 + 1$$

$$Tamt = 10$$

Furthermore, if it is supported by the profile generators, the capacity model can also be extended to determine the gender of the selected profiles as expressed in Equation (6). In this case, it is applicable to LPG, since LPG provides detail characters of the occupants gender information:

$$Tg = (1.03 + 0.96) + (3.51 + 3.48) + (0.46 + 0.54)$$

$$Tg = (1m + 1f) + (4m + 3f) + 1f$$

As shown in the Equation (5), age group 1 has two allocations, age group 2 has seven allocations and age group 3 has one allocation. Thus, there are currently two resources for two allocations, which after the division between them, resulting in 1. Furthermore, AG1m has an excess of 0.03, where the excess can be taken and divided among the remaining demands, which is only AG1f. Therefore, AG1f = 1. As a result of the capacity and fairness of allocation model depicted in Figure 3, there will be two occupants: one male and one female in age group 0–17. Furthermore for the case Age group 2 and Age group 3, we cannot fully apply the max-min fairness. We simply apply rounding number because we have only two resources per age group. For instance, for age group 3, there are two resources for only one allocation. Therefore, rounding number is applied to the highest weight between the resources.

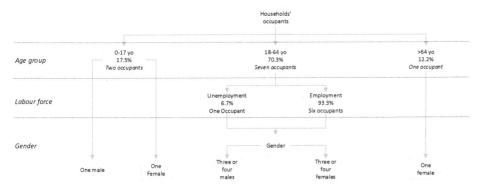

Figure 3. The application of the Wepro model's structure to the case-study city, namely amsterdam, The Netherlands. It consists of the amsterdam age group share, labour force composition share and gender share of each age group and their capacity of the occupants to be modelled.

As a result, the age group 18–64 should consist of seven adult occupants with six of them working people and one person not working. Considering the gender share is quite balance in this age group, then it is either four females and three males, or four males and three females in the occupants' list. Lastly, for the aged over 64, which has only one allocation, based on the results of the capacity and fairness of allocation model, we apply rounding value to the one which has the highest share to represent the senior age group. Therefore, we selected a female senior to represent this age group.

2.1.2. Profile Generators: LPG and ALPG

To produce the load profiles of the selected households profiles as the result of the Wepro model between the city's main characteristics and the households occupants, we use LPG and ALPG as the load profiles generators. Thus, in this case we optimise a bottom-up approach provided by the generators, scale-up from the household level to the city level based on the down-scale task perform previously in the weighting model, and employ the profile generator's model at the former level.

The main reason of choosing LPG and ALPG because both of them are developed based on behavioral model, which is in line with ClairCity project's goal to model the citizen's behaviour. LPG's model has been selected for use in our model, as it offers a mature model with which to synthesise household energy load profiles based on various occupants' profiles. Pflugrandt has developed the model with a strong focus on modelling the behavioural aspect. The basic elements for modelling a single household in Figure 4 are the desire to do so and expressions of the need to do something. The model specifies weight, threshold and decay time as desired properties [15].

Weight is the relative weight of a need compared to all a person's other needs. In selecting for the next action, the minimisation of the deviation requirement is used as a criterion, the weighting acting as a multiplier in this calculation. *Threshold* determines when the person really feels a need, that is, when it is included in the next action selection of the calculation. For example, in reality there is usually no eating after lunch because only 10% of the hunger sensation is evident. Instead, one generally waits until a noticeable feeling of hunger has built up before having dinner. Finally, *Decay Time* describes the half-life, until 50% of the requirement is reached. It has been found that activities at 50% threshold mostly after the two to three times the decay time, depending on the weighting and the other available activities. The decay constant is calculated from the decay time by which the current value of the need is multiplied in each time step [15]. When creating households, it has been found that activities at the 50% threshold are usually executed after two to three times the decay time, depending on the weighting and the other available activities. Furthermore, besides desire, it is also essential to identify the individual's properties (age, gender, sick leave in the year, average duration of illness, needs when healthy, needs when ill) and load type, which in this case is electricity [14,15]. LPG provides various pre-defined German household profiles.

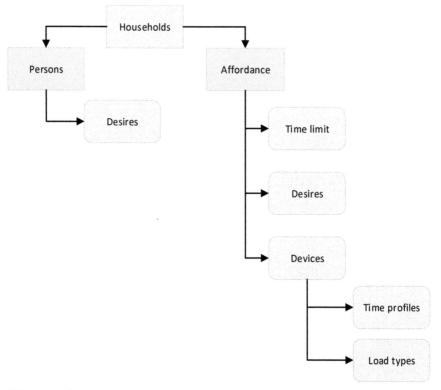

Figure 4. LPG's minimum necessary elements in modelling a decision-making process of a single household [15], where the basic elements are the desire to do so and expressions of the need to do something.

The second profile generator used in our work is ALPG. ALPG employs household occupancy profiles generated by a simple behavioural model, which creates consistent profiles for the devices. The devices' flexibility is specified through four classes: timeshiftables, buffer-timeshiftables, buffers and curtailable. The inflexible electricity profiles are grouped into the following categories: stand-by load, consumer electronics, lighting, inductive devices, fridges, and other. Furthermore, to show annual electricity consumption, the individual profiles are scaled in magnitude, making it easier to alter the profile if there is a change in electricity usage by the external factors. An example of such a change could be the adoption of a new technology, for instance, light-emitting diode (LED) lights. Moreover, the following classes in Figure 5 are implemented in the simulation model: neighbourhood, household, person, device, house, writer and ALPG. Electricity usage in a typical Dutch setting is the focus of ALPG, which is also in line with our work in modelling residential electricity load profiles, with Amsterdam as the case-study city [16,17].

Furthermore, we after applying the capacity allocation into LPG and ALPG the following are closest profiles that reflect the city's proportion of the age groups, gender and labour force mentioned above.

- LPG

The following are the simplified Wepro-based selected pre-defined households profiles in LPG although there could be also several other options that may fulfill the Wepro model composition:

Couple, *both of whom work,* with **one child**

Couple, *one at work, one at home*, with **one child**

Couple *both of whom work*

Single *with work*

Senior *at home*

The **underlined** entities indicate the age groups, the *blue italic* entities represent the labour force. Moreover, to express the gender shares of each age group, we selected the characters of LPG pre-defined household profiles in Table 3, as follows:

Table 3. The selected pre-defined household profiles in LPG based on Wepro model.

Households Profiles	Household ID in LPG	Character—Name (Age and Gender) in LPG
Couple with **one child,** *both at work*	CHR3	Ava (40 female), Fin (43 male) and Luka (10 male)
Couple with **one child,** *one at work, one at home*	CHR45	Susann (45 female), Alexander (48 male) and Claudia (16 female)
Couple *both at work*	CHR1	Sami (25 male), Rubi (23 female)
Single *with work*	CHR7	Christian (23 male)
Senior *at home*	CHR31	Monika (68 female)

Furthermore, we can insert these occupant's list to the Wepro composition in order to validate the model. As illustrated in Figure 6, the selected household profiles can fulfill the Wepro's model composition. Then, we generate these LPG's pre-defined households' load profiles one by one. The LPG can be downloaded free from https://www.loadprofilegenerator.de/. In generating one pre-defined household's load profile, after we download and open the windows program, we can go to "calculation" menu.

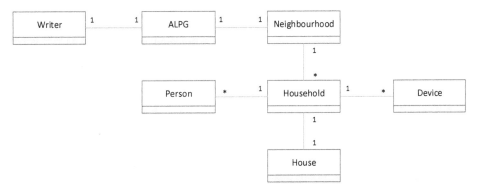

Figure 5. ALPG's class diagram [17] that shows the cardinality of a class in relation to another. The example of one-to-one (1..1) relationship is depicted between Household and House, where a household lives in a house and a house belongs to a household. The one-to-many(1..*) relationship is shown between Household and Device, where a household has one or more devices, and each device belongs to a household. Each class from these multiple classes represents a part of the model, which makes the software flexible to be extended in the future work.

Furthermore, we should select some options such as which pre-defined profile to be modelled, geographic location and temperature profile based on temperature dataset that we input before, if the temperature dataset is not provided yet by LPG. That is why we need to pre-process our input data such as temperature dataset in order to be matched with LPG's format. Then we can calculate the household profile one by one which may require a computational processing time and the result is generated in comma-separated values (.CSV) file.

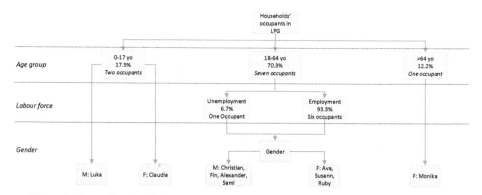

Figure 6. The application of the Wepro model's structure for amsterdam's household occupancy profiles in LPG. It consists of the amsterdam's age group share, labour force composition share and gender share of each age group, their capacity of the occupants to be modelled and the selected gender character provided in LPG.

- ALPG

As shown in Table 4, the pre-defined households profiles in ALPG are not as detailed as in LPG, but they simply can fulfill the Wepro model. The pre-defined households class contains seven types of households: Single worker, dual worker, family dual worker, family single parent, dual retired and single retired. Dual profile means a couple. In this case, each type of household corresponds to a category of electricity annual consumption in Kilowatt hour and amount of occupants or persons.

Table 4. Pre-defined households configurations in ALPG based [17].

Name	Annual Consumption	Persons (Adults)
SingleWorker	1610–2410 kWh	1(1)
DualWorker	2660–4060 kWh	2(2)
FamilyDualWorker	3460–7060 kWh	3–6(2)
FamilySingleWorker	3460–7060 kWh	3–6(2)
FamilySingleParent	2600–6200 kWh	2–5(1)
DualRetired	2660–4060 kWh	2(2)
SingleRetired	1610–2410 kWh	1(1)

To fulfill the Wepro model and simplify the process, we selected: one single worker, one single retired, two dual worker and one family dual worker. ALPG is open-source code and the code is available at it's github page. Figure 7 shows the snipped code of the households profiles selection, where the ALPG program runs by executing profilegenerator.py.:

Furthermore, the same procedure with LPG, in Figure 8 we inserted these occupant's list to the Wepro composition in order to validate the model.

Accordingly, it indicates a different result in comparison with LPG because in ALPG there is no need to identify the gender characteristics as it has simplified and consistent pre-defined profiles list as provided in Table 4. Moreover, these selected occupancy's list in ALPG may fulfill the Wepro model regardless the gender detail. In consequences, there are five generated households load profiles both in LPG and ALPG. We used the average load profile's value of these generated load profiles in the analysis.

```
#Select the types of households
import households


for i in range(0,1):
        householdList.append(households.HouseholdSingleRetired())

for i in range(0,1):
        householdList.append(households.HouseholdSingleWorker())

for i in range(0,2):
        householdList.append(households.HouseholdDualWorker(False))

for i in range(0,1):
        householdList.append(households.HouseholdFamilyDualWorker(True))
```

Figure 7. The snipped code of the configuration of the selected household profiles in ALPG based on Wepro model.

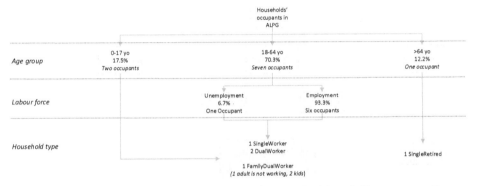

Figure 8. The application of the Wepro model's structure for amsterdam's household occupancy profiles in ALPG. It consists of the amsterdam's age group share, labour force composition share and gender share of each age group, their capacity of the occupants to be modelled and the selected pre-defined profiles provided in LPG.

2.2. Load Profile Analyses Based on Time-Division

As the model has produced residential electricity load profiles in high resolution, we focus on analysis of the load profile results in this section. The visualisation, charting and plotting of the hourly resolution are executed in Python. The residential electricity load profile is analysed at four levels: seasonal analysis, monthly analysis, days analysis and hourly analysis.

2.2.1. Seasonal Analysis

Electricity consumption patterns based on the seasons is interesting to distinguish, as the temperature influences the interval of the seasons. A time-division according to the four seasons in the year has been defined based on the meteorological concept (Table 5).

2.2.2. Monthly Analysis

Monthly characteristics are examined through the monthly average share to identify the monthly pattern of residential electricity consumption in the city. The analyses cover the 12 months electricity data from the load profiles results. Besides to identify the potential energy savings, the monthly analysis is beneficial to plan the generation and distribution of power utilities.

Table 5. Division of the seasons based on meteorological concept in the selected year: 2015 (*date format: dd-mm-yyyy*). In this case, the start day of the winter season is 01 December 2015. Winter lasts from 01 December 2015 until 28 February 2015, spring lasts from 01 March 2015 to 31 May 2015, summer lasts from 01 June 2015 to 31 August 2015, and autumn from 01 September 2015 to 30 November 2015. Therefore, the winter season has the fewest number of days.

Seasons	Date Period	Number of Days
Winter	1 January 2015 to 28 February 2015 1 December 2015 to 31 December 2015	90
Spring	1 March 2015 to 31 May 2015	92
Summer	1 June 2015 to 31 August 2015	92
Autumn	1 September 2015 to 30 November 2015	91

The meteorological concept (Table 5) is quite simple and is the most widely used, being broken down into four three-month periods. Winter has the three coldest months in the Northern Hemisphere, namely December, January and February. Spring runs from March to May, summer from June to August, and the other months belong to autumn [59]. Hence, a seasonal electricity load profiles model is proposed as follows in Equation (7):

$$Ts\% = Sw\% + Ssp\% + Ssm\% + Sa\%$$ (7)

where $Ts\%$ is the total of seasons share, $Sw\%$ is the share of Winter season, $Ssp\%$ is the share of Spring season, $Ssm\%$ is the share of Summer season and Sa is the share of Autumn season.

2.2.3. Days Analysis

The days analysis is provided based on the hourly average share load of the days in each season and the typical days share in each season. The typical days are the selected days, of one weekday and one weekend day in each season as listed in Table 6. None of the selected days listed below in Table 6 is a national holiday in the selected city, meaning that the selected days represent people's normal daily activities on a weekday and at weekends.

Table 6. Selected typical days (*date format: yyyy-mm-dd*).

Typical Day (TD) in Seasons	Week Date; Weekend Date
Winter TD	11 February 2015; 15 February 2015
Spring TD	15 April 2015; 19 April 2019
Summer TD	15 July 2015; 19 July 2015
Autumn TD	11 November 2015; 15 November 2015

2.2.4. Hourly Analysis

In this part, we will process the output from the load profile generators as one minute resolution and create a time series with an hourly resolution. The objective is to show the hourly characteristics of electricity consumption on the hourly average load profiles in the selected year and the hourly average of the seasonal load profiles. Hence, the average load profiles model is proposed as follows in Equation (8):

$$\widetilde{h}_n = \frac{1}{d} \sum_{i=1}^{d} x_i$$ (8)

where $\widetilde{h}_n$ is the hourly average. n is the number of hours which is in the range of 0 to 23. d is the number of days in a year, which is in the range of 1 to 365 for the selected year 2015. x_i is the data *i*-th. To create the hourly average of the seasonal load profiles, we replace d with the number of the days in each season.

3. Results: Load Profile Analyses in amsterdam as the Case Study

The analyses of the generated load profiles by the model will be presented based on the time variation of the case-study city, namely amsterdam (The Netherlands). The hourly temporal results will be moderately validated by the standard average of Dutch household load profile.

3.1. Load-Profile Analyses Based on Time-Division

The generated load profiles produced by the model will be analysed at four levels: seasonal analysis, monthly analysis, days analysis and hourly analysis, where hourly resolution is the core output of our temporal profile.

3.1.1. Seasonal Analysis

The seasonal variations based on the meteorological concept (Table 5) are provided in two generated models: Wepro-LPG and Wepro-ALPG, where we used Equation (7). In this concept, Winter has the fewest days, Autumn has one day more compared to winter, while spring and summer have two days more compared to winter. Based on the generated load profiles of Wepro-LPG and Wepro-ALPG in Figure 9, it indicates that Winter is the highest consumption share, slightly followed by Autumn, and Spring. Both models show Summer as the lowest consumption share.

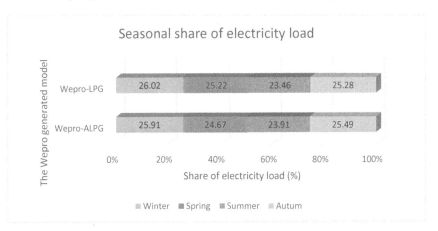

Figure 9. Seasonal share of electricity load based on the models: Wepro model-LPG and Wepro-ALPG. Both models show similar seasonal characteristics of the consumption share from the highest season to the lowest season.

Wepro-LPG

$$Ts\% = 26.02\% + 25.22\% + 23.46\% + 25.28\%$$

$$Ts = 100\%$$

while for Wepro-ALPG, the highest consumption share occurred in winter, slightly followed by autumn, then spring. Summer is recorded as the lowest consumption period.

Wepro-ALPG

$$Ts\% = 25.91\% + 24.67\% + 23.91\% + 25.49\%$$

$$Ts = 100\%$$

3.1.2. Monthly Analysis

Amsterdam's monthly electricity load share is illustrated in Figure 10, which shows a distinct profile in the Wepro-LPG model. This demonstrates that December has the highest consumption share compared to the other months, which may exhibit seasonal variations. Surprisingly, this load profile identifies May as having the second highest electricity share in 2015, followed by October, August and January. The lowest monthly consumption share is in July, which concurs with the seasonal analysis result that summer has the lowest consumption share in all load profiles. The second lowest consumption share is in March, followed by September.

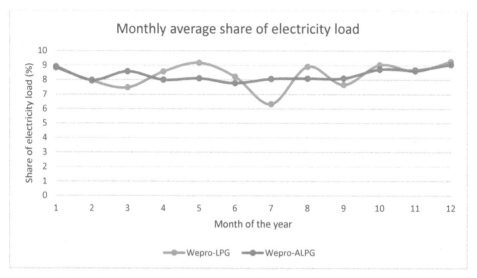

Figure 10. Monthly average electricity load share based on the results of the generated Wepro-LPG and Wepro-ALPG models.

The Wepro-ALPG model indicates December as having the highest consumption share, the same as in Wepro-LPG model. The second highest consumption share is in January, followed by October and November. The lowest consumption share is in June, followed by February and April.

3.1.3. Days Analysis

The days analysis is provided based on the hourly average share load of the days in each season which are depicted in Figure 11, and the daily load share of the typical selected days, which is illustrated in Figure 12.

Figure 11 depicts the hourly average load share in each season based on the days Monday, Tuesday, Wednesday, Thursday, Friday, Saturday and Sunday, where the load profiles for Wepro-LPG are shown in dashed lines and the load profiles for Wepro-ALPG are shown in solid lines. The Winter load profiles are shown in red, the Spring load profiles are shown in blue, the Summer load profiles are shown in green and the Autumn load profiles are shown in black, where the weekday colours are in a lighter shade then the weekend colour.

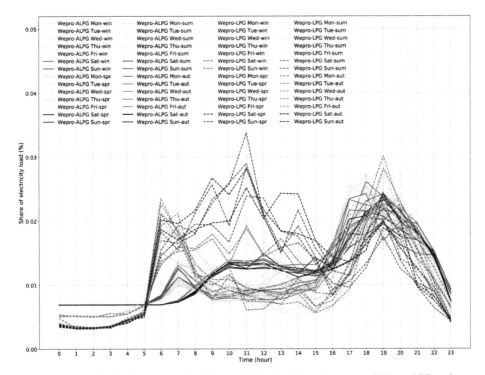

Figure 11. The hourly average load share of the days in each season of Wepro-LPG and Wepro-ALPG models.

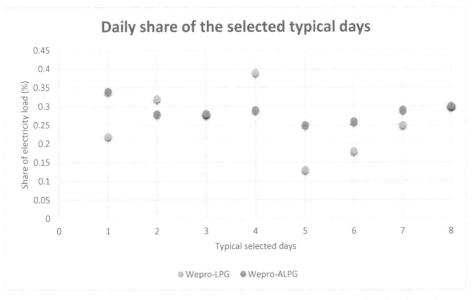

Figure 12. Daily share of electricity load of the selected typical days in each season based on the results of Wepro-LPG and Wepro-ALPG load profiles.

For the winter period in Wepro-LPG, the top morning peak appears around 7 am for all weekdays. For some weekdays, the morning peak then continues with a light peak between 9 am and 10 am. The following daylight peaks are identified around lunchtime, from 12 am to 1 pm, while for weekend days, the curve show several daylight peaks from 7 am to late lunchtime, around 1 pm. The morning and daylight peaks appear around 7 am, 9 am, 11 am and 1 pm, among which 11 am is identified as the top morning peak, which may be associated with the brunch time. Furthermore, the evening peaks for all days started from about 5 pm to 8 pm and mostly reach the top value around 7 pm, while for the weekend days, the curves show a longer evening peak from 6 pm to around 7:30 pm. The weekend days show a quite higher daylight share than the weekdays' daylight share. Furthermore, for Wepro-ALPG, the top morning peak is shown around 7 am for all weekdays, followed by a light peak around 8 am on some weekdays. For some weekdays, the morning peak then continues with a light peak between 10 am to 12 am. The load share continues to increase until 2 pm, while for the weekend days, the morning peaks are characterized by a light peak around 7 am that continues to increase to 10 am. The top morning peak is around 12 am. The weekend days show a higher daylight share than the weekdays' daylight share. Most of the days indicate 6 pm as the top evening peak, some weekdays identify 5 pm as the top evening peak and one weekend day shows 7 pm as the top evening peak.

The hourly average load share in Spring period for Wepro-LPG illustrates the top morning peak around 6 am for all weekdays. The following morning and daylight peaks occur around lunchtime from 12 am to 2 pm, while for weekend days, the curves show several morning peaks from 6 am to late lunchtime around 2 pm. The morning and daylight peaks are shown around 6 am, 9 am, 11 am and 2 pm, where 11 am is identified as the top morning peak, which may be associated with brunch. Furthermore, the evening peaks for all days start from about 6 pm to 8 pm and mostly reach the top peak around 7 pm. It is obvious that the weekend days show a quite significant higher daylight share than the weekdays' daylight share. Furthermore, the hourly average load share in Spring period for Wepro-ALPG shows the top morning peak around 7 am for all weekdays, followed by a light peak around 8 am on some weekdays. For some weekdays, the morning and daylight peaks then continue with a light peak at 10 am, 11 am, 1 pm and 2 pm. After 7 am, the curves are continually declining until 9 am. The load share continues to increase again with a slight share from 9 am to 2 pm, while for the weekend days, the morning peaks start with a slight peak from 7 am, and gradually increase to reach the top on 10 am. It then increases slightly at 12 am, which is identified as the top morning peak in the weekend days. The weekend days show a higher daylight share than the weekdays' daylight share. Most of the days indicate 6 pm as the top evening peak, one weekday identifies 5 pm as the top evening peak and some days shows 7 pm as the top evening peak.

Furthermore, the Wepro-LPG in Summer period indicates the top morning peak on 6 am and 7 am for all weekdays. The following morning peak is around 10 am to 2 pm, while for weekend days, the curve shows several morning and daylight peaks from 6 am to late lunchtime, around 2 pm. These peaks are evident at 6 am, 7 am, 8 am, 11 am and 2 pm, where 11 am is identified as the top morning peak, which may be associated with brunch. Furthermore, the evening peaks for all days have started from about 6 pm to 8 pm, which all days reach the top peak on 7 pm. The weekend days show a quite significant higher daylight share than the weekdays' daylight share, while for Wepro-ALPG in Summer period, the top morning peak is shown around 7 am for all weekdays, followed by a light peak around 11 am for most weekdays. The load share continues to increase again with a slight share from 11 am to 2 pm, while for the weekend days, the morning peaks start with a slight peak at 7 am, then a gradual slight one increasing each next hour and reaching the top on 10 am. It then slightly increases further at 12 am. The weekend days show a higher daylight share than the weekdays' daylight share. Most of the days indicate 6 pm as the top evening peak, two weekdays show 5 pm as the top evening peak and the weekend days shows 7 pm as the top evening peak.

Furthermore, the hourly average load share in Autumn period for Wepro-LPG illustrates the top morning peak on 6 am on most weekdays and one weekday has 7 am as the top morning peak.

The following morning peak occurs on 10 am on most weekdays, followed by another daylight peak at 2 pm, while for the weekend days, the curve identifies several peaks at 6 am, 8 am, 9 am and 11 am. The morning peaks are seen around 6 am, 9 am, 11 am and an afternoon one at 2 pm, where 11 am is identified as the top morning peak, which may be associated with brunch. Furthermore, the evening peaks for all days start to increase from about 5 pm or 6 pm and all days reach the maximum evening peak on 7 pm. It is obvious that the weekend days show a quite significantly higher daylight share than the weekdays' daylight share. Lastly, the hourly average load share in Autumn period for Wepro-ALPG shows the top morning peak around 7 am for all weekdays, with a slight peak occurring before at 6 am. The next peak happens at 10 am, with the load share increasing gradually from 11 am to 3 pm on all weekdays, while for the weekend days, the morning peaks start with a slight peak at 7 am, and the load share keeps increasing until it reaches another peak at 10 am. It then increases further to reach the top morning peak at 12 am. The weekend days show a higher daylight share than the weekdays' daylight share. Most of the days indicate 7 pm as the top evening peak, one day identifies 5 pm as the top evening peak, another day shows 6 pm as the top evening peak and another day has 8 pm as the top evening peak.

In addition, as an overview of the daily total share load, we present the selected typical days analysis in Figure 12, where the selected days represent weekdays and weekend days of each season.

For the weekdays, we selected 1: 11 February 2015, 3: 15 April 2015, 5: 15 July 2015 and 7: 11 November 2015. The load profile of the Wepro-LPG model in Figure 12 shows that 15 April 2015 has the highest consumption share among the selected weekdays, followed by 11 November 2015, 11 February 2015 and 15 July 2015. For the weekend days, we chose 2: 15 February 2015, 4: 19 April 2015, 6: 19 July 2015 and 8: 15 November 2015, showing that 19 April 2015 has the highest consumption share among the selected weekend days, followed by 15 February 2015, 15 November 2015 and 19 July 2015. Weekdays and weekends both show that the lowest consumption share is in the selected days in July, which concurs with the seasonal and monthly analyses. In addition, this also shows that the weekends have higher consumption shares than the weekdays.

In the Wepro-ALPG model, the load profile indicates 11 February 2015 as having the highest consumption share among the selected weekdays, followed by 11 November 2015. 15 April 2015 comes next, but with only a subtle difference. The lowest share is on 15 July 2015. The Wepro-ALPG model for weekends shows 15 November 2015 as having the highest consumption share, followed by 19 April 2015, then 15 February 2015, then 19 July 2015. Both Wepro-LPG and Wepro-ALPG are having the same values on 15 April 2015 and 15 November 2015.

3.1.4. Hourly Analysis

The hourly average load profiles in a year are provided in Figure 13 based on the expression in Equation (8). Figure 13 also illustrates the seasonal hourly average load profiles, where the load profiles for Wepro-LPG are shown in dashed lines and the load profiles for Wepro-ALPG are shown in solid lines. The Winter load profiles are shown in red, the Spring load profiles are shown in purple, the Summer load profiles are shown in green and the Autumn load profiles are shown in blue, where the hourly average load profiles in a year are shown in grey bold lines.

The Wepro-ALPG curve illustrates an increasing load from 5 am and reaches the morning peak around 7 am. Then, the load decreases gradually until 9 am and increases again to 10 am. After that, the curve remains flat from 10 am to 1 pm although there is a subtle peak in between around 12 am or during lunchtime. It is then increases slightly from 1 pm to 3 pm, and after 3 pm the curve is increasing significantly and is reaching the evening peak around 6 pm. Furthermore, after 6 pm the curve is decreasing gradually until midnight. After that, the curve remains flat until 5 am. While for the Wepro-LPG, the morning peak starts to increase significantly from 5 am and reaches the peak at 6 am. After 6 am, the curve is gradually decreasing until 4 pm although there is a subtle peak around 11 am. It starts to increase again significantly and reaches the evening peak at 7 pm. The curve decreases significantly after 7 pm to midnight. Furthermore, it remains quite flat until 3 am. There is a slightly increase load between 3 am to 5 am before the morning peak.

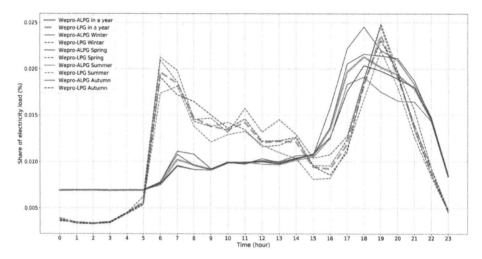

Figure 13. The hourly average load share in a year and the hourly average load share in each season based on the results of Wepro-LPG and Wepro-ALPG models.

Furthermore, the hourly average load per season for both models indicate the consistent curve shape within the season and model, either Wepro LPG or Wepro ALPG. The winter curve indicates the highest load profile among the hourly season curves, and it is more obvious for Wepro-ALPG whereas the winter's curve is shown as the highest load and slightly followed by autumn's curve for Wepro-LPG. The demand peaks show similarity with the hourly average in a year as the top peak is in the evening, followed by the morning peak and a subtle peak during the lunch time, with both models identifying the same peak hours as the peak hours for the hourly average in a year. In general, Wepro-LPG's load profiles for all seasons have higher load share than the Wepro-ALPG's load share for all seasons during the day. Conversely, the Wepro-ALPG's load indicate longer peak share than the Wepro-LPG's load during the night time.

3.2. Validation with Case Study's Measured Data

Validation can be done by comparing the data generated by Wepro with the city's measured data such as smart-meter data, TUS data or data from the utilities. In this case, we cannot make an in-depth validation as the measured city's data is unavailable. Therefore, a future study would follow to improve our current work when the city's measured data is available.

In practice, we can still compare our model with the standard load profiles for Dutch households published by the Energy Data Services Netherlands (EDSN) to validate whether our hourly average generated load profiles have the same trends the standard Dutch residential load profile. The average normalised standard household load in The Netherlands based on EDSN is provided in Figure 1 of [11]. It is shown that the morning peak starts to increase from 5 am, similar to both our generated models. It then reaches the peak around 10 am, while both our models identify the morning peak around 6 am to 7 am. The EDSN's load remains flat from 10 am to 13 pm, although there is a subtle peak at 12 am during lunchtime. This curve from 10 am to 13 pm is quite similar to the Wepro-ALPG model one. Furthermore, like the Wepro-LPG model, the ESDN's load is decreasing gradually to 4 pm. After that, the curve starts to increase significantly like the curves of both our generated models. The EDSN's model reaches the peak between 19:00 and 19:30 similar to the Wepro-LPG. Furthermore, the load is decreasing quite significantly until 2 am. It remains flat from 2 am to 5 am which is similar to our generated models. In general, it can be concluded that the generated hourly average share of the Wepro models have similar curve trends as the EDSN's load trend, although the morning peaks in the generated Wepro models have different time characteristics from EDSN's morning peak. Furthermore, both our models and the EDSN's model show a subtle peak during lunchtime. The evening peak occurs after dinner in the Wepro-LPG and EDSN model, while the the the evening peak is occurring exactly at the dinner time in Wepro-ALPG.

As an update, the load profile data in EDSN have been moved to de Vereniging Nederlandse Energie Data Uitwisseling's (NEDU) page [33]. The data provided in NEDU's page start from year 2016, therefore data 2016 are used in this initial validation. Smart-meter data is used as a basis for the consumption/production profiles as described in 'Profielenmethodiek elektriciteit', where the documentation is available in Dutch. The raw data are provided in 15 min resolution, which show how much electricity is allocated in that 15 min. The data are obtained from 3,002,450 households type E1A in 2016. The comparison of the standard average Dutch household load profile in 2016, which has similar trends with Figure 1 of [11] for E1A residential type and the hourly average load profile in a year of Wepro-LPG and Wepro-ALPG is plotted in Figure 14.

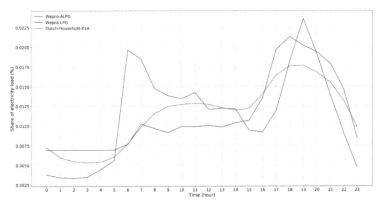

Figure 14. The comparison of hourly average standard residential load profile in The Netherlands based on NEDU's data of 2016, E1A and the hourly average load profile in a year of Wepro-LPG and Wepro-ALPG.

This simple validation is an initial check to see whether our generated load profiles resemble the standard Dutch's household load profile characteristics before going into an in-depth validation with the city's measure data. Moreover, further study in the future is required.

4. Discussion

Based on the results, our weighted proportion (Wepro) model can be applied to generate the residential electricity load profiles at the city level by utilising the exisiting household profile generators, either LPG or ALPG, which we have employed here, given that they both have specific behavioural profile models. The seasonal share analysis based on Wepro-LPG and Wepro-ALPG, shows each season's consumption share is in the range of 23% to 26%. The 1% share consists of approximately 80 h of load or about 3 days of load when calculated on the basis of the hourly dataset. For instance, if we compare the winter and summer seasons to the whole year in Wepro-LPG as shown in Figure 9, where winter is 26.02% and summer is 23.46%, it indicates that the electricity load in winter is almost 3% higher than in summer to the whole year, which is equal to approximately 240 h or about 9 days. In addition, both seasonal profiles indicate Winter as having the highest consumption share, which concurs with the known seasonal pattern in energy demands studies [60–62]. In addition, the seasonal analyses based on meteorological is important to be mentioned as some studies did not mention which time-division concept they used for analysing the seasonal electricity profile. Furthermore, the monthly analysis results illustrate that December is having the highest consumption share, which accords with the result of some monthly electricity studies [61,63].

The hourly average share based on the days in each season show that the weekend days indicate a higher daylight share than the weekdays' daylight share in both models. The result of the daily share of the selected typical days for all models indicates that most weekend days have a higher consumption share than weekdays in the same season. It concurs with an analysis of weekday and weekend variation, where weekend days show slightly more electricity use than weekdays [64]. Exception found in the Wepro-ALPG model's selected days in winter, where weekday consumption is higher than at weekend.

The hourly average load profiles identify the morning and evening peaks in Wepro-ALPG and Wepro-LPG, where the Wepro-LPG model has a higher load than the Wepro-ALPG model for both peaks. It is also identified that the evening peak has a significant higher load value than the morning peak load value in both models. All the hourly average loads in a year and per season demonstrate a consistent curve shape within season and model, either Wepro LPG or Wepro ALPG. The consistency is also shown within the curve shape of the hourly seasonal average load share with the hourly seasonal load share based on the days within the model.

As a consequence, the application of our model requires a profile generator as an external tool to match the weighted city's profile with the representative occupants' profiles at the household level, since we are not building our own profile generator. It also influences the results of the generated load profiles where they will be based on the characteristics of the developed model in profile generator, include relying on the few selected input profiles as a result of the approach taken in this study. The issue of relying on the few selected input profiles may result in the less fluctuations load profiles as shown in the Wepro-ALPG load profiles for the morning curves. The main difference of the hourly average in a year between the models is shown in the morning curve, where for Wepro-LPG after reaches the peak on 6am, the load share is declined gradually until 4 pm, with some light peaks in between, while for Wepro-ALPG, the curve declines slightly until 9 am after reaching a peak at 7 am. It increases again at 10 am and remains stable until 1 pm. This issue is also has been initially identified in [16] where the generated profiles show less fluctuations on the single household level, while the fluctuations at the neighbourhood level matched with the measured values. We assume that the less fluctuations during the morning period generated in Wepro-ALPG might be caused by the consistent pre-defined profiles in ALPG, where they are developed based on the simple behavioural model of an occupancy profile. The occupancy model for general events in ALPG is configured using mean times to change the state of a person. In this case, it is limited to the three person's states: active (being home), inactive (e.g., sleeping) and away (e.g., to work) [16], while in the generated load profiles of Wepro-LPG, the fluctuations are obviously shown during the morning period which might be caused by the detailed behavioural model that emphasised on the person's desire developed in LPG model. Although, it requires a future analysis. In general, the Wepro-ALPG has more aligned curve shape with the average standard Dutch residential load profile as illustrated in Figure 14 than the Wepro-LPG, where it could be because ALPG model is built based on Dutch dwelling setting. Moreover, a measured dataset that adequately represents the case study is required for validation purposes although in general our generated hourly average load profiles have similar curve's trend with the standard Dutch residential load profile provided by NEDU.

In addition, our model is found to be more efficient in respect of its computational time. In this case processing the load profiles of the city's residential sector, which consists of a large number of households is more efficient rather than generating each household in LPG or a certain number of city's households in ALPG. It takes about ten minutes computation to generate a single-person household load profile in LPG and about fifteen minutes computation to generate a multi-occupants household load profile in LPG, for instance profile: Family, 3 children, both adults at work. Thus, in takes 60-min to generate the Wepro's selected five profiles of Table 3 in LPG, where we used LPG version 8.9.0. Furthermore, the simulation of the current configuration that consists of five households from four types of pre-defined profiles in ALPG takes about eight minutes. We use Python 3.7 (64-bit) to run this configuration. All of these simulations either LPG or ALPG were conducted on a computer using an Intel core i5-5300U CPU processor @2.3 GHz and 8 GB of installed memory (RAM). Thus, the computation will take much longer than our approach to generate a single or the few load profiles at the city level. In this case, our approach to model the residential sector at the city level has also tackle the limitation addressed by the ALPG that the tool is aimed at small group of houses which is maximum about 100 households per simulation. Consequently, our approach also creates efficiencies in the size and storage of the generated files. For instance, the output folder of one "single with work" profile generated in LPG has 2.6 GB size and the output folder of our selected pre-defined profiles in ALPG has 1.5 GB size.

5. Conclusions

This work has developed a simplified and practical approach to model residential electricity load profiles where the model can match the main city's characteristics with the representative pre-defined households profiles proportionally. The Wepro model is advantageous as an efficient approach to develop the residential electricity load profiles at the city level, especially where survey data, smart-meter data or any other local temporal profiles dataset are unavailable. The findings concur with some load profile studies from the similar climate profile which indicate Winter as the highest consumption share and illustrate either December or January is having the highest consumption share. The results of the selected typical days for all load profiles indicate that most weekend days have a higher consumption share than weekdays in the same season. Moreover, all the hourly average load profiles in a year and per season demonstrate the consistent curve shapes, demand peaks and the peak hours within the season and model, either using Wepro-LPG or Wepro-ALPG. In terms of the curve shape and daylight characteristics between the models, the hourly average in a year of Wepro-ALPG is preferred to be used because it also shows a high similarity with the shape of the standard Dutch household provided by NEDU or previously EDSN, although the Wepro-ALPG load profiles illustrate less morning fluctuations as a result of the few input profiles taken by the approach. In addition, in terms of the evening peak, the hourly average in a year of Wepro-LPG is preferable to be used, because it resembles the evening peak time of the Dutch household characteristics, where the evening peak takes place after dinner time, which concurs with a Dutch load profile study that the evening peak takes place after dinnertime when e.g., TV, dishwasher, etc., are on because within the average Dutch household, cooking is done using gas instead of electricity.

Moreover, our work contributes by evaluating the characteristics of residential electricity load profiles based on time variation analyses: seasonal analysis, monthly analysis, days analysis and hourly analysis. In addition, this method is applicable to model previous year, current year and future year, where for current year and future year are used city's projected numbers.

Furthermore, the few selected household profiles which are the representative of the city's profile may dominate the shape of the output profiles where all of input have represented the city's age group, labour force composition and gender share. Although the few selected profiles may dominantly influence the output profile, based on the results, they still resemble the Dutch average household profile and concur with the common peak demands characteristics. In addition, although the Wepro model depends on external household profile generators such as LPG and ALPG, the Wepro model is found to be more efficient in storage capacity and computational process of the residential sector's load profiles, given the number of households in the city that can represent the local profile.

In future work, it would be interesting to identify the potential of energy savings based on the generated load profiles using a relevant machine-learning technique. We also look forward to add more main input parameter to the model and compare with the case study's measured data. Further work might also be conducted to extend residential electricity temporal profiles into spatial profiles.

Author Contributions: The idea, method and analysis of the study is designed by A.K. A.K., P.D.K.M. and P.S.N. wrote the paper. P.D.K.M. performed the complex pre-processing and modelling tasks in Python. P.S.N. reviewed and proofread the paper. All authors have read and agreed to the published version of the manuscript.

Funding: The research described in this paper is being conducted as part of the ClairCity project, funded by the European Union's Horizon 2020 research and innovation programme under grant agreement No. 689289, and a PhD fellowship within the CITIES project at Denmark Technical University (DTU) funded by the Indonesia Endowment Fund for Education (LPDP) under Letter of Guarantee: Ref:S-1401/LPDP.3/2016. The CITIES project is funded by InnovationsFund Denmark under contract: 1305-00027B.

Acknowledgments: We acknowledge ClairCity partners within the Technical work package UWE–United Kingdom, TML-Belgium, UAVR-Portugal, Techne-Italy, NILU-Norway, PBL-The Netherlands, CBS-The Netherlands, and other partners for supplying the related datasets and other large-scale inputs. We also acknowledge Noah Pflugradt for developing and publishing the LPG, and Gerwin Hoogsteen, the University of Twente, The Netherlands for developing and publishing ALPG. Furthermore, we thank Elke Klaassen for sharing her publication and The Netherlands' load profile information.

Conflicts of Interest: The authors declare no conflict of interest.

References

1. Daioglou, V.; van Ruijven, B.J.; van Vuuren, D.P. Model projections for household energy use in developing countries. *Energy* **2012**, *37*, 601–615. [CrossRef]
2. Pablo-Romero, M.d.P.; Pozo-Barajas, R.; Yñiguez, R. Global changes in residential energy consumption. *Energy Policy* **2017**, *101*, 342–352. [CrossRef]
3. Zuo, C.; Birkin, M.; Malleson, N. Spatial microsimulation modeling for residential energy demand of England in an uncertain future. *Geo-Spat. Inf. Sci.* **2014**, *17*, 153–169. [CrossRef]
4. Wang, F.; Li, K.; Duić, N.; Mi, Z.; Hodge, B.M.; Shafie-khah, M.; Catalão, J.P.S. Association rule mining based quantitative analysis approach of household characteristics impacts on residential electricity consumption patterns. *Energy Convers. Manag.* **2018**, *171*, 839–854. [CrossRef]
5. To, W.M.; Lee, P.K.C.; Lai, T.M. Modeling of monthly residential and commercial electricity consumption using nonlinear seasonal models—The case of Hong Kong. *Energies* **2017**, *10*, 885. [CrossRef]
6. Andersen, F.M.; Larsen, H.V.; Gaardestrup, R.B. Long term forecasting of hourly electricity consumption in local areas in Denmark. *Appl. Energy* **2013**, *110*, 147–162. [CrossRef]
7. *SET-Plan ACTION n°3.2 Implementation Plan: Europe to Become a Global Role Model in Integrated, Innovative Solutions for the Planning, Deployment, and Replication of Positive Energy Districts*; European Commission Brussels: Brussels, Belgium, 2018.
8. Granell, R.; Axon, C.J.; Wallom, D.C.H. Impacts of Raw Data Temporal Resolution Using Selected Clustering Methods on Residential Electricity Load Profiles. *IEEE Trans. Power Syst.* **2014**, *30*, 3217–3224. [CrossRef]
9. Beck, T.; Kondziella, H.; Huard, G.; Bruckner, T. Assessing the influence of the temporal resolution of electrical load and PV generation profiles on self-consumption and sizing of PV-battery systems. *Appl. Energy* **2016**, *173*, 331–342. [CrossRef]
10. Linssen, J.; Stenzel, P.; Fleer, J. Techno-economic analysis of photovoltaic battery systems and the influence of different consumer load profiles. *Appl. Energy* **2017**, *185*, 2019–2025. [CrossRef]
11. Klaassen, E.; Frunt, J.; Slootweg, H. Assessing the Impact of Distributed Energy Resources on LV Grids Using Practical Measurements. In Proceedings of the 23rd International Conference on Electricity Distribution (CIRED), Lyon, France, 15–18 June 2015.
12. Ahn, Y.H.; Woo, J.H.; Wagner, F.; Yoo, S.J. Downscaled energy demand projection at the local level using the Iterative Proportional Fitting procedure. *Appl. Energy* **2019**, *238*, 384–400. [CrossRef]
13. Ropuszy, E. Residential Electricity Consumption in Poland. *Oper. Res. Decis.* **2016**, *26*, 69–82.
14. Pflugradt, N.; Muntwyler, U. Synthesizing residential load profiles using behavior simulation. *Energy Procedia* **2017**, *122*, 655–660. [CrossRef]
15. Pflugradt, N.D. Modellierung von Wasser und Energieverbräuchen in Haushalten. Ph.D. Thesis, Chemnitz University of Technology, Chemnitz, Germany, 2016.
16. Hoogsteen, G.; Molderink, A.; Hurink, J.L.; Smit, G.J.M. Generation of flexible domestic load profiles to evaluate Demand Side Management approaches. In Proceedings of the 2016 IEEE International Energy Conference, ENERGYCON 2016, Leuven, Belgium, 4–8 April 2016; pp. 1–6.

17. Hoogsteen, G. A Cyber-Physical Systems Perspective on Decentralized Energy Management. Ph.D. Thesis, the University of Twente, Enschede, The Netherlands, 2017.
18. Richardson, I.; Thomson, M.; Infield, D.; Clifford, C. Domestic electricity use: A high-resolution energy demand model. *Energy Build.* **2010**, *42*, 1878–1887. [CrossRef]
19. Widén, J.; Wäckelgård, E. A high-resolution stochastic model of domestic activity patterns and electricity demand. *Appl. Energy* **2010**, *87*, 1880–1892. [CrossRef]
20. McKenna, E.; Thomson, M. High-resolution stochastic integrated thermal-electrical domestic demand model. *Appl. Energy* **2016**, *165*, 445–461. [CrossRef]
21. Eggimann, S.; Hall, J.W.; Eyre, N. A high-resolution spatio-temporal energy demand simulation to explore the potential of heating demand side management with large-scale heat pump diffusion. *Appl. Energy* **2019**, *236*, 997–1010. [CrossRef]
22. Marszal-Pomianowska, A.; Heiselberg, P.; Kalyanova Larsen, O. Household electricity demand profiles—A high-resolution load model to facilitate modelling of energy flexible buildings. *Energy* **2016**, *103*, 487–501. [CrossRef]
23. Birkin, M.; Clarke, M. *Population Dynamics and Projection Methods*; Springer: Dordrecht, The Netherlands, 2011; pp. 193–208.
24. Kipping, A.; Trømborg, E. Modeling aggregate hourly energy consumption in a regional building stock. *Energies* **2018**, *11*, 78. [CrossRef]
25. Afshari, A.; Liu, N. Inverse modeling of the urban energy system using hourly electricity demand and weather measurements, Part 2: Gray-box model. *Energy Build.* **2017**, *157*, 139–156. [CrossRef]
26. Andersen, F.M.; Baldini, M.; Hansen, L.G.; Jensen, C.L. Households' hourly electricity consumption and peak demand in Denmark. *Appl. Energy* **2017**, *208*, 607–619. [CrossRef]
27. Kipping, A.; Trømborg, E. Hourly electricity consumption in Norwegian households—Assessing the impacts of different heating systems. *Energy* **2015**, *93*, 655–671. [CrossRef]
28. Oliveira Panão, M.J.N.; Brito, M.C. Modelling aggregate hourly electricity consumption based on bottom-up building stock. *Energy Build.* **2018**, *170*, 170–182. [CrossRef]
29. Räsänen, T.; Voukantsis, D.; Niska, H.; Karatzas, K.; Kolehmainen, M. Data-based method for creating electricity use load profiles using large amount of customer-specific hourly measured electricity use data. *Appl. Energy* **2010**, *87*, 3538–3545. [CrossRef]
30. Widén, J.; Lundh, M.; Vassileva, I.; Dahlquist, E.; Ellegård, K.; Wäckelgård, E. Constructing load profiles for household electricity and hot water from time-use data-Modelling approach and validation. *Energy Build.* **2009**, *41*, 753–768. [CrossRef]
31. OPSD Data Platform—Open Power System Data. Available online: https://data.open-power-system-data.org/time_series/ (accessed on 28 September 2018).
32. Data View. Available online: https://transparency.entsoe.eu/load-domain/r2/totalLoadR2/show?name=&defaultValue=false&viewType=TABLE&areaType=BZN&atch=false&dateTime.dateTime=04.03.2020+00:00%7CCET%7CDAY&biddingZone.values=CTY%7C10YNL----------L!BZN%7C10YNL----------L&dateTime.timezone=CET_CEST&dateTime.timezone_input=CET+(UTC+1)+/+CEST+(UTC+2) (accessed on 4 March 2020).
33. Verbruiksprofielen—NEDU. Available online: https://www.nedu.nl/documenten/verbruiksprofielen/ (accessed on 25 June 2020).
34. Guo, Z.; Zhou, K.; Zhang, X.; Yang, S.; Shao, Z. Data mining based framework for exploring household electricity consumption patterns: A case study in China context. *J. Clean. Prod.* **2018**, *195*, 773–785. [CrossRef]
35. Yang, T.; Ren, M.; Zhou, K. Identifying household electricity consumption patterns: A case study of Kunshan, China. *Renew. Sustain. Energy Rev.* **2018**, *91*, 861–868. [CrossRef]
36. Klaassen, E.A.M. *Demand Response Benefits from a Power System Perspective*; Eindhoven University of Technology: Eindhoven, The Netherlands, 2016; ISBN 9789038641768.
37. Fan, H.; MacGill, I.F.; Sproul, A.B. Statistical analysis of drivers of residential peak electricity demand. *Energy Build.* **2017**, *141*, 205–217. [CrossRef]
38. Kewo, A.; Munir, R.; Lapu, A.K. IntelligEnSia based electricity consumption prediction analytics using regression method. In Proceedings of the 2015 IEEE 5th International Conference on Electrical Engineering and Informatics: Bridging the Knowledge between Academic, Industry, and Community (ICEEI), Denpasar, Indonesia, 10–11 August 2015.

39. Kewo, A.; Manembu, P.; Liu, X.; Nielsen, P.S. Statistical Analysis for Factors Influencing Electricity Consumption at Regional Level. In Proceedings of the 2018 IEEE 7th International Conference on Power and Energy (PECon), Kuala Lumpur, Malaysia, 3–4 December 2018; pp. 132–137.

40. Manembu, P.; Kewo, A.; Liu, X.; Nielsen, P.S. Multi-Grained Household Load Profile Analysis Using Smart Meter Data: The Case of Indonesia. In Proceedings of the 2018 2nd Borneo International Conference on Applied Mathematics and Engineering (BICAME), Balikpapan, Indonesia, 10–11 December 2018; pp. 213–217.

41. Papachristos, G. Household electricity consumption and CO_2 emissions in the Netherlands: A model-based analysis. *Energy Build.* **2015**, *86*, 403–414. [CrossRef]

42. Bedir, M.; Kara, E.C. Behavioral patterns and profiles of electricity consumption in dutch dwellings. *Energy Build.* **2017**, *150*, 339–352. [CrossRef]

43. Bedir, M.; Hasselaar, E.; Itard, L. Determinants of electricity consumption in Dutch dwellings. *Energy Build.* **2013**, *58*, 194–207. [CrossRef]

44. Kobus, C.B.A.; Klaassen, E.A.M.; Mugge, R.; Schoormans, J.P.L. A real-life assessment on the effect of smart appliances for shifting households' electricity demand. *Appl. Energy* **2015**, *147*, 335–343. [CrossRef]

45. ClairCity.eu ClairCity Technical Summary. Available online: http://www.claircity.eu/about/technical-summary/ (accessed on 11 February 2019).

46. Oliveira, K.; Rodrigues, V.; Coelho, S.; Fernandes, A.; Rafael, S.; Faria, C.; Ferreira, J.; Borrego, C.; Husby, T.; Diafas, I.; et al. Assesment of Source Contributions to the Urban Air Quality for the Bristol Claircity Pilot Case. *WIT Trans. Ecol. Environ.* **2019**, *236*, 89–98.

47. Rodrigues, V.; Oliveira, K.; Coelho, S.; Ferreira, J.; Fernandes, A.P.; Rafael, S.; Borrego, C.; Faria, C.; Vanherle, K.; Papics, P.; et al. H2020 ClairCity project: Assessment of air quality impacts for Bristol City Council. In Proceedings of the 19th International Conference on Harmonisation within Atmospheric Dispersion Modelling for Regulatory Purposes, Bruges, Belgium, 3–6 June 2019.

48. Coelho, S.; Rodrigues, V.; Barnes, J.; Boushel, C.; Devito, L.; Lopes, M. Air pollution in the Aveiro region, Portugal: A citizens' engagement approach. *WIT Trans. Ecol. Environ.* **2018**, *230*, 253–262.

49. Trozzi, C.; Piscitello, E.; Vaccaro, R. Air pollutants, emissions and carbon footprint at city level: The ClairCity project. *WIT Trans. Ecol. Environ.* **2018**, *230*, 263–275.

50. Hayes, E.; King, A.; Callum, A.; Williams, B.; Vanherle, K.; Boushel, C.; Barnes, J.; Chatterton, T.; Bolscher, H.; Csobod, E.; et al. Claircity project: Citizen-led scenarios to improve air quality in European cities. *WIT Trans. Ecol. Environ.* **2018**, *230*, 233–241.

51. Boushel, C.; Barnes, J.; Chatterton, T.; Vito, L.D.E.; Edwards, A.; Rogers, L.F.; Leach, M.; Prestwood, E.; Hayes, E. "Unfortunately, I use my car": Commuter transport choices in Bristol, UK. *WIT Trans. Ecol. Environ.* **2018**, *230*, 243–252.

52. Kewo, A.; Manembu, P.; Nielsen, P.S. Data Pre-Processing Techniques in the Regional Emissions Load Profile Case. In Proceedings of the 2019 6th International Conference on Control, Decision and Information Technologies (CoDIT), Paris, France, 23–26 April 2019.

53. Manembu, P.; Kewo, A.; Welang, B. Missing data solution of electricity consumption based on Lagrange Interpolation case study: IntelligEnSia data monitoring. In Proceedings of the 2015 IEEE 5th International Conference on Electrical Engineering and Informatics: Bridging the Knowledge between Academic, Industry, and Community (ICEEI), Denpasar, Indonesia, 10–11 August 2015.

54. L'Huillier, G.; Velásquez, J.D. *Advanced Techniques in Web Intelligence-2*; Springer: Berlin/Heidelberg, Germany, 2013; Volume 452, ISBN 978-3-642-33325-5.

55. MIT Critical Data. *Secondary Analysis of Electronic Health Records*; Springer: Cham, Switzerland, 2016; ISBN 978-3-319-43740-8.

56. OECD. *Working Together for Local Integration of Migrants and Refugees in Amsterdam*; OECD Publishing: Paris, France, 2018. Available online: https://books.google.dk/books?id=O-dVDwAAQBAJ&pg=PA71&lpg=PA71&dq=amsterdam+labour+force+unemployment+rate+2015&source=bl&ots=yd61WrhIY_&sig=ACfU3U0u_zNNIckca2JzEl6aUQDx7GpN0w&hl=en&sa=X&ved=2ahUKEwjw3fepxOLmAhWCy6QKHYqKDUg4ChDoATAAegQICRAB#v=onepage&q=unemploymentrate&f=false (accessed on 1 January 2020).

57. Amsterdam (Municipality, Noord-Holland, Netherlands)—Population Statistics, Charts, Map and Location. Available online: https://www.citypopulation.de/en/netherlands/admin/noord_holland/0363__amsterdam/ (accessed on 9 March 2020).

58. Age Classes by Gender Municipality of amSTERDAM, Old-Age Index and Average Age of Residents. Available online: https://ugeo.urbistat.com/AdminStat/en/nl/demografia/eta/amsterdam/23055764/4 (accessed on 1 January 2020).

59. Trenberth, K.E. What are the Seasons? *Bull. am. Meteorol. Soc.* **1983**, *64*, 1276–1282. [CrossRef]

60. Torriti, J. Understanding the timing of energy demand through time use data: Time of the day dependence of social practices. *Energy Res. Soc. Sci.* **2017**, *25*, 37–47. [CrossRef]

61. Do, L.P.C.; Lin, K.H.; Molnár, P. Electricity consumption modelling: A case of Germany. *Econ. Model.* **2016**, *55*, 92–101. [CrossRef]

62. Satre-Meloy, A.; Diakonova, M.; Grünewald, P. Daily life and demand: An analysis of intra-day variations in residential electricity consumption with time-use data. *Energy Effic.* **2020**, *13*, 433–458. [CrossRef]

63. Meng, M.; Niu, D.; Sun, W. Forecasting monthly electric energy consumption using feature extraction. *Energies* **2011**, *4*, 1495–1507. [CrossRef]

64. Lee, S.; Whaley, D.; Saman, W. Electricity demand profile of Australian low energy houses. *Energy Procedia* **2014**, *62*, 91–100. [CrossRef]

 © 2020 by the authors. Licensee MDPI, Basel, Switzerland. This article is an open access article distributed under the terms and conditions of the Creative Commons Attribution (CC BY) license (http://creativecommons.org/licenses/by/4.0/).

Article

An Integrated Energy and Environmental Audit Process for Historic Buildings

Elena Mazzola, Tiziano Dalla Mora *, Fabio Peron and Piercarlo Romagnoni

Department of Architecture and Arts, IUAV University of Venice, Dorsoduro 2206, 30123 Venice, Italy;
elenoire_me@libero.it (E.M.); fperon@iuav.it (F.P.); pierca@iuav.it (P.R.)
* Correspondence: tdallamora@iuav.it

Received: 6 August 2019; Accepted: 15 October 2019; Published: 17 October 2019

Abstract: The valorization and sustainable management of historic centers is a topic relevant to the cultural identity and heritage of European cities. A rational strategy to preserve the centers must consider both energy and environmental retrofitting, even if this is a complex issue requiring interdisciplinary approaches, dedicated diagnostic procedures, and specific tools. Within this context, this paper proposes an integrated method for energy and environmental analysis specifically devoted to historical building retrofit. Attention is focused on cases in which building management is not interested in renovation or in a deep conservation project, but instead in green management and maintenance overhaul. The basis of the procedure is the Leadership in Energy and Environmental Design for Existing Buildings: Operations and Maintenance (LEED O+M) rating protocol. The global goal was the definition of an intervention strategy indicating the principal direction of action. The first step is identifying critical issues in the operation of the building through energy diagnosis and dynamic thermophysical simulations. The second step is defining a panel of appropriate retrofit measures. The third step is choosing between alternatives to increase the sustainability performance following an environmental assessment scheme. Ca' Rezzonico in Venice (Italy), a 17th-century palace, nowadays the seat of a museum, was used as a case study to apply the proposed methodology.

Keywords: energy audit; green buildings; LEED rating system; operation and management; methodology; workflow; historic buildings

---

1. Introduction

According to the United Nations previsions [1], in 2050, most people will live in cities or urban centers; therefore, it is increasingly vital to work toward a more sustainable urban environment and to guarantee adequate public services realizing greener cities [2]. In European countries like Italy, this presents a significant challenge due to the historical context and important cultural heritage witnesses.

Historical buildings express the cultural identity of European countries, characterize cities, and provide continuity of the connection from our past to our future [3]. Historic centers have the potential to valorize different cultures and to attract financial capital, real estate investments, and building renovation projects, so it is necessary to think about how to coordinate the continuous intervention and management of historic centers to increase citizen and tourist attendance and improve relevant economic and cultural activities. A main goal of managing these centers is to detect and promote new tools for the sustainable management of historic centers. This management would enhance the attractiveness of city centers and their surroundings, increasing their suitability for both citizens and tourists [4]. National authorities are committed to valorization policies for the buildings of their historical heritage. Energy retrofitting could provide an effective strategy to protect the cultural heritage through operational costs reduction and environmental quality improvement [5].

Unfortunately, the evaluation of environmental and energy performance of historical buildings is complex and requires dedicated tools, sophisticated diagnostic procedures, and an interdisciplinary approach [6–8]. The energy requalification process must not work against the conservation necessities; it has to be an instrument of protection [9,10].

Energy and environmental diagnosis should be integrated for better identifying inefficiencies and wastefulness and to define the most appropriate retrofit measures [11]. In this context, two tools exist: the green energy audit that integrates the methodologies for evaluating energy performance (energy audit) and environmental impacts (green assessment) tools to guide green retrofits [12], and the green assessment protocols [13]. The most common of these analysis tools are multi-criteria, and evaluations are based on comparisons with real or reference performance [14,15]. Developed by the United States Green Building Council (USGBC) in 1998, currently Leadership in Energy and Environmental Design (LEED), represents the most influential and widespread rating system [16]. This certification system has been set for all types of buildings and proposes different protocols according to the typology, from home to hospital, from data center to school. The USGBC database reports that more than 100,000 projects are listed or certified by LEED, making it the most used certification system in the world [17].

The application of sustainability assessment protocols to the energy retrofit of historic buildings faces various difficulties [18,19]. Even if sustainability aspects were originally integrated into historical buildings, some rehabilitation processes ignore some of the sustainability aspects, and specific categories and criteria of rating systems, such as indoor environmental quality, conservation of materials and resources, and sustainability in the site management, have more effective and considerable impacts on sustainable rehabilitation [20]. Rating systems can be applicable to the interventions involved in the thorough renovation of historic buildings but may not address the specific issues related to a sustainable valorization of the historical and cultural aspects of this particular segment of the built environment [21].

GBC Italia developed a protocol dedicated to architectural heritage, GBC HB (historic buildings), which has been applied a few times [22,23]. LEED protocols (new construction, homes, core and shell, neighborhood development) are addressed to new constructions or major renovations; only the Italian GBC HB considers the refurbishment and the certification of the sustainability level of interventions. GBC Italia has developed a guide dedicated to neighborhoods, historic buildings, and the management of existing buildings. These studies have highlighted the compatibility between the safeguard requirement, maintenance, and preservation of historical contexts with current needs and future provision for energy efficiency [24]. An exemplary model is Savona, Italy [25]: the project reached the gold level of USGBC's LEED for Cities, increasing the efficiency of the energy management of the whole urban area by the adoption of LEED certification as a planning tool and the fulfilment of city development interventions, with the purpose of improving the lives of citizens.

USGBC guidance for applying LEED certification does not propose a method or a strategy for the calculation of LEED requirements, but refers to the professional experience of technicians and stakeholders for achieving the certification. The complexity of options and the required documentation complicate the process to achieving a LEED certification, often deterring technicians and surveyors from approaching the rating system process. The goal of this work was to create a methodology for selecting aspects to consider and the credits to calculate according to the project characteristics [16]. This paper presents a new procedure for optimizing the integrated environmental and energy audit dedicated to historical buildings, referring to the general scheme of the energy diagnosis process defined in the UNI CEI EN 16247-1:2012 standard [26] and to the LEED Operation and Management (LEED O+M) rating system that focuses on the management and operative aspects of a building. A specific procedure for the application to historic buildings was implemented starting from previous proposals [27,28]. A univocal and unambiguous workflow that optimizes the effort on assessment process and the resources, reaching higher levels of sustainability and energy efficiency, is presented.

LEED O+M is used to analyze the operative and management aspects usually aimed at existing buildings [18], even if it has been applied in a few cases to historic buildings [29]. LEED O+M can be usefully applied to historical buildings where the management is not interested in a complete renovation or in a complete conservation project. In Italy, the protocol was applied to one historical building, the Ca' Foscari University headquarters in Venice [30], and the Galleria Borghese in Rome is a case study for a future application [31].

Here, following some previews works [32–35], the authors propose integrating LEED O+M with green audits to guarantee a sounder evaluation of the operating strategies to apply during the preliminary analysis of a retrofitting project. A case study of a museum is considered, Ca' Rezzonico in Venice (Italy), that is not interested in renovation or a thorough conservation project (as required for the adoption of standard LEED protocols) but is interested in green management and maintenance. The green audit is used to identify a better framework of the critical issues and the potential for sustainability of the building. The environmental assessment protocol was applied, choosing the issues and credits that most optimize time and costs to result in a high level of sustainability, good performance assessment by the protocol, and to ensure the effectiveness of retrofitting.

2. Materials and Methods

The specific issues connected with the analyses of historic buildings in the framework of sustainable and green retrofit must be considered. For creating a procedure to lead environmental retrofitting, the examination and deconstruction of different approaches available in standards and legislations are necessary. Here is considered the general scheme of the process of energy diagnosis defined in the UNI CEI EN 16247-1:2012 standard [26] and the green energy audit referring to the UNI EN 16883:2017 standard [36]. It is also considered the LEED O+M rating system that focuses on management and operative aspects.

2.1. The Green Energy Audit

The energy diagnosis was introduced by Directive 2006/32/EC [37] and modified by Directive 2012/27/EU [38]: these directives request this procedure for all requalification actions. The interventions on historic building are usually considered voluntary: standard regulations for these cases are lacking [39]. The energy diagnosis general procedure was introduced by the UNI CEI EN 16247-1:2012 standard [15] that defines energy audits as a "systematic inspection and analysis of energy use and energy consumption of a site, building, system or organization with the objective of identifying energy flows and the potential for energy efficiency improvements and reporting them". The green energy audit retains the basic features of an energy audit but is aimed at a more important goal: improving the overall sustainability of the building. The main difference with the general energy audit's process is that during the analysis phase, only sustainability retrofits are evaluated. The audit is strictly related to environmental assessment protocols and the retro-commissioning process, presenting a systematic scheme to investigate the level of maintenance and operation of the systems in existing buildings, proposing operative interventions for improving the overall performance.

2.2. The LEED O+M Rating System

A different approach can be adopted in the management of the retrofit of an historical building based on LEED assessment scheme. Frequently, the complexity generated by cultural preservation and technical innovation and the necessity to find proofs of sustainability action through consistent documentation can discourage surveyors and technicians from pursuing the certification. Here, is considered the LEED O+M for buildings [37], which is normally intended for operative and management aspects for existing buildings undergoing limited retrofitting.

This protocol is subdivided into 20 mandatory prerequisites and 37 credits that indicate the points obtained from the characteristics of the structure and its management. The rating system organizes the prerequisites and credits into categories: Location and Transportation (LT), referring to the building site and the effect on commuting patterns; Sustainable Sites (SS), referring to environment surrounding the building and highlighting the relationship among services, ecosystems and buildings; Water Efficiency (WE), which considers water holistically, including indoor use, outdoor use, specialized uses, and metering, and recognizes the use of non-potable and alternative sources of water; Energy and Atmosphere (EA) focuses on the energy use reduction, renewable energy sources, and energy-efficient design strategies; Materials and Resources (MR), which considers the constant flow of products purchased and discarded to support building operations; Indoor Environmental Quality (EQ), which considers the satisfaction of occupants, the visual and thermal comfort, and the indoor air quality; Innovation (IN) identifies exemplary and innovative features or practices able to generate environmental benefits; and Regional Priority (RP), which identifies specific priorities according to the location and type of rating system.

The LEED performance credit system allocates points to each credit considering human benefits and the potential environmental impacts, so some categories are weighted according to the score of the associated credits, the relevance of the topic, and the intent described in the credit. As such, LEED O+M states that the categories EQ and EA are weighted higher than the total value of the other categories combined.

The structure of credits and prerequisites is organized in different sections: intent and requirements, behind the intent, step-by-step guidance, further explanation, required documentation and related credit tips, changes from LEED 2009, referenced standards, exemplary performance, and definitions [38]. It is a voluntary assessment tool that provides guideline to enhance the use of natural resources, to encourage restorative and regenerative policies, to maximize the positive and to minimize the negative environmental and human health consequences of the buildings sector, and to produce high quality indoor environments. LEED systems pursue sustainability goals by achieving mandatory prerequisites and choice credits. Four levels of sustainability are reachable according to the achieved points, platinum, gold, silver, and certified [23].

2.3. The Proposed Methodology

The proposed methodology starts from the green energy audit, then adding specifications in terms of:

(1) Collecting data: in historic buildings, it is crucial to dedicate a long period of time to researching historic data as well as planning field surveys to investigate stratigraphy; in new construction, all the project and decisions are registered, but in this case, it is necessary to examine all the building properties.
(2) Energy opportunities: the retrofit and the retro-commissioning are presented in this section because they pursue sustainable objectives; with the aim of producing an energy certification, it is possible to inspect a building's energy systems and their operating procedures.
(3) Analysis: considering the costs and benefits is insufficient for historic buildings because the compatibility of interventions must be considered. As previously mentioned, in this case, all the analyses were applied for the improvement of and not for the adaptation to standards.

A phase of monitoring energy values post-intervention is added at the end of the process. The effects of the energy requalification interventions are introduced to the scheme, where the auditor examines indicators such as energy consumption for heating, cooling, or domestic hot water.

The green energy audit aims to improve the sustainability of the building. For this reason, the selection of intervention measures must be evaluated according to the contribution in terms of energy savings, economic costs, and environmental impacts. This evaluation should be assessed by the adoption of a rating system that certifies a level of sustainability with a global score determined by the adopted design strategy and the achievement of selected credits, so, the proposal is to follow the environmental assessment on the basis of LEED O+M scheme. A workflow is proposed for achieving the certification score using a new classification of prerequisites and credits that consider the points of credits and the document to be delivered. This method references previous studies [40] that aimed to identify the credits necessary to achieve the minimum score to attain the certification label with the better use of resources in term of time and costs. This step consists of two phases:

(1) Phase 1 applies a prerequisites classification, assigning a score to the parameters selected within the LEED guide that describe the requirements and documentation for the achieving the prerequisites [41,42];

(2) Phase 2 considers the credits and is split into two different steps:

    (a) Sub-phase 2A involves the selection of credits

    (b) Sub-phase 2B applies a credits classification according to the same approach in phase 1.

All the sections described for each prerequisite and credit are considered, for example, intent, requirements, relations, score, and options, according to the structure fixed by the LEED rating system (Figure 1).

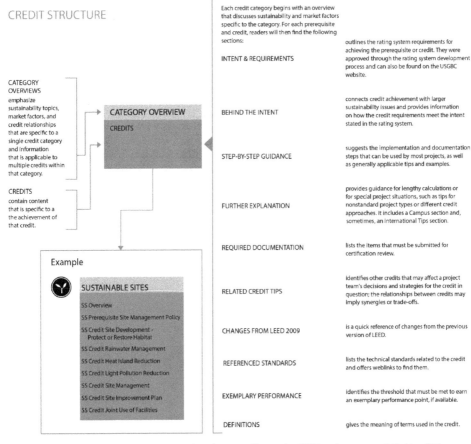

Figure 1. Structure of prerequisites and credits according to the LEED rating system definition [16].

Subsequently, a scoring system, described in Table 1, was developed considering the following parameters: the number of required documents, (listed in the required documentation section), the connected prerequisites (listed in the related credit tips section), and the effort level to fulfil the forms requested by USGBC (as described in the intent and requirement section).

Table 1. Scoring system for prerequisites according to options: parameters are the requirements in each prerequisite and the score is the score system. In detail: 1 point is assigned for each document required for the achievement of the intent; 1 point is assigned for each prerequisite listed in the section of related credits tips; different points are assigned related to the procedure of the performance period; different points are assigned in relation to the different levels of commitment difficulty in completing and collecting data.

Parameter	Score
Documents requested	1 point = 1 document
Related prerequisites	1 point = 1 prerequisite listed according to related credit tips section
Performance period	0 point = not present 2 points = five-yearly audit or maintenance after certification 3 points = collection of data before the certification
Type of form	1 point = easy to fill in 2 points = calculation required 3 points = form is more complex

As an example, the possible score for the prerequisite p2 of the Minimum Energy Performance (EA category, Table 2) is presented with two options requiring a total amount of four or eight documents to be completed according to the chosen option; there are two related prerequisites: EA p1 Energy Efficiency Best Management Practices and EA p3 Building-Level Energy Metering. The performance period requires 12 continuous months of metered energy data collected before the end of the performance period; the form includes the data collected to fulfil the Energy Star Rating or similar energy audit. Therefore, a partial score could be achieved for each prerequisite option by the application of the method, as explained in Table 1, and the total score of the prerequisite is determined by the average values of the options.

Table 2. Example of a score calculation for prerequisite EA p2 Minimum Energy Performance: the number of options proposed by the prerequisite requirement; the amount of documentation, listed in the documentation required section; the number and types of prerequisites; period and description of performance period; forms requested from USGBC; partial score for each option; and normalization of total score through calculation of average partial scores.

Name	Options	Documentation	Prerequisites	Performance Period	Form	Partial Score	Total Score
EA p2 Minimum Energy Performance	1.1	4	2	3	2	12	14.4
	1.2	4	2	3	2	12	
	2.1.1	6	2	3	3	15	
	2.1.2	8	2	3	3	17	
	2.1.3	7	2	3	3	16	

As shown for prerequisite EA p2, the procedure concludes with the assignment of a final score for each prerequisite, obtained by the normalization of the partial score and the number of options contained in the prerequisite description.

The result is a classification of prerequisites for LEED O+M v.4 (Figure 2), organized from higher to lower scores, also listing the relationships. It represents a workflow for applying the certification process as it lists the prerequisites in order of importance. In case of a correlation (for example EA p3, EA p1, and EQ p1 with EA p2) the prerequisites with a lower score (EA p1 and EQ p1) lose the score because the relationship allows pursuing the same documentation and data for the item with the higher score (EA p2), receiving the same higher score and the same relevance in the classification and workflow.

WORK CLASSIFICATION

	PREREQUISITE	SCORE
EA p2	Minimum Energy Performance	14.4
EA p1	Energy Efficiency Best Management Practicies	~~9~~
EQ p1	Minimum Indoor Air Quality Performance	9
EA p3	Building-Level Energy Metering	~~10~~
MR p1	Ongoing Purchasing and Waste Policy	9.25
EQ p3	Green Cleaning Policy	7
MR p2	Facility Maintenance and Renovation Policy	~~2~~
EA p4	Fundamental Refrigerant Management	6.6
WE p1	Indoor Water Use Reduction	6.5
WE p2	Building-Level Water Metering	~~6~~
EQ p2	Environmental Tobacco Smoke Control	6
SS p1	Site Management Policy	3

Figure 2. Work classification of prerequisites for LEED O+M; scores of prerequisites related to other prerequisites are struck through. LEED's goals drive the weighting of points toward certification. Each credit is allocated points based on the relative importance of its contribution toward the goals. The results present a weighted average: credits that most directly address the most important goals are assigned the highest weight [42].

The classification proposed in Figure 2 reveals the most important areas for attaining the certification according to the LEED O+M perspective. The main area of concern for the management of energy performance, the EA category, is the most important topic, followed by signed policies such as requested in the EQ and MR category.

After pursuing mandatory prerequisites, credits allow receiving a score to determine the level of certification: USGBC assigns different points to each option of each credit. Since the complexity of the requirements and the large number of credits and documents, this study tries to simplify the selection process with the aim of receiving higher LEED certification by evaluating the minimum number of documentations for each credit and its relevance to the system. A calculation was developed for assessing the weighing of each credit and for credit selection considering the following parameters: score, relationship, and frequency. Relationship considers the number of credits listed in the related credit tips section of the same credit; frequency counts the quotes for the considered credit in the related credit tips section of other credits.

Phase 2A involves selection process. First, credits are listed and ranked in relation to the number of documents/reports to be completed according to the options. Then, the methodology proposes a new parameter called the "summary credit", as defined in Equation (1), which considers the maximum points achievable (score), the number of correlated prerequisites and credits (relationship), and the quote in other prerequisites/credits (frequency):

$$\text{Summary credit} = \text{point} + \text{frequency} + \text{relationship} \tag{1}$$

The method identifies a choice of credits with the best value as defined using Equation (2). Considering the required documentation (y) and the calculated summary credit (x), the result is a list of best credits (Figure 3) for LEED O+M v.4:

$$y \leq 3/10\, x \tag{2}$$

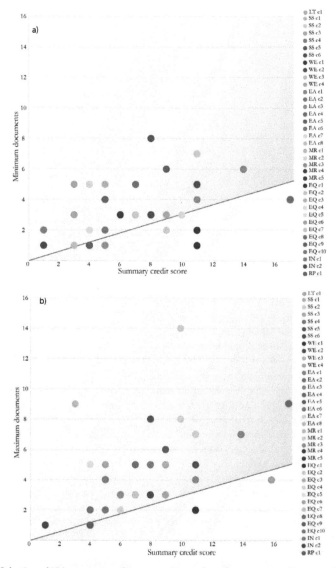

Figure 3. Selection of 10 important credits: on x axis, number of summary credit, on y axis, number of documents, in particular minimum documents in (**a**) minimum documents and (**b**) maximum documents; the chosen credits lay below the line, according to function $y \le 3/10x$.

Credits are organized in phase 2B, developing a score system that considers the internal options (Table 3) in the requirement for the credit structure: one point is assigned for each requested document, for each connection with prerequisites and credits; different points are assigned based on the performance period and on the level of complexity and difficulty in completing the forms requested from USGBC.

Table 3. Scoring system for credits according to internal options: parameters are the requirements for each credit and score is the scoring system. The system is the same for prerequisites, but more points are assigned in relation to the number of prerequisites and credits listed in the tips section.

Parameter	Score
Documents requested	1 point = 1 document
Relation with prerequisites	1 point = 1 relation with prerequisite
Credits inside	1 point = 1 internal credit
Performance period	0 point = not present 2 points = five-yearly audit or maintenance after the certification 3 points = collection of data before the certification
Type of form	1 point = easy to fill in . 2 points = calculation required 3 points = form is more complex

While the previous analysis was only dedicated to the prerequisites, this process was also developed for classifying the credits. The classification of credits has been implemented with the correlation between both credits and prerequisites (Figure 4).

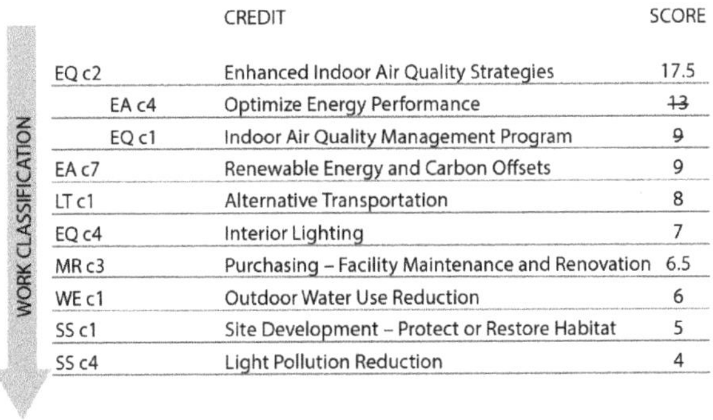

	CREDIT	SCORE
EQ c2	Enhanced Indoor Air Quality Strategies	17.5
EA c4	Optimize Energy Performance	~~13~~
EQ c1	Indoor Air Quality Management Program	9
EA c7	Renewable Energy and Carbon Offsets	9
LT c1	Alternative Transportation	8
EQ c4	Interior Lighting	7
MR c3	Purchasing – Facility Maintenance and Renovation	6.5
WE c1	Outdoor Water Use Reduction	6
SS c1	Site Development – Protect or Restore Habitat	5
SS c4	Light Pollution Reduction	4

WORK CLASSIFICATION

Figure 4. Work classification of credits for LEED O+M; scores of credits related to other credits are crossed out.

The credits classification shows how the management of energy use is relevant, as with the prerequisite classification. Particular relevance is assigned to the human health topic presented in the EQ and LT categories, as listed in the management of air quality, the interior lighting, and the incentive to use alternative transportation.

The methodology identifies a list of 10 credits. The application and calculation of the requirements of these credits could achieve a total score of 53 points according to the scorecard, achieving the Silver level of certification [41] for LEED O+M systems, achievable when a project earns 50–59 points.

3. The Application on a Case Study

3.1. Ca' Rezzonico Museum

A case study was considered for the application of the method: Ca' Rezzonico (Figure 5), Museum of 18th Century Venice, in Venice, Italy. Many Italian museums are hosted in historical buildings: 28 museums are pre-12th century, 483 were built between the 12th and 16th centuries, and 544 between the 17th and 19th centuries [43].

(a)
(b)

Figure 5. Ca' Rezzonico: (**a**) main front on the Grand Canal (Fondazione Musei Civici di Venezia s.d.); (**b**) ballroom on the first floor.

This palace was built during the Baroque age and was converted into a museum in 1936 after refurbishment interventions. The quality of architecture and exhibited works make Ca' Rezzonico an interesting and unique witness of the Venetian 19th century. It has four floors that host several museum rooms, a library shop, and a coffee bar, for a total surface are of 6400 m^2. Seven different types of external walls and five different types of windows exist in the building. The energy consumption is about 142 kWh/m^2a, including about 81 kWh/m^2a for electricity, determined by averaging the bills of three consecutive years from 2014 to 2016 (Table 4).

Table 4. Energy consumption of Ca' Rezzonico for 2014–2016. The data represent the average use for the three years and are reported for each month; the large consumption is due to electricity; heating and domestic hot water are provided by natural gas. Note that heating is not required from May to September; the values are listed using kWh/m^2a.

2014–2016 Energy Type	Jan	Feb	Mar	Apr	May	Jun	Jul	Aug	Sep	Oct	Nov	Dec	Annual
Electricity use (kWh/m^2a)	5.79	5.34	5.85	5.62	6.26	8.41	9.99	9.42	7.23	6.06	5.27	5.54	80.77
Natural Gas use (kWh/m^2a)	13.93	11.41	9.00	2.36	0.38	0.41	0.57	0.59	0.54	2.69	7.20	12.28	61.35

The museum is managed and promoted by the Fondazione Musei Civici di Venezia foundation, which chose Ca' Rezzonico as a pilot case to test LEED requirements for achieving the certification for all museum systems.

3.2. First Step: Green Audit

According to the previous above of the integrated energy and environmental audits of historic buildings, in this case study, different surveys were developed, including a thermography analysis, data were collected about the schedule and system plan, and a dynamic energy model was created to evaluate the building energy performance. Using this method, some energy efficiency measures were identified.

The entire building envelope does not have thermal characteristics similar to the energy behavior required by actual normative; the historical protection status and heritage value do not allow energy efficient interventions such as thermal insulation of external/internal walls or window substitution, so the best energy improvements cannot be adopted.

The energy performance of the building envelope is low, especially in some zones (such as the attic) or in some local points (for example, near the external systems placement or where, in previous years, a replacement and refurbishment has been completed with the use of different materials causing thermal bridges), so interventions should completed to maintain the integrity of the building structure.

The thermal energy lost through the windows is high, thermal loss and need improvement, especially into the curved partition. The intervention involves redoing the sealing between the frame and glass to maintain the historical elements and reduce the thermal bridge problem.

An electrical system intervention should be considered as the most important measure due to the high consumption and costs; the energy and economic savings should be achieved without altering the historical elements of the buildings that are listed and protected by the Historical Superintendent.

Intervention on the reduction of domestic hot water (DHW) should not be considered relevant due to its low use and cost.

Another useful tool in the audit step is dynamic simulations. A numerical model of Ca' Rezzonico was set up by Design Builder®(powered by EnergyPlus®) to validate simulated values with real consumption. As shown in Table 5, the deviation was 1% on average for natural gas and electricity use.

Table 5. Comparison of energy consumption between real data from bills and output simulation by the Design Builder model.

Energy Type	Real data (kWh/m^2a)	Simulation (kWh/m^2a)	Deviation (%)
Electricity use	80.77	81.7	1%
Natural gas use	55.16	52.4	5%

3.3. Second Step

3.3.1. Part A: Application to Prerequisites

Phase 2A is the completion of prerequisites that are mandatory to be admitted to the LEED certification process. According to the classification of prerequisites (Figure 2), prerequisite EA p2, concerning operating energy performance, was developed first. For Ca' Rezzonico, the prerequisite was achieved in comparison with similar buildings and the recently completed energy performance assessment. A 25% improvement in the energy consumption was verified (with reference to the previous 12 months) in comparison with the usage data of the three contiguous years (with reference to the last five), using a normalized index for occupancy, building use, and climate.

The work program indicates the need for an investigation into the real connections between other prerequisites through the analysis of required data and documentation. The documents needed for prerequisite p2 in the EA category can be used for other prerequisites (Table 6). The meter calibration report requires data collection from permanently installed meters, according to prerequisite p3 in the EA category; the early assessment for energy performance required by prerequisite EA p1 could be integrated into the utility bill summary. Prerequisite EQ p1, regarding minimum indoor air quality, requires the same occupation schedules as in the energy audit. The table presents an example of the relationships between credits. The documents that manage the same kind of information are highlighted in the same color, showing that they could be treated together as proposed in the methodology.

Table 6. Example of relationship between the first four prerequisites according to the work program in Figure 2. The required documentation is listed for each prerequisite and the colors indicate the similar documents because they manage the same kind of information.

Prerequisite	Required Documentation
EA p2	Meter calibration report Energy Star portfolio Utility bill summary pages of performance period for each fuel source Weather-normalized source EUI Calculation supporting additional normalization

Table 6. *Cont.*

Prerequisite	Required Documentation
EA p1	Preliminary energy use analysis Energy audit Current facility requirements and operations and maintenance plan
EA p3	Confirmation of permanently installed meters Letter of commitment Confirmation of data sharing source
EQ p1	Measured outdoor airflow rates Information about ventilation Ventilation maintenance program Table with occupied rooms, spaces, or zones

3.3.2. Part B: Application to Credits

A selection of 10 credits was applied according to the methodology to produce a draft of energy and environmental certification by achieving the minimum score necessary and minimizing the internal documents to achieve the highest possible score. This score and the consequent level of certification are integrated with the evaluation of other issues and credits by the design team.

In Ca' Rezzonico, the evaluation strategy was conducted considering the requests of the museum administration, who had expressed the desire to evaluate some specific aspect such as the energy efficiency and management, the internal lighting quality, and the ventilation system. These requests were consistent with what is expressed in the documentation necessary for the selection of the 10 credits, as previously described in Figure 4.

The information in Table 7 focuses on the application of 10 credits in the case study. The administration of the museum will have to apply some specific requirements (highlighted in red) to obtain validation and achieve certification. According to the case study characteristics, a preview showed the museum could earn 47 points toward LEED O+M certification. In detail Table 7 shows the credits and what their characteristics and documentation are [42].

EQ c2, Enhanced Indoor Air Quality Strategies: the intent is to ensure better indoor air quality for users' productivity, well-being, and comfort. The requests include permanent installations (such as slotted systems and grilles). Currently Ca' Rezzonico does not have such systems.

EA c4, Optimize Energy Performance: the intent is to increase the energy performance beyond the prerequisite standard for reducing economic and environmental problems in relation to the unnecessary use of energy. The requirements include a demonstration of continuous energy efficiency improvement during the performance period in comparison to a baseline, and Ca' Rezzonico has an energy use 43% lower with respect to similar buildings in terms of typology, use, and characteristics.

EQ c1, Indoor Air Quality Management Program: the intent is to maintain users' well-being by modifying and preventing indoor air quality problems. The requirement includes conducting an I-BEAM audit on a regular basis and revising the IAQ management program.

EA c7, Renewable Energy Carbon Offsets: the intent is to reduce greenhouse gas (GHG) emissions through the use of local and grid-source renewable energy technologies and carbon mitigation projects. The requirements include a demonstration that renewable energy systems determine the total energy use or the engagement of contracts to purchase carbon offsets, green power, or Renewable Energy Certificates (RECs) as the annual renewal of the energy supply contract for Ca' Rezzonico.

LT c1, Alternative Transportation: the intent is to reduce pollution and land development effects from automobile use for transportation. Alternative transportation strategies that contribute to this reduction include human-powered transport (e.g., walking or biking), public transit, telecommuting, informal transit options, compressed workweeks, carpooling, and green vehicles. For Ca' Rezzonico, the credit is achievable as for all buildings on the Venice isle.

Table 7. Analysis of the 10 selected credits in Figure 4 in application to the case study. The requests of Ca' Rezzonico management are highlighted in red color, the already requests are in black. The score obtainable is listed, compared with the maximum achievable with the LEED O+M rating system.

Credit	Requirements	Max. Score Achievable	Points for Ca' Rezzonico
EQ c2 Enhanced Indoor Air Quality Strategies	Install permanent entryway systems; each ventilation system that supplies outdoor air to occupied spaces must have particle filters or air cleaning devices.	2	2
EA c4 Optimize Energy Performance	Demonstrate energy efficiency performance that is at least 26% better than the median energy performance for typical buildings of similar type.	20	18
EQ c1 Indoor Air Quality Management Program	Develop and implement an indoor air quality management program.	2	2
EA c7 Renewable Energy Carbon Offsets	Demonstrate that the total energy use is met directly with renewable energy systems.	5	4
LT c1 Alternative Transportation	Demonstrate that regular building occupants and visitors use alternative transportation.	15	15
EQ c4 Interior Lighting	Implement individual lighting controls; analyze internal lighting quality level and obtain an improvement.	2	1
MR c3 Purchasing: Facility Maintenance and Renovation	Purchase maintenance and renovation materials that are environmentally sustainable.	2	1
WE c1 Outdoor Water Use Reduction	Calculate the landscape water requirement and install an irrigation meter.	2	2
SS c1 Site Development – Protect or Restore Habitat	Provide financial support to a nationally or locally recognized land trust or conservation organization.	2	1
SS c4 Light Pollution Reduction	Measure the night illumination levels, which must not be more than 20% above the level measured with the lights off.	1	1
Total		53	47

EQ c4, Interior Lighting: the intent is to improve occupants' well-being, comfort, and productivity through the provision of high-quality lighting. The requirements include an analysis of the quality of light control system. Currently, for the case study, only some changes to lighting consumption were possible because the requirements for by this credit are constrained by the Superintendent.

MR c3, Purchasing—Facility Maintenance and Renovation: the intent is to reduce the environmental harm due to the materials used in building renovations. The requirement includes purchasing at least 50%, by cost, of the total maintenance and renovation materials that meet at least one of the criteria of being recyclable, reusable, bio-based, cradle-to-cradle certification, and low emissions of volatile organic compounds. In this case, Ca' Rezzonico is a building listed by the Superintendent, so the requirements for renovation and credit will have to be analyzed more in-depth in accordance with the various stakeholders, even if no particular difficulties have yet been detected.

WE c1, Outdoor Water Use Reduction: the intent is to reduce outdoor water consumption. The requirement is reducing the project's landscape water requirement (LWR) by at least 50% from the calculated baseline for the site's peak water use month. Reductions must first be achieved through plant species selection and irrigation system efficiency as calculated in the Environmental Protection Agency (EPA) Water, Sense Water Budget Tool. The museum administration is active in monitoring and validating the consumption reduction.

SS c1, Site Development—Protect or Restore Habitat: the intent is to maintain existing natural areas and restore damaged areas for habitat provision and biodiversity promotion. The requirement is the coverage by vegetation (adapted or in place native) of a minimum area during the performance period. Another option, effectively chosen for the case study, is the provision of financial support equivalent to at least USD $4 per square meter for the total site area (including the building footprint), to a nationally- or locally-recognized land trust or conservation organization within the same EPA Level III ecoregion or the project's state.

SS c4, Light Pollution Reduction: the intent is to minimize the light escaping from the site and building, by reducing sky-glow, improving night sky access, enhancing the night-time visibility, and reducing the impact from lighting on nocturnal environments. The requirement includes the use of an external shading device or reducing the measured illuminance level of external lights by 20% compared with lights off. In the case study, this second option is achievable due the installation of external light pointed only on the main external surface of the building.

3.4. Overall Results

As described in Table 7, the certification process in the case study could achieve 47 points toward LEED O+M certification, corresponding to a Certified level (40–49 points). This is a good result because the application of the methodology guarantees the certification only by the calculation of 10 credits, but above all, confirms a good level of sustainability focusing on the management of energy use and the improvement of indoor quality. The same procedure could be applied and verified for other LEED rating systems given the identical structure, but also to other certification systems based on criteria, indicators, ratings, and the certification process.

With the adoption of a LEED protocol, a single intervention measure could result in the achievement of different credits. For example, the intervention for the same inefficiencies, analyzed by energy diagnosis, could be evaluated by environmental impact; the improvement involves the selection and calculation of credits that concern n these items and inefficiencies (Table 8). A higher the score evaluated based on available credits, the higher the assessment of the environmental improvement achieved.

Table 8. Description of the analyzed inefficiencies. Each intervention is defined using a qualitative assessment according to the energy improvement, sustained costs, economic benefits, and preservation of the historical asset (+ positive value, - negative value).

Type of Inefficiency	Type of Analysis	Energy Improvement	Costs	Heritage Conservation
Electric energy use	Consumption data, benchmark comparison	+++	++	+++
Opaque envelope (local element)	Thermographic analysis	++	+++	+++
Transparent envelope (local windows)	Thermographic analysis	++	+	+++
Whole envelope	Minimum requirements by normative	+++	+	- - -
DHW use	Consumption data, benchmark comparison	+	++	+

In the description each credit, the rating system considers a list of related credits that are similar or comparable in terms of items or calculation approach. Table 8 shows how to address the inefficiencies and the calculation of the requirements for a list of credits. For example, in the Ca' Rezzonico analysis, a Base level of certification should be achieved by the application of recommended credits, but the calculation of related credits, as proposed in Table 9, could increase the level.

Table 9. Environmental assessment of the interventions examined using energy diagnosis. The recommended measures are selected according to the credits in LEED O+M, specifying the nomenclature of the reference credit and the related credits. The last column reports a qualitative environmental assessment.

Type of Inefficiency	Recommended Intervention by LEED	LEED Credit	Related Achievable Credits	Environmental Improvement
Electric energy use	Indoor light management and metering; management plan for inner air quality	EQ c4	EQ c3 Thermal Comfort. EA c2 Existing Building Commissioning—Analysis; EA c3 Existing Building Commissioning—Implementation; MR c2 Purchasing—Lamps	+++
		EQ c1	EQ c9 Integrated Pest Management	
Opaque envelope (local analysis)	Energy use improvement	EA c4	EA c2 Existing Building Commissioning—Analysis	+
Transparent envelope (single windows)	Energy use improvement	EA c4	EA c2 Existing Building Commissioning—Analysis	+
Whole envelope	Energy use improvement	EA c4	EA c2 Existing Building Commissioning—Analysis	++
DHW use	Management and metering for water use on green areas	WE c1	WE c3 Cooling Tower Water Use; WE c4 Credit Water Metering	+

4. Discussion and Conclusions

Historic buildings require special consideration because they represent a large proportion of Italian buildings. The desire to achieve energy saving, global costs management, and environmental impact goals is growing, aiming to reduce CO_2 emissions and other greenhouse gases, and to improve in internal quality air and comfort. In fact, the objective of this research was to investigate the energy and environmental assessment systems and the tools that allow their implementation.

The research proposes different approaches to obtain an energy and environmental audit for historic buildings:

(1) A new formulation for the operative workflow of the energy audit that considers energy evaluations and the characteristics in the analysis of an historic building. The research underlines the importance of non-destructive investigations and post-intervention monitoring, and the selection of a rating system able to select the most appropriate intervention measures.

(2) An environmental analysis developed through the assessment of the operational and management aspects through the application of the LEED O+M rating system with the addition of a new strategy to organize and optimize the use and the calculation of the requirements.

(3) A validation with a case study of Ca' Rezzonico museum. The building was analyzed according to the normative by the completion of an operative check list, using data from the archive of the Superintendent and through the development of non-destructive investigations. The energy audit according to normative and an environmental assessment was developed according to the LEED O+M.

This paper highlights some other findings. The energy diagnosis requires benchmarks that refer only to the museums [12], and the research lacks quantitative analysis of the interventions from economic and financial viewpoints. The investigation into supply costs, time of return of investments, and comparisons with the Superintendent references need to be further analyzed.

The proposed method was tested on to LEED rating system and was developed according to the characteristics of the LEED O+M credit system. Even if LEED rating systems have a standard structure, each protocol includes different requirements, connections, scores, and weighing. Future developments should focus on validating the proposed method and finding a robust system for the credits selection that is applicable for different LEED protocols.

Notably, the application of the methodology indicated a Silver level LEED O+M certification cold be attained through the calculation of a list of 10 credits for a maximum total score of 53 points, which could be implemented with other credits in relation to the characteristics of the projects.

As previously described, the proposed methodology is an upgrade of the GBC Historic Building system proposal [44] and the research is revising and deepening the application to other protocols with the aim of defining Equation (3) and improving the method to increase its applicability:

$$\text{ratio} = \frac{\text{summary credit}}{\text{required documents}} \tag{3}$$

This study was conducted as part of a research program that includes different phases; therefore, some weaknesses and uncertainties still need to be studied. For example, for Ca' Rezzonico, the certification process and the credits completion are still ongoing, so the methodology is being verified with the progression of the credits achievement. The paper presents a calculation method that has only been analyzed in some historical buildings and therefore, in future developments, we intend to validate the method on other cases, including both museum and other types of buildings.

A weakness of the study is the lack of applicability to all LEED protocols, precisely because the structure of the credits and categories in O+M is substantially different from most rating systems. The research intends to develop the application for other protocols to create a method for preliminary evaluation of certification achievement in terms of documentation, score, and difficulties. After verifying the prerequisites and the selected credits using the generic formula in Equation (3), in the case of non-achievement of a satisfactory score or obstacles, a change of rating system could be considered during in a first phase of a check.

Author Contributions: Conceptualization, E.M. and T.D.M.; methodology, E.M. and T.D.M.; formal analysis, E.M. resources, E.M. and T.D.M.; data curation, E.M. and T.D.M. and F.P.; writing-original-draft preparation, E.M. and F.P.; writing—review and editing, T.D.M. and P.R.; visualization, E.M.; supervision, F.P. and P.R.; project administration, T.D.M.

Funding: This research received no external funding.

Conflicts of Interest: The authors declare no conflict of interest.

References

1. United Nations, Department of Economic and Social Affairs, Population Division (2019). World Urbanization Prospects: The 2018 Revision (ST/ESA/SER.A/420). New York: United Nations. 2019. Available online: https://population.un.org/wup/Publications/Files/WUP2018-Report.pdf (accessed on 16 March 2019).
2. Saleem, H.A. Green Cities: Urban Growth and the Environment. *J. Am. Plan. Assoc.* **2008**, *74*, 143. [CrossRef]
3. Ragni, M.; Maurano, A.; Scoppola, F.; Soragni, U.; Baraldi, M.; D'Amico, S.; Mercalli, M.; Banchini, R.; Bellisario, M.G.; Rubino, C.; et al. *Linee di Indirizzo per il Miglioramento Dell'efficienza Energetica nel Patrimonio Culturale*; Architettura Centri e Nuclei Storici ed Urbani, Ministero dei Beni Culturali: Roma, Italy, 2013; pp. 1–200. Available online: http://soprintendenza.pdve.beniculturali.it/wp-content/uploads/2018/04/Linee_indirizzo_miglioramento_efficienza_energetica_nel_patrimonio_culturale.pdf (accessed on 16 March 2019).
4. Martinez-Molina, A.; Tort-Austina, I.; Cho, S.; Vivancos, J. Energy efficiency and thermal comfort in historic buildings: A review. *Renew. Sustain. Energy Rev.* **2016**, *61*, 70–85. [CrossRef]
5. Vieites, E.; Vassileva, I.; Arias, J.E. European initiatives towards improving the energy efficiency in existing and historic buildings. *Energy Procedia* **2015**, *75*, 1679–1685. [CrossRef]
6. Roberti, F.; Oberegger, U.F.; Gasparella, A. Calibrating historic building energy models to hourly indoor air and surface temperatures: Methodology and case study. *Energy Build.* **2015**, *108*, 236–243. [CrossRef]
7. Lucchi, E.; Pracchi, V. *Efficienza Energetica e Patrimonio Costruito: La Sfida del Miglioramento Delle Prestazioni Nell'edilizia Storica*; Ed. Maggioli: Milano, Italy, 2013.

8. Ma, Z.; Cooper, P.; Daly, D.; Ledo, L. Existing building retrofits: Methodology and state-of-the-art. *Energy Build.* **2012**, *55*, 889–902. [CrossRef]

9. De Santoli, L.; Mancini, F.; Rossetti, S. Studio di interventi di riqualificazione energetica e impiantistica per la Galleria Borghese a Roma. *AiCARR J.* **2016**, *36*, 32–40.

10. Ascione, F.; Bianco, N.; de Masi, R.F.; de Rossi, F.; Vanoli, G.P. Energy retrofit of an educational building in the ancient center of Benevento. Feasibility study of energy savings and respect of the historical value. *Energy Build.* **2015**, *95*, 172–183. [CrossRef]

11. Mustafaraj, G.; Marini, D.; Costa, A.; Keane, M. Model calibration for building energy efficiency simulation. *Appl. Energy* **2014**, *130*, 72–85. [CrossRef]

12. Dall'O', G.; Speccher, A.; Bruni, E. The Green Energy Audit, a new procedure for the sustainable auditing of existing buildings integrated with the LEED Protocols. *Sustain. Cities Soc.* **2012**, *3*, 54–65. [CrossRef]

13. Jagarajan, R.; Asmoni, M.N.A.M.; Mohammed, A.H.; Jaafar, M.N.; Mei, J.L.Y.; Baba, M. Green retrofitting—A review of current status, implementations and challenges. *Renew. Sustain. Energy Rev.* **2017**, *67*, 1360–1368. [CrossRef]

14. Berardi, U. Comparison of sustainability rating systems for buildings and evaluation of trends. In Proceedings of the SB11 Helsinki: World Sustainable Building Conference, Helsinki, Finland, 18–21 October 2011; pp. 1696–1702.

15. El Yamany, S.; Afifi, M.; Hassan, A. Applicability and Implementation of U.S. Green Building Council Rating System (LEED) in Egypt. *Procedia Environ. Sci.* **2016**, *34*, 594–604. [CrossRef]

16. U.S. Green Building Council, LEED Rating System. 2009. Available online: http://www.usgbc.org/leed/leed_main.asp. (accessed on 26 March 2019).

17. Gurgun, A.P.; Polat, G.; Damci, A.; Bayhan, H.G. Performance of LEED energy credit requirements in European countries. In Proceedings of the Creative Construction Conference, Budapest, Hungary, 25–28 June 2016; pp. 25–28.

18. Sun, X.; Gou, Z.; Lu, Y.; Tao, Y. Strengths and Weaknesses of Existing Building Green Retrofits: Case Study of a LEED EBOM Gold Project. *Energies* **2019**, *11*, 1936. [CrossRef]

19. Stephens, J.F.; Siddiqi, K. LEED Rating Systems for Historical Restorations. In Proceedings of the 49th ASC Annual International Conference, San Luis Obispo, CA, USA, 10–13 April 2013; pp. 1–6.

20. Sadrykia, S.; Medghalchi, L.; Mahdavinejad, M. Sustainability assessment, rating systems and historical buildings Case study: Rehabilitated construction in a university site. In Proceedings of the 4th International Building Control Conference (IBCC 2016), Kuala Lumpur, Malaysia, 7–8 March 2016; pp. 1–9.

21. Boarin, P.; Guglielmino, D.; Pisello, A.L.; Cotana, F. Sustainability assessment of historic buildings: Lesson learnt from an Italian case study through LEED®rating system. *Energy Procedia* **2014**, *61*, 1029–1032. [CrossRef]

22. Lucchi, E.; Boarin, P.; Zuppiroli, M. GBC Historic Building®: A new certification tool for orienting and assessing environmental sustainability and energy efficiency of historic buildings. In Proceedings of the EECHB on Energy Efficiency and Comfort in Historic Buildings, Brussels, Belgium, 19–21 October 2016; pp. 1–8.

23. Troi, A.; Lucchi, E. Cultural Heritage Preservation. In Proceedings of the 3rd European Workshop on Cultural Heritage Preservation; Felix Verlag: Bozen/Bolzano, Italy, 2013; pp. 16–18.

24. Dall'O', G.; Galante, A.; Sanna, N.; Miller, K. On the Integration of Leadership in Energy and Environmental Design (LEED)®ND Protocol with the energy planning and management tools in Italy: Strengths and weaknesses. *Energies* **2013**, *6*, 5990–6015. [CrossRef]

25. Bisello, A.; Vettorato, D.; Stephens, R.; Elisei, P. *Smart and Sustainable Planning for Cities and Regions*; Springer: Berlin/Heidelberg, Germany, 2016; pp. 389–401.

26. Ente Nazionale Italiano di Unificazione. *Diagnosi Energetiche—Parte 1: Requisiti Generali*; Norma CEI UNI EN 16247-1:2012; Ente Nazionale Italiano di Unificazione: Milano, Italy, 2012.

27. Roberti, F.; Exner, D.; Oberegger, U.F.; Gasparella, A. Diagnosi energetica e simulazione di un edificio storico. In Proceedings of the 49th AICARR Conference, Venice, Italy, 26–28 February 2014.

28. Ascione, F.; de Rossi, F.; Vanoli, G.P. Energy retrofit of historical buildings: Theoretical and experimental investigations for the modelling of reliable performance scenarios. *Energy Build.* **2011**, *43*, 1925–1936. [CrossRef]

29. Sudo, C. The 11 Oldest LEED Certified Buildings in the U.S., LEED Ed., 2017, 25. Available online: https://www.bisnow.com/national/news/construction-development/its-all-about-the-shell-the-10-oldest-leed-certified-buildings-in-america-72560 (accessed on 16 March 2019).

30. Fedrizzi, R. The oldest LEED-Certified Building in the World, LEED Ed., 2013, 25. Available online: https://www.usgbc.org/articles/oldest-leed-certified-building-world (accessed on 26 March 2019).

31. De Santoli, L.; Perini, G.P.; Rossetti, S. Come affrontare e gestire un progetto di riqualificazione energetica di un bene culturale con l'obiettivo di certificarne la sostenibilità? Il caso della Galleria Borghese a Roma, Quine Ed. *AiCARR J.* **2017**, *43*, 34–39.

32. Mazzola, E.; Mora, T.D.; Peron, F.; Romagnoni, P. Proposal of a methodology for achieving a LEED O+M certification in historic buildings. *Energy Procedia* **2017**, *140*, 277–287. [CrossRef]

33. Mora, T.D.; Cappelletti, F.; Peron, F.; Romagnoni, P.; Bauman, F. Retrofit of an historical building toward NZEB. *Energy Procedia* **2015**, *78*, 1359–1364. [CrossRef]

34. Mora, T.D.; Righi, A.; Peron, F.; Romagnoni, P. Historical buildings retrofit: The city hall of the city of Motta di Livenza (TV). *Energy Procedia* **2017**, *133*, 392–400.

35. Cappelletti, F.; Mora, T.D.; Peron, F.; Romagnoni, P.; Ruggeri, P. Building renovation: Which kind of guidelines could be proposed for policy makers and professional owners? *Energy Procedia* **2015**, *78*, 2366–2371. [CrossRef]

36. Ente Nazionale Italiano di Unificazione. *Conservazione dei Beni Culturali—Linee Guida per Migliorare la Prestazione Energetica Degli Edifici Storici*; UNI EN 16883; Ente Nazionale Italiano di Unificazione: Milano, Italy, 2017.

37. Commission, European, Directive 2006/32/EC on Energy End-use Efficiency and Energy Services. 2006. Available online: https://eur-lex.europa.eu/LexUriServ/LexUriServ.do?uri=OJ:L:2006:114:0064:0085:EN:PDF (accessed on 16 March 2019).

38. European Parliament, Directive 2012/27/UE of The European Parliament and of the Council of 25 October 2012 on energy efficiency, amending Directives 2009/125/EC and 2010/30/EU and repealing Directives 2004/8/EC and 2006/32/EC. Available online: https://eur-lex.europa.eu/LexUriServ/LexUriServ.do?uri=OJ:L:2012:315:0001:0056:en:PDF (accessed on 16 March 2019).

39. Dall'O', G. *Green Energy Audit—Manuale Operativo per la Diagnosi Energetica e Ambientale Degli Edifici*; Ed. Ambiente: Milano, Italy, 2011.

40. Baggio, M.; Tinterri, C.; Dalla Mora, T.; Righi, A.; Peron, F.; Romagnoni, P. Sustainability of a Historical Building Renovation Design through the Application of LEED®Rating System. *Energy Procedia* **2017**, *113*, 382–389. [CrossRef]

41. U.S. Green Building Council, LEED v4 for Building Operations and Maintenance. 2014. Available online: https://www.usgbc.org/resources/leed-v4-building-operations-and-maintenance (accessed on 16 March 2019).

42. U.S. Green Building Council, LEED v4, Reference Guide for Building Operations and Maintenance. 2016. Available online: https://www.usgbc.org/resources/leed-reference-guide-building-operations-and-maintenance (accessed on 16 March 2019).

43. De Santoli, L.; Bellia, L.; Corgnati, S.P.; d'Ambrosio Alfano, F.R.; Filippi, M.; Mazzarella, L.; Romagnoni, P.; Sciurpi, F. *Efficienza Energetica Degli Edifici Storici*; Ed Delfino: Milano, Italy, 2014.

44. Green Building Council Italia. *Sistema di Verifica GBC Historic Building®—Parte 1*; Green Building Council Italia: Rovereto, Italy, 2014.

 © 2019 by the authors. Licensee MDPI, Basel, Switzerland. This article is an open access article distributed under the terms and conditions of the Creative Commons Attribution (CC BY) license (http://creativecommons.org/licenses/by/4.0/).

Article

Quantifying the Building Energy Dynamics of Manhattan, New York City, Using an Urban Building Energy Model and Localized Weather Data

Wenliang Li

Department of Geography, Environment, and Sustainability, The University of North Carolina at Greensboro, Greensboro, NC 27412, USA; w_li3@uncg.edu

Received: 12 May 2020; Accepted: 17 June 2020; Published: 23 June 2020

Abstract: Building sectors account for major energy use and greenhouse gas emissions in the US. While urban building energy-use modeling has been widely applied in many studies, limited studies have been conducted for Manhattan, New York City (NYC). Since the release of the new "80-by-50" law, the NYC government has committed to reducing carbon emissions by 80% by 2050; indeed, the government is facing a big challenge for reducing the energy use and carbon emissions. Therefore, understanding the building energy use of NYC with a high spatial and temporal resolution is essential for the government and local citizens in managing building energy use. This study quantified the building energy use of Manhattan in NYC with consideration of the local microclimate by integrating two popular modeling platforms, the Urban Weather Generator (UWG) and Urban Building Energy Modeling (UBEM). The research results suggest that (1) the largest building energy use is in central Manhattan, which is composed of large numbers of commercial buildings; (2) a similar seasonal electricity-use pattern and significantly different seasonal gas-use patterns could be found in Manhattan, NYC, due to the varied seasonal cooling and heating demand; and (3) the hourly energy-use profiles suggest only one electricity-use peak in the summer and two gas-use peaks in the winter.

Keywords: building energy use; localized weather data; urban building energy use model; Manhattan

---

1. Introduction

In the past decades, the world has experienced rapid economic development, population growth, and urban sprawl [1]. So far, over 55% of the world's population lives in cities, and it is predicted that 2.5 billion more people will be dwelling in cities by 2050 [2]. This rapid urbanization has brought several challenging issues, such as the significant increases in energy consumption and CO_2 emissions [1]. Scholars project that urban energy consumption will be over 20,000 Mtoe (million tons of oil equivalent) by 2050, which, in turn, would result in the shortage of energy and environmental degradation [3]. In response to these challenging issues, city governments throughout the whole world have proposed ambitious greenhouse gas emission reduction plans. For instance, the City of San Francisco and the City of London have set the emission reduction target at 40% and 60% by 2025, respectively [4]. The City of Boston proposed a Greenovate Climate Action Plan and is targeting an emission reduction of 25% and 80% by 2020 and 2050, respectively [5]. No exception for the City of New York, where an 80% emission reduction by 2050 has been set as the goal [6]. Buildings, as the foundation and major component of a city, are contributing the majority of the energy consumption and greenhouse gas emissions within the city [3]. According to past studies, up to 75% of the energy consumption is contributed by urban buildings [7,8], and over 50% of the electricity consumption is consumed by residential and commercial buildings in a city [3,9]. Therefore, understanding urban building energy dynamics is essential for managing urban energy consumption, reducing greenhouse gas emissions, improving energy-use efficiency, developing urban sustainable development plans, and optimizing urban system design [3,10–14].

Urban Building Energy Modeling (UBEM) has been proved effective in simulating and understanding urban building energy consumption [15,16]. With UBEM, city governments can manage the existing urban building energy consumption and investigate future potential energy savings through testing new techniques and building codes [17]. UBEM can be generally grouped into two branches: the top-down models and bottom-up models [11,18]. The top-down models analyze urban building energy consumption based on a group of buildings, and thus not able to analyze and explain the energy use of every single building [19,20]. Therefore, these models cannot provide a detailed energy-use analysis for a specific neighborhood. Moreover, most top-down models rely on historical data, which makes them difficult in testing the consequence of different energy retrofit strategies and technological advances. For instance, Hirst et al. [21] simulated the annual residential energy consumption of the US based on an econometric model. Zhang [22] examined the potential changes in regional energy use in China using the residents and corresponding energy consumption information, and also compared the results with other countries. Ozturk et al. [23] and Canyurt et al. [24] analyzed the relationship between energy use and demographic and economic factors using the genetic algorithms method in Turkey. While these studies have included major demographic, economic, and technological factors in energy-use modeling, new energy retrofit strategies and technological advances cannot be tested and verified as the models were only built based on past historical data on a large scale. In contrast, the bottom-up models focus on single buildings, where the energy use is thus analyzed for each building and, further, aggregated to the city, county, state, or national level. The bottom-up models are categorized into two types based on the modeling mechanisms: statistical models and physics-based models [25]. The statistical model simulates the energy use of single buildings based on the collected historical energy-use data and social-economic data. Hirst et al. [26] applied a regression model to analyze the impact of weather elements on household energy use based on utility data. Fung et al. [27] used a regression model to explore the impact of demographics, weather, and other equipment characteristics on residential energy use in Canada. Parti and Parti [28] used conditional demand analysis to analyze the relationship between household occupancy and electricity consumption in San Diego. Aydinalp et al. [29,30] proposed a national residential energy-use model based on neural networks. However, access to historical energy use and economic data may not be available for all cities. In contrast, the physics-based models estimate building energy use based on the physical characteristics of every single building. These models do not require any historical data as required by the top-down models and bottom-up statistical models, but require the knowledge of the building's physical parameters, including the building's shape, orientation, glazing, occupancy rates and schedule, envelope thermal properties, etc.

Several physics-based UBEM models have been proposed and applied in investigating urban building energy use in the past years. CitySim was developed by the Ecole Polytechnique Federale de Lausanne University in 2009, and it used a simplified thermal model to estimate urban building energy use at the district scale [31]. While the accuracy of the proposed CitySim is limited as a simplified model used in energy-use estimations, it still can provide decision support for energy-use management and greenhouse gas emission reduction. Reinhart et al. [32] developed an Urban Modeling Interface (UMI) in assessing building energy use performance, neighborhood walkability, and daylight potential under a Rhino-based environment. The sustainable design lab from the Massachusetts Institute of Technology proposed a UBEM model for the City of Boston in 2016. Specifically, the UBEM was developed based on GIS datasets and a custom-building archetype, and 83,541 buildings were generated using the CAD modelling and environment Rhinoceros 3D [4]. The model has been calibrated and validated and is capable of estimating city-wide building energy use at the building level and hourly scale. City Building Energy Saver (CityBES), a web-based city-scale energy-use simulation and management platform, was developed by the Lawrence Berkeley National Laboratory. In particular, CityGML, an open data model for the storage and exchange of virtual 3D city models, was adopted by the

CityBES for simulating building energy use and creating 3D building energy-use visualization [15]. Li et al. [12] simulated building energy use of the City of Des Moines, IA, with the newly developed CityBEUM model. Specifically, the energy-use mapping has been improved to the building level and hourly scale. Moreover, they also reported significant underestimation of electricity consumption in the summer and gas consumption in the winter, as well as overestimation of gas use in the spring when applying the Typical Meteorological Year (TMY) data in the model calibration and building energy-use simulation. Therefore, they emphasized the importance of applying actual weather data in urban building energy-use simulation.

Nowadays, the physics-based UBEMs have been widely applied in supporting urban energy-use management and greenhouse gas emission reduction throughout the world, such as in Boston [4], Chicago [33], Lisbon [34], Kuwait [35], Cambridge [36], Des Moines [12], Arriyadh [37], etc. Numerous works have been conducted for New York City (NYC) as well. Specifically, Howard and Parshall [19] proposed a model of energy consumption for NYC at a parcel level. Scofield [38] analyzed the effect of certification on energy consumption in NYC. Ma and Cheng [39] applied a geographic information system integrated data mining technology framework for estimating building energy-use intensity for NYC at an urban scale. Olivo and Hamidi [40] analyzed the spatiotemporal variability of building energy use in NYC. However, most studies have been conducted at an urban scale or parcel scale, no study has been implemented at the building level yet. NYC, especially the Manhattan borough, is the most urbanized and populated area in the US, and NYC is facing a big challenge in reducing energy use and emissions. In April 2019, the Climate Mobilization Act, the most aggressive climate bill in the US, was passed by NYC to abide by the Paris climate change agreement, and NYC committed to reducing the carbon emission by 80% by 2050. Buildings contribute to almost 70% of the energy use and carbon emissions in NYC, and to reach the proposed carbon emission reduction target, several benchmarks have been prescribed in the new "80-by-50" law. Some buildings are required to reach the reduction goal earlier and different building types are subject to a specific target. For instance, buildings with total areas over 25,000 square feet need to reduce the emissions by 40% by 2030, and that is about 500,000 buildings in NYC. Therefore, an urban building energy-use model with a high spatial (building level) and temporal resolution (hourly scale) is essential for the city government and citizens in NYC for managing building energy use and implementing effective ways to reduce carbon emissions.

When implementing UBEM, weather data has been considered as one of the most important components, and most UBEM tools use the TMY weather data or the weather data from a local weather station in the model calibration and simulation. The importance of applying actual weather data in the model calibration and simulation has already been clarified by Li et al. [12]. However, actual weather data from local weather stations may still not be enough for urban building energy use as actual weather data is commonly collected from the weather station from the airport, which is usually distributed in rural areas and far away from the downtown area in a city. Therefore, the impacts from the local microclimate have not been considered in the actual weather data. Several studies reported that the local microclimate, such as the urban heat island effect, could increase the temperature of the city's downtown areas more than the surrounding rural areas [41]. Therefore, it will increase the use of air conditioning, which, in turn, has a positive feedback on the urban heat island effect. Instead of applying actual weather data, localized weather data is needed in the urban building energy calibration and simulation process.

In this study, I proposed a work to quantify the building energy use of Manhattan in NYC with consideration of the local microclimate by integrating two popular modeling platforms, the Urban Weather Generator (UWG) and UBEM. The UWG was developed by Bueno and Norford [42], and it can generate localized hourly weather data based on the referenced hourly weather data and local physical parameters. The UBEM has been widely used in many studies, and it is powerful in estimating building energy use at the building level and hourly scale. The paper is organized as follows: the study area, Manhattan in NYC, is introduced in Section 2. the UWG and UBEM are described in Section 3.

The modeling results, including the spatial and temporal pattern of annual, monthly, and hourly building energy use, are reported in Section 4. Conclusions are included in Section 5.

2. Study Area and Data

The borough of Manhattan, situated in the northwest part of NYC, was chosen as the study area (Figure 1). Manhattan is one of the most urbanized and populated boroughs in NYC, with a population of 1.6 million in 2017 and a geographic area of 59.13 km^2. Manhattan features a humid subtropical climate, the winter is cold and damp, and the summer is warm to hot and humid. Manhattan has been classified as Climate Zone 4A by the ASHRAE. Manhattan also suffers the urban heat island effect due to a high building density and little vegetation cover. The temperature difference between Manhattan and the surrounding areas could be up to 15 °C. Manhattan is mainly covered by commercial buildings (e.g., offices, retails, restaurants, hotels) and residential buildings (e.g., apartments and houses), and they are contributing around 70% of the energy use in Manhattan.

New York City   Manhattan

Figure 1. Study area: Manhattan, New York City, US.

To model the building energy use for the borough of Manhattan, several GIS data were collected from the New York City Open Data platform and the State of New York government website. Specifically, the GIS building footprint data, which include all city-wide building information, was collected from the New York Open Data Platform (https://opendata.cityofnewyork.us/). The building footprint data include accurate information about building construction year, number of floors, and building location. In addition, the land-use parcel data was obtained from the website of the State of New York government (http://gis.ny.gov/parcels/). It includes information about building type and building HVAC information. For model calibration and simulation purposes, the actual weather data at Central Park, Manhattan, in 2009 and 2012 were obtained from the Whitebox technique [43]. To calibrate the new model, the Residential Energy Consumption Survey (RECS) [44] and Commercial Buildings Energy Consumption Survey (CBECS) [45] in 2009 and 2012 were collected from the Energy Information Administration (EIA), respectively.

3. Methodology

In order to quantify the building energy use in Manhattan, NYC, a new building energy-use model was constructed (Figure 2); it could be detailed using the following steps. Firstly, this study generated localized weather data based on existing hourly weather data and localized physical parameters using the Urban Weather Generator (UWG). Secondly, the UBEM was employed and calibrated for modeling the building energy use of Manhattan. Finally, the building energy consumption of Manhattan was simulated using the calibrated UBEM model and the localized weather data.

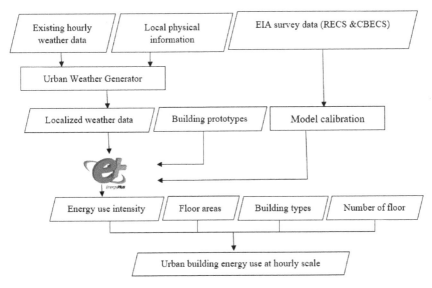

Figure 2. Flow chart of the proposed study.

3.1. Generating Localized Weather Data

The UWG is developed by Bueno et al. [42], and it can estimate hourly air temperature with consideration of the local microclimate based on the collected hourly weather data situated outside the city. It composes four modules: the rural station model, vertical diffusion model, the urban boundary layer model, and the urban canopy and building energy model. In UWG, the user can identify and describe an urban area geometrically through the average building height, horizontal building intensity, and vertical to horizontal urban area ratio. In general, users need to input the parameters into the UWG in four categories: geometric and local parameters, radiative parameters, thermal parameters, and building model parameters. Currently, the UWG has been updated to version 4.1 and could be requested from the website of the building technology program at MIT directly (https://urbanmicroclimate.scripts.mit.edu/uwg.php).

3.2. Modelling Building Energy Use

In this study, an urban building energy-use model (UBEM) was developed and used to model the building energy use of Manhattan. The UBEM modelled the city-wide building energy use by combing the building floor area, number of floors, and the modelled building energy-use intensity [12].

$$EU_j = EUI_m \times FA_j \times NF_j \tag{1}$$

where EU_j is the simulated electricity or gas consumption for building j, EUI_m is the electricity or gas use intensity for building type m, FA_j is the footprint area of building j, and NF_j is the total amount of floors of building j.

The floor areas of the buildings were derived from the GIS database of the building footprints. To simulate building energy-use intensity, this study aggregated all buildings within the study area into twenty-eight commercial and six residential building prototypes [46,47] (Figure 3). Specifically, commercial buildings were categorized as hotel, primary school, secondary school, shopping mall, warehouse, retail store, supermarket, office, hospital, quick service restaurant, and full-service restaurant. They were further categorized based on the built year (pre-1980 or post-1980) as varied energy consumption for buildings constructed before and after 1980. Moreover, office buildings were reclassified as large (>5110 m²), medium (511–5110 m²), and small offices (<511 m²), based on the floor areas; hotel buildings were regrouped into two classes: large and small hotels, based on floor areas larger or smaller than 5110 m². Residential buildings were classified as mid-rise apartments, single-family, and multiple-family. The mid-rise apartments were further subdivided into two classes based on the built year before or after 1980. Single-family and multi-family were subdivided into four types based on the primary heating methods: electrical heating or gas heating.

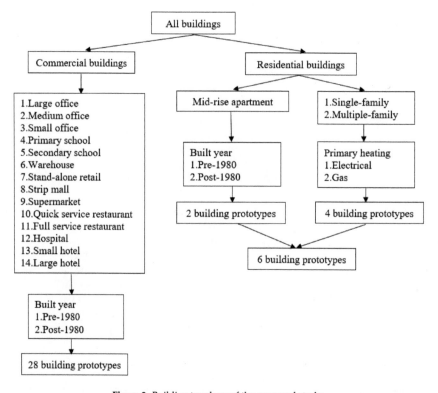

Figure 3. Building typology of the proposed study.

An engineering model, EnergyPlus v9.2, was employed to estimate the energy-use intensity for each building prototype. To establish the energy-use intensity model for each building prototype, the reference commercial and residential building models from the Department of Energy (DOE) and the Pacific Northwest National Laboratory (PNNL) were collected and used in this study. The commercial building models were developed by the DOE directly, and it covers different climate zones [47]. The residential building models were developed by the PNNL and governed by the DOE; the models are available for each state [46]. Specifically, the energy-use intensity model of the 28 commercial buildings and the mid-rise apartment buildings were obtained from the designed models of Baltimore developed by the DOE as NYC is situated in the same climate zone as Baltimore, and they also share similar building constructions. In addition, four residential building energy-use intensity models were collected from the designed models of NYC developed by the PNNL.

The thirty-four building energy-use models that were designed were calibrated for simulating the energy use of Manhattan. Model calibration is the key for energy-use simulation: Without calibration, the collected models may not be good enough for reflecting the actual building energy use as a discrepancy may exist between the collected models and the actual practical operation. We first updated most of the local parameters, such as latitude, longitude, and elevation, in the models, and then we calibrated the models through adjusting the buildings' internal information, such as lighting intensity, electric equipment consumption intensity, and occupancy schedule, to minimize the difference between the simulated results and the reference data. In this study, we calibrated all models using the US EIA's RECS and CBECS data in 2009 and 2012, respectively.

4. Results and Discussion

4.1. Localized Weather Data Generated by UWG

The Urban Weather Generator was developed by the MIT, with the actual weather data from weather stations in rural areas and with localized physical parameters input; the UWG can revise the actual weather data with consideration of the variations of the local environment. There are several physical parameters that need to be included in the UWG, such as location, latitude, longitude, city diameter, average building height, horizontal building density, wall construction, wall albedo, building glazing ratio, building window construction, building cooling and heating system, the surface albedo of weather station, and the vegetated faction of the weather station. The generated local weather data and the differences between the generated weather data and the weather data from the weather stations are included in Figure 4. It shows that urban temperatures are much higher than the temperature observed from the surrounding rural areas, and the differences are much higher in the summer. It is consistent with our knowledge that the urban heat island effect can increase the temperature in the downtown area, and such an increased temperature will definitely cause a much higher cooling demand for buildings in the downtown area.

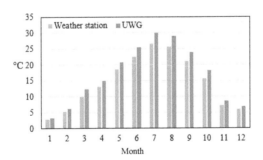

Figure 4. Localized monthly average based on hourly temperature.

4.2. Building Energy Use of Manhattan Simulated by UBEM

4.2.1. UBEM Input

To run the UBEM, to quantify the building energy use of Manhattan, NYC, several pieces of important information need to be put into the model. In this study, most parameters were collected from the technical report of the US Department of Energy Reference Building Models of the National Building

Stock provided by the National Renewable Energy Laboratory, to represent a typical performance of the different building types [48]. In general, the model input could be listed as program, form, fabric, and equipment (see Table 1.). Occupancy is one of the most important parameters in the model; it can be collected from different sources, such as CBECS, RECS, and ASHRAE. In this study, the occupancy rates for all the reference building models were collected from Standard 62.2 from ASHRAE. Table 2 lists the occupancy rate by space types, and most buildings are composed of one or more of the space types listed below. Ventilation/Outside air (OA) requirements are included in Table 3 by space types, and they are also collected using Standard 62 from ASHRAE. As limited information is available for old buildings, this study assumes all reference buildings are having the same ventilation requirements, and a reevaluation is expected when more information is available in the future. The occupancy schedule was applied with Standard 90.1 from ASHRAE. Different building types have quite different schedules. For instance, a restaurant may have a kitchen electric (gas) equipment schedule and dining area schedule. A hospital has an administrative area schedule, ER schedule, lab schedule, inpatient area schedule, and outpatient schedule. Residential buildings have a kitchen schedule, dining room schedule, and bedroom schedule. In general, some schedules are included in most building models, such as a building occupancy schedule, building the electric equipment schedule, and the HAVC system schedule (including both cooling and heating systems). All the occupancy schedules can also be divided as a weekday schedule, weekend schedule, and holiday schedule. Figure 5 shows the general weekday building occupancy schedules of the different building types. Due to the different functions they have, quite different hourly patterns could be found. The model input is the first and one of the most important steps for establishing the building energy-use model; more input parameter information could also be found from the technical report of the US Department of Energy Reference Building Models of the National Building Stock provided by the National Renewable Energy Laboratory [48].

Table 1. The general model input information [48].

Program	Form	Fabric	Equipment
Ventilation requirements	Orientation	Roof	Lighting
Service hot water demand	Floor height	Floors	Efficiency
Operating schedules	Shading	Windows	HVAC system
Total floor area	Window location	Infiltration	Water heating
Occupancy	Number of floors	Wall	Control settings

Table 2. Occupancy by space type [48].

Space Type	Occupancy per space	Occupancy m²/person	Space Type	Occupancy per space	Occupancy m²/person
Apartment	3		Supermarket		11.6
Fast food dinning		1.4	Hospital (ER)		4.7
Classrooms		4	Hospital (lab)		18.6
Corridor (school)		10	Hospital (ICU)		4.7
Hotel guest room	1.5		Warehouse		0
Lobby (hotel)		3	Office (school)		20
Office		18.6	Library		4.4
Restaurant		1.4	Restroom (school)		100
Sales		6.2	Reception areas		3.1
Storage		28	Lobby (office building)		9.3

Table 3. Outside air requirements (ventilation) [48].

Space Type	OA		Total OA
	L/s/person	L/s/m²	L/s/m²
Apartment			
Fast food dinning	9.44		6.77
Classrooms	7.08		1.77
Corridor (school)		0.51	0.51
Hotel guest room (cfm/room)	14.16		
Lobby (hotel)	9.44		3.05
Office	9.44		0.51
Restaurant	9.44		6.77
Sales		1.52	1.52
Storage		0.76	0.76
Supermarket	7.08		0.61
Hospital (ER)			
Hospital (lab)			
Hospital (ICU)			
Warehouse		0.25	0.25
Office (school)			
Library			
Restroom (school)	23.6		
Reception areas	7.08		2.29
Lobby (office building)	9.44		1.02

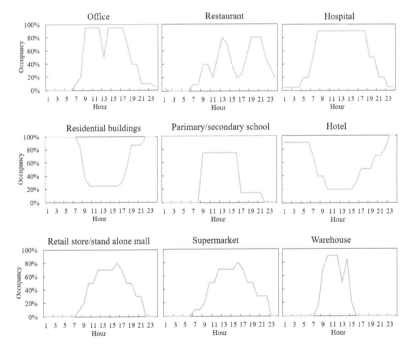

Figure 5. Building weekday hourly occupancy schedules.

4.2.2. UBEM Calibration

With the established UBEM model, the hourly energy-use intensity of all the designed building prototypes could be calculated. To further apply the simulated results for the final building energy-use calculation, the model calibration needs to be implemented first. In this study, the energy-use reference data from RECS and CBECS, including electricity and gas consumption data, were collected from the EIA for model calibration. RECS and CBECS are the only two nationwide statistical information sets on building energy consumption. RECS and CBECS data are collected in two phases: Phase 1 is the building survey, which collects basic information about the buildings, such as structural characteristics, building size, building type, and energy-use equipment; Phase 2 is the energy consumption survey that collects, through a website or mail, the basic energy-use information, such as electricity consumption, gas consumption, and heating oil consumption. The RECS and CBECS data are widely used by building managers, energy modelers, government leaders, and the Energy Star program. There are more than 1000 itemized information about buildings and their associated energy-use information included in the RECS and CBECS data sets. Selected important building and energy-use information is listed in Table 4. For instance, primary and more specific building activity delivers information about building types; construction year could help to separate the reference data into two categories, pre-1980 built buildings and post-1980 built buildings; the number of floors and building footprint helps the calculation of the referenced energy-use intensity; and electricity and gas consumption deliver direct information about the building's energy-use amount. With the all-important building and corresponding energy-use information listed in Table 4, the referenced building energy-use intensity for all 34 building types was calculated and used for further model calibration.

Table 4. Building and energy-use information included in RECS and CBECS.

General Information	Building Typology	Energy Use
Census region	Number of floors	Electricity used
Construction year	Main heating equipment	Natural gas used
Primary building activity	Main cooling equipment	Electricity used for cooling
Final full sample building weight	Water heating equipment	Gas used for heating
More specific building activity	Building footprint (area)	

To minimize the discrepancy between the modeled energy-use intensity and actual energy-use intensity, several important building parameters, such as the set point, occupancy schedule, usage pattern, etc., have all been optimized. Specifically, the setpoint of the cooling and heating system is very essential in modeling building energy use. Different building types may have a significantly varied cooling and heating demand. In this study, the minimum acceptable room temperature and the optimum room temperature in the summer from the engineering toolbox [49] were collected and used as reference data for adjusting the cooling and heating set point of the HVAC system in the model calibration (see Table 5). Table 5 shows that the accepted room temperature in winter for the school (classroom or lecture room) is 20 °C; the hotel is 21 °C; the office is 20 °C; the restaurant is 18 °C; and warehouse is 16 °C. Moreover, the general optimum room temperature in the summer is between 20 °C and 22 °C for most rooms. Therefore, when the calibration is conducted, the cooling and heating set point of the HVAC system has to be set with the consideration of the recommended room temperatures. Moreover, the occupancy schedule is another very important parameter. Business buildings, school buildings, and residential buildings may have different schedules. People may have different timing for getting up, leaving home, starting work or study, going back home, or going to bed. Therefore, different schedules must be considered for different buildings. In this study, the most optimum building occupancy schedule (Figure 5) recommended by the technical report of the US Department of Energy Reference Building Models of the National Building Stock provided by the National Renewable Energy Laboratory was applied. Furthermore, schools may have spring, summer, fall, and winter breaks, which result in lower energy consumption. They all must be considered in the schedule section during model calibration. The primary school and secondary school operating schedules were collected from the Department of Education in New York City [50]. It shows the spring semester starts in late January and ends in late June, and the fall semester starts in early September and ends in late December. Therefore, the summer break (July and August) and spring break (January) were set as time points of limited operation with relatively low energy consumption [50].

Table 5. The minimum acceptable room temperature in the winter and the optimal room temperature in the summer of different room types [49].

Season	Room Type	Temperature (°C)	Room Type	Temperature (°C)
	Bathrooms	22	Lecture rooms	20
	Bedrooms	18	Libraries	20
	Classrooms	20	Living rooms	21
	Corridors	16	Offices	20
Winter	Dining rooms	20	Recreation rooms	18
	Exhibition halls	18	Restaurants	18
	Hotel rooms	21	Shops	18
	Laboratories	20	Stores	15
	Wards	18	Warehouses	16
Summer	All rooms	20–22		

In addition, both electricity and gas consumption are coming from different components, such as lighting, cooking, heating, cooling, refrigerator, machines in the lab, machines in the office, etc. In general, one or more listed lighting, electric, and gas equipment are included in each specific building type (see Table 6). For instance, schools may include lighting, electric equipment, and gas equipment for a dorm, classroom, lab, cafeteria, library, and auditorium. The office only has office lights and corridor lights in lighting, electric equipment for the office, meeting room, and employee lounge, and no gas equipment. Residential buildings include more specific equipment, such as a refrigerator, microwave, laundry machine, TV set, stove for cooking, and lighting in different rooms. In this study, the reference data collected from the Pacific Northwest National Lab were used for updating all models for model calibration purposes [51]. In summary, energy plus has hundreds of parameters. On the one hand, it is impossible for us to make the change for all parameters; on the other hand, not all reference data are available to be used for the calibration. Therefore, the goal of the model calibration is to minimize the discrepancy between the modeled results and the referenced number with the available reference information.

Table 6. Selected lighting, electric, and gas equipment inside buildings.

Lighting	Electric Equipment	Gas Equipment
Dinning lights, kitchen lights	Dining room equipment	Kitchen cooking equipment
Lab lights, ER lights, office lights	Nurse station equipment	Water heating furnace
Corridor lights, apartment lights	Kitchen room equipment	Heating (HVAC) equipment
Bathroom lights, auditorium lights	Auditorium equipment	Laundry equipment
Cafeteria lights, gym lights	Cafeteria equipment	
Library lights, classroom lights	Library equipment	
Guest room lights, employee lounge lights	Employee lounge equipment	
Admin office lights	Meeting room equipment	
Restroom lights, deli lights	Guest room equipment	
Produce lights	Laundry room equipment	
sales lights	Refrigerator (residential)	
storage room lights	Microwave (residential)	

Figure 6 indicates that, after calibration, the difference between the simulated electricity- and gas-use intensity and the actual energy-use intensity were all reaching the evaluation criteria (within ± 10%). Therefore, all the proposed energy-use intensity models are qualified to estimate the actual energy-use intensity of all the building prototypes. The annual energy-use intensity included in Figure 6 shows that for commercial buildings, the quick-service restaurant has the highest energy-use intensity for electricity consumption and the full-service restaurant has the highest energy-use intensity for gas consumption. Moreover, the warehouse has the lowest electricity- and gas-use intensity. In terms of residential buildings, the multi-family residences have a much higher electricity- and gas-use intensity than single-family residences. After model calibration, the modeled total electricity and gas consumption in Manhattan was also compared with the real energy-use information from the City of New York, to make sure the modeled energy consumption is reasonable.

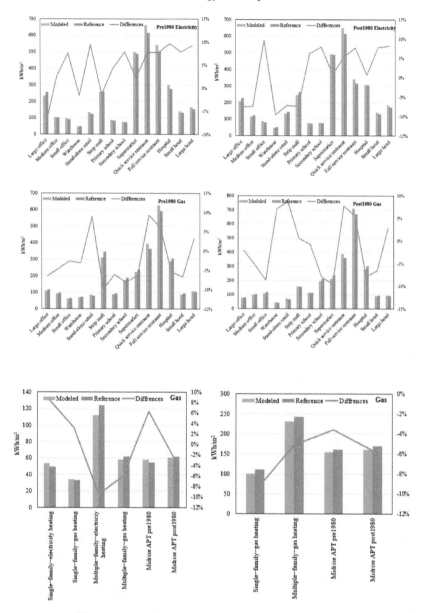

Figure 6. Comparison of the modeled and referenced energy-use intensity for residential and commercial buildings.

4.2.3. The Spatial Distribution of Energy Consumption in Manhattan

Figure 7 shows the spatial distribution patterns of energy-use intensity in Manhattan, and quite different spatial patterns could be found between electricity-use intensity and gas-use intensity. Specifically, the highest electricity-use intensity is located in the center and southern corner of

Manhattan, which are mainly composed of large offices with an annual electricity-use intensity over 200 kWh/m². From the central area to the outlier of Manhattan, the electricity-use intensity drops significantly to around 100 kWh/m², or even much lower as most buildings clustered here are medium offices, small offices, primary schools, secondary schools, retail stores, single-family houses, and midrise apartments. Moreover, some buildings, such as quick-service restaurants, full-service restaurants, and supermarkets, are dispersed in Manhattan with a much higher electricity-use intensity, around 500 kWh/m². In contrast, quite different gas-use intensity patterns could be found in Manhattan. A very similar gas-use intensity could be found throughout Manhattan. Manhattan is very cold in the winter, gas is majorly used for heating purposes in the winter, and most buildings have a very similar gas-use intensity. Only some buildings located in the center and southern corner of Manhattan show a relatively lower gas-use intensity, which is mainly composed of large offices built after 1980 with improved energy-use efficiency. There are also some red spots with a high gas-use intensity dispersed in Manhattan, which is mainly composed of restaurants. With the modeled energy-use intensity of all the designed building prototypes, the building energy consumption could be quantified for all buildings in Manhattan through combing the corresponding building floor areas and number of floors information. The modeled building energy use is very straightforward as the total energy use was calculated for each building, and it is highly associated with building height. The energy use of Manhattan is progressively decreasing from the urban core, which is mainly covered by commercial buildings such as offices, hotels, and retail stores, to suburban areas, which are mainly composed of residential buildings (mostly apartments, single-family, and multi-family houses).

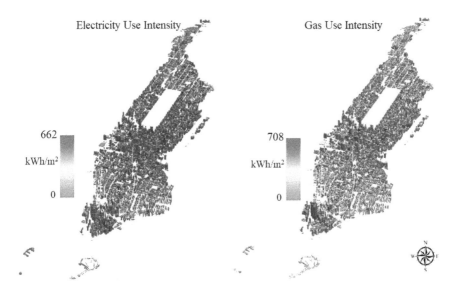

Figure 7. Modeled annual building electricity- and gas-use intensity in Manhattan, NYC, in 2012.

4.3. The Temporal Profiles of Energy Consumption in Manhattan

Figure 8 illustrates similar seasonal electricity-use intensity patterns but different seasonal gas-use intensity patterns. Specifically, the electricity-use intensity is very similar in four seasons except in summer. In addition to the general electricity use, electricity for cooling purposes is another major electricity consumption source in the summer. Therefore, a slight electricity-use intensity increase could be found in the summer. Significantly different seasonal gas-use intensity patterns could be found for Manhattan. In particular, gas-use intensity is the highest in the winter for heating purposes and much lower in the other three seasons. Moreover, spatially varied patterns of gas-use intensity could also be found in Figure 8. The central area and southern corner of Manhattan have a little bit lower gas-use intensity in the winter as some buildings are renovated with improved HVAC systems or built after 1980 with improved energy-use efficiency.

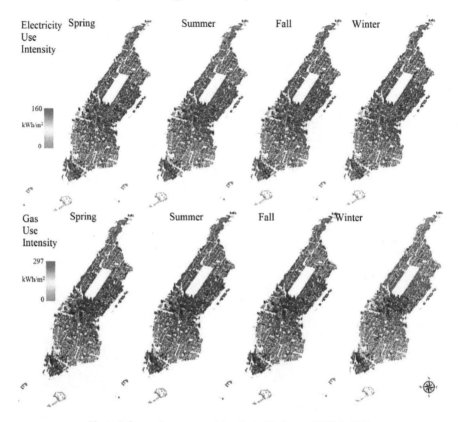

Figure 8. Seasonal energy-use intensity in Manhattan, NYC, in 2012.

To examine the monthly profiles of the building energy use in Manhattan, I aggregated the hourly electricity and gas consumption to the monthly scale. Figure 9 illustrates strong monthly electricity- and gas-use variations. Both residential and commercial buildings show only one peak for both electricity and gas consumption in 2012. Specifically, the peak of electricity use is in the summer (around July and August) due to high cooling demand, and the peak of gas consumption is in the winter (around December and January) owing to high heating demand. In particular, the electricity use is stable from January to April and October to December; it starts jumping up in May, reaching the peak in July and August owing to high cooling demand, and finally drops in September. The gas consumption is relatively stable from May to September but starts jumping in October, reaching a peak in December and January due to high heating demand, and finally drops in April.

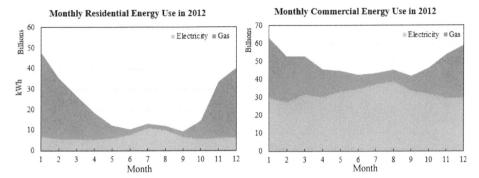

Figure 9. Monthly electricity and gas consumption in Manhattan in 2012.

Figures 10 and 11 illustrate hourly building energy use and energy-use intensity for the hottest (07-18-2012) and coldest (01-04-2012) days in Manhattan in 2012. The summer energy-use profiles show only one peak around noon, and the summer peak is mainly contributed by the high cooling demand from both residential and commercial buildings as it is the hottest time during a day. It is very consistent with the hourly building occupancy schedule provided in Figure 5 and hourly energy-use intensity provided in Figure 11. Most buildings such as offices, schools, retail stores, and supermarkets are opening around 7 or 8 a.m. in the morning, with the highest occupancy around noon from 11 a.m. to 1 p.m. The summer energy-use peak is contributed by both high building occupancy and high outside temperature. Figure 10 also shows a low demand for gas consumption as gas is only used for water heating at this time. In winter, energy consumption is much higher than in the summer. Two peaks could be found in Figures 10 and 11, with one significant peak in the morning and another peak in the evening. The first peak is mainly caused by high heating demand from commercial buildings. The residential building occupancy in Figure 5 shows that people are leaving home around 7 a.m. and most commercial buildings, such as offices, retail stores, and supermarkets, open at 7 or 8 a.m. It does support the conclusion that the first-morning energy-use peak is caused by high heating demand in the morning. The second peak is mainly contributed by residential buildings, as illustrated in Figure 5, in that people finish their work and return home around 6 p.m., and a high heating demand was caused by low outside temperatures.

Figure 11 also shows the improvement in energy-use efficiency for buildings built after 1980. Significant energy-use reduction could be found for some specific building types. For building electricity consumption, the strip mall, large office, and secondary school have all been improved significantly. The peak electricity-use intensity of strip mall, large office, and secondary school drops from around 0.09 kWh/m^2 to around 0.08 kWh/m^2, around 0.06 kWh/m^2 to 0.05 kWh/m^2, and around 0.04 kWh/m^2 to 0.02 kWh/m^2, respectively. Moreover, the efficiency of gas consumption was also improved. The peak gas-use intensity of the secondary schools also drops from around 0.25 kWh/m^2 to 0.19 kWh/m^2, and the peak gas-use intensity of the strip malls drops from 0.3 kWh/m^2 to 0.2 kWh/m^2. A similar situation could also be detected in Figure 9 for other building types. In summary, the energy-use efficiency of buildings built after 1980 has been improved significantly.

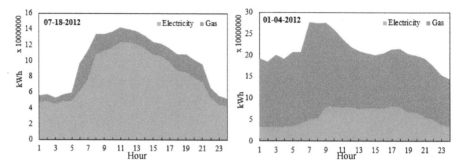

Figure 10. Hourly building energy use for summer and winter peak days.

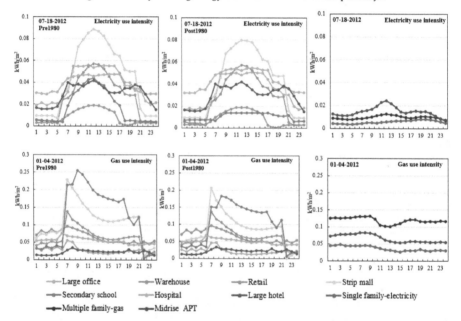

Figure 11. Hourly energy-use intensity (major building types) in Manhattan, NYC.

4.4. Sensitivity Analysis

Figure 12 illustrates the significant differences in building energy use between applying the TMY weather data and the localized weather data. In particular, residential buildings have a much higher electricity consumption in the summer and lower gas consumption in the winter in 2012 compared to the TMY as the temperature in 2012 was much higher than in other years. When the TMY weather data are applied, significant underestimation of electricity consumption (up to 16%) and overestimation of gas consumption (up to 24%) occur, due to underestimating the cooling demand and overestimating the heating demand. Similar patterns could also be found for commercial buildings. The application of TMY weather data in building energy modeling could result in underestimation of electricity use (up to 18%) in the summer and overestimation of gas consumption (up to 21%) in the winter, as there is unreasonable cooling and heating demand generated by the TMY weather data. In summary, electricity consumption for cooling and gas consumption for heating are all very important components of building energy consumption. When inappropriate weather data are applied, the building energy consumption will be highly misunderstood. Therefore, it is important to generate and apply localized weather data in building energy-use modeling.

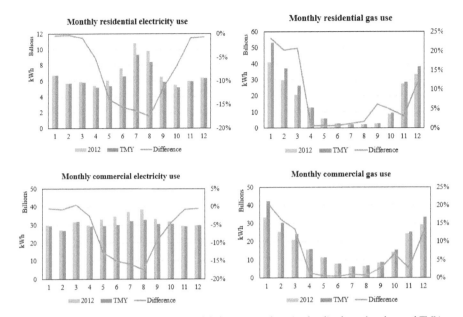

Figure 12. Comparative analysis of the modeled energy use by using localized weather data and TMY weather data.

5. Conclusions

In this study, the building energy-use dynamics of Manhattan, NYC, was modeled through integrating localized weather data and UBEM. Specifically, this study generated localized weather data based on the collected urban physical parameters and observed hourly weather data using UWG. A building energy-use model was established and calibrated for Manhattan, NYC, based on the collected RECS and CBEC reference data. Finally, building energy use was simulated and explored, to observe the spatial and temporal patterns of Manhattan, NYC.

The analysis results suggest several major conclusions. Firstly, the largest building electricity and gas uses are located in the center of Manhattan, which is mainly covered by commercial buildings with the largest building density and height. Secondly, similar seasonal electricity-use patterns and different seasonal gas-use patterns could be found in Manhattan. Specifically, the building electricity use is stable throughout all seasons. The largest gas consumption could be found in the winter due to high heating demand and low gas consumption in the summer as the gas is only used for water heating and cooking purpose. Thirdly, the summer energy use hourly profiles show only one peak for electricity use, mainly contributed by the high cooling demand. Winter energy use hourly profiles suggest two gas-use peaks. The first one is in the morning as people started working with high heating demand, and the second peak is associated with high heating demand from residential buildings when people finish their daily work and get back home.

While building energy use has been improved with localized weather data, there are still some other issues that need to be considered in the future, such as including the economic activity in the energy-use model. This study only modeled building energy use in the past. However, the understanding of future building energy use may be even more important as it could provide reference support for sustainable city planning. In 2014, the Intergovernmental Panel on Climate Change (IPCC) has released the fifth assessment report about future climate change, and the simulated future weather under different socio-development scenarios have been widely used in many studies already [52–54]. Therefore, one possible future research direction could be estimating future building energy use with consideration of both the local microclimate and future climate change under different scenarios.

In addition, the same building occupancy schedule was applied in the same building group in this study. However, buildings located in a different part of the city may have different occupancy schedules. Therefore, another future research direction could be improving building energy-use modeling with actual building occupancy schedules extracted from other data sources, such as socio-media data (e.g., Twitter. Facebook, etc.). Moreover, more accurate reference data is needed to improve the model performance. In this study, only the RECS and CBECS data from EIA in 2009 and 2012 were used as the reference data for model calibration. While the calibration performance is acceptable, the collected RECS and CBECS data are not very recent data; thus, the calibrated model may not be able to consider the current energy use conditions as impacted by the economy. The EIA is going to release new data in the future. The model could be updated later with new recent data to improve the performance. Moreover, the RECS and CBECS data are reported only at the regional level and the calibrated model may have a much better reflection of energy use at the regional level instead of the individual building level. In addition, the spatial information of the reference data from RECS and CBECS has been blocked to for privacy purposes. Only one energy-use model can be calibrated for one building type, and the spatial variation in energy use of each building type was ignored. When smart-metered utility data become available, the proposed model can be updated and improved for better modeling of building energy use at the individual building level, with consideration of the spatial variation in energy use within each building type.

Funding: This research was supported by the Faculty First Award and Sustainability Faculty Fellowship from the University of North Carolina at Greensboro.

Acknowledgments: I would like to thank three reviewers for their constructive suggestions on an earlier version of this manuscript.

Conflicts of Interest: The author declares no conflict of interest.

References

1. Li, W.; Wu, C.; Zang, S. Modeling urban land use conversion of Daqing City, China: A comparative analysis of "top-down" and "bottom-up" approaches. *Stoch. Environ. Res. Risk Assess.* **2012**, *28*, 817–828. [CrossRef]
2. United Nations, Department of Economic and Social Affairs, Population Division. *World Urbanization Prospects: The 2018 Revision (ST/ESA/SER.A/420)*; United Nations: New York, NY, USA, 2019.
3. Ma, R.; Geng, C.; Yu, Z.; Chen, J.; Luo, X. Modeling city-scale building energy dynamics through inter-connected distributed adjacency blocks. *Energy Build.* **2019**, *202*, 109391. [CrossRef]
4. Davila, C.C.; Reinhart, C.F.; Bemis, J.L. Modeling Boston: A workflow for the efficient generation and maintenance of urban building energy models from existing geospatial datasets. *Energy* **2016**, *117*, 237–250. [CrossRef]
5. Boston, G. *Climate Action Plan Update*; The City of Boston: Boston, MA, USA, 2014.
6. City of New York. *One City Built to Last—Transforming New York City Buildings for a Low-Carbon Future*; City of New York: New York, NY, USA, 2014.
7. Ei, D.; Usdoe, E.I.A. *Annual Energy Outlook 2009 with Projections to 2030*; Government Printing Office: Washington, DC, USA, 2009.
8. Parshall, L.; Gurney, K.; Hammer, S.A.; Mendoza, D.; Zhou, Y.; Geethakumar, S. Modeling energy consumption and CO2 emissions at the urban scale: Methodological challenges and insights from the United States. *Energy Policy* **2010**, *38*, 4765–4782. [CrossRef]
9. IEEJ. *IEEJ Outlook 2018*; The Institute of Energy Economics: Tokyo, Japan, 2018; pp. 1–116. Available online: https://www.ief.org/_resources/files/events/ief-lecture---ieej-energy-outlook-2018--prospects/ieej -outlook-2018-executive-summary.pdf (accessed on 10 August 2019).
10. Zhou, Y.; Clarke, L.; Eom, J.; Kyle, P.; Patel, P.; Kim, S.H.; Dirks, J.; Jensen, E.; Liu, Y.; Rice, J.; et al. Modeling the effect of climate change on U.S. state-level buildings energy demands in an integrated assessment framework. *Appl. Energy* **2014**, *113*, 1077–1088. [CrossRef]
11. Li, W.; Zhou, Y.; Cetin, K.; Eom, J.; Wang, Y.; Chen, G.; Zhang, X. Modeling urban building energy use: A review of modeling approaches and procedures. *Energy* **2017**, *141*, 2445–2457. [CrossRef]

12. Li, W.; Zhou, Y.; Cetin, K.S.; Yu, S.; Wang, Y.; Liang, B. Developing a landscape of urban building energy use with improved spatiotemporal representations in a cool-humid climate. *Build. Environ.* **2018**, *136*, 107–117. [CrossRef]

13. Zhou, Y.; Eom, J.; Clarke, L. The effect of global climate change, population distribution, and climate mitigation on building energy use in the U.S. and China. *Clim. Chang.* **2013**, *119*, 979–992. [CrossRef]

14. Yu, S.; Eom, J.; Zhou, Y.; Evans, M.; Clarke, L. Scenarios of building energy demand for China with a detailed regional representation. *Energy* **2014**, *67*, 284–297. [CrossRef]

15. Chen, Y.; Hong, T.; Piette, M.A. Automatic generation and simulation of urban building energy models based on city datasets for city-scale building retrofit analysis. *Appl. Energy* **2017**, *205*, 323–335. [CrossRef]

16. Reinhart, C.F.; Cerezo Davila, C. Urban building energy modeling—A review of a nascent field. *Build. Environ.* **2016**, *97*, 196–202. [CrossRef]

17. Ching, F.D.; Winkel, S.R. *Building Codes Illustrated: A Guide to Understanding the 2018 International Building Code*; John Wiley & Sons: Hoboken, NJ, USA, 2018.

18. Swan, L.G.; Ugursal, V.I. Modeling of end-use energy consumption in the residential sector: A review of modeling techniques. *Renew. Sustain. Energy Rev.* **2009**, *13*, 1819–1835. [CrossRef]

19. Howard, B.; Parshall, L.; Thompson, J.; Hammer, S.; Dickinson, J.; Modi, V. Spatial distribution of urban building energy consumption by end use. *Energy Build.* **2012**, *45*, 141–151. [CrossRef]

20. Kavgic, M.; Mavrogianni, A.; Mumovic, D.; Summerfield, A.; Stevanovic, Z.; Djurovic-Petrovic, M. A review of bottom-up building stock models for energy consumption in the residential sector. *Build. Environ.* **2010**, *45*, 1683–1697. [CrossRef]

21. Hirst, E.; Lin, W.; Cope, J. A residential energy use model sensitive to demographic, economic, and technological factors. *Q. Rev. Econ. Financ.* **1977**, *17*, 7–22.

22. Zhang, Q. Residential energy consumption in China and its comparison with Japan, Canada, and USA. *Energy Build.* **2004**, *36*, 1217–1225. [CrossRef]

23. Öztürk, H.K.; Canyurt, O.E.; Hepbasli, A.; Utlu, Z. Residential-commercial energy input estimation based on genetic algorithm (GA) approaches: An application of Turkey. *Energy Build.* **2004**, *36*, 175–183. [CrossRef]

24. Canyurt, O.E.; Öztürk, H.K.; Hepbasli, A.; Utlu, Z. Estimating the Turkish residential–commercial energy output based on genetic algorithm (GA) approaches. *Energy Policy* **2005**, *33*, 1011–1019. [CrossRef]

25. Li, X.; Zhou, Y.; Sha, Y.; Jia, G.; Li, H.; Li, W. Urban heat island impacts on building energy consumption: A review of approaches and findings. *Energy* **2019**, *174*, 407–419. [CrossRef]

26. Hirst, E.; Goeltz, R.; White, D. Determination of household energy using 'finger-prints' from energy billing data. *Energy Res.* **1986**, *10*, 393–405. [CrossRef]

27. Fung, A.S.; Aydinalp, M.; Ugursal, V.I. *Econometric Models for Major Residential Energy End-Uses*; CREEDAC-1999-04-05 Report; Dalhousie University: Halifax, NS, Canada, 1999.

28. Parti, M.; Parti, C. The total and appliance-specific conditional demand for electricity in the household sector. *Bell J. Econ.* **1980**, *11*, 309. [CrossRef]

29. Aydinalp, M.; Ugursal, V.I.; Fung, A.S. Modeling of the appliance, lighting, and space-cooling energy consumptions in the residential sector using neural networks. *Appl. Energy* **2002**, *71*, 87–110. [CrossRef]

30. Aydinalp, M.; Ugursal, V.I.; Fung, A.S. Effects of socioeconomic factors on household appliance, lighting, and space cooling electricity consumption. *Int. J. Glob. Energy Issues* **2003**, *20*, 302. [CrossRef]

31. Robinson, D.; Haldi, F.; Kämpf, J.H.; Leroux, P.; Perez, D.; Rasheed, A.; Wilke, U. CitySim: Comprehensive micro-simulation of resource flows for sustainable urban planning. In Proceedings of the Eleventh International IBPSA Conference, Glasgow, UK, 27–30 July 2009.

32. Reinhart, C.; Dogan, T.; Jakubiec, J.A.; Rakha, T.; Sang, A. Umi-an urban simulation environment for building energy use, daylighting and walkability. In Proceedings of the 13th Conference of International Building Performance Simulation Association, Chambery, France, 25–28 August 2013; Available online: https://www.aivc.org/sites/default/files/p_1404.pdf (accessed on 10 August 2019).

33. Reinhart, C.; Nagpal, S.; Davila, C.C. Chicago Energy Bazar. 2017. Available online: http://web.mit.edu/sustainabledesignlab/projects/UBEM_Chicago/index.html (accessed on 10 August 2019).

34. Reinhart, C.; Monteiro, C.S.; Davila, C.C.; Arsano, A.; Turan, I.; Benis, K. UBEM Lisbon—A New Look at Old Buildings; Workshop Held in Lisbon on March 21 2018. Available online: http://web.mit.edu/sustainabledesignlab/projects/UBEM_Lisbon/Lisbon_ANewLookAtOldBuildings.pdf (accessed on 10 August 2019).

35. De Wolf, C.; Cerezo, C.; Murtadhawi, Z.; Hajiah, A.; Al Mumin, A.; Ochsendorf, J.; Reinhart, C. Life cycle building impact of a Middle Eastern residential neighborhood. *Energy* **2017**, *134*, 336–348. [CrossRef]
36. Sokol, J.; Davila, C.C.; Reinhart, C.F. Validation of a Bayesian-based method for defining residential archetypes in urban building energy models. *Energy Build.* **2017**, *134*, 11–24. [CrossRef]
37. Rose, C.M.; Saratsis, E.; Aldawood, S.; Dogan, T.; Reinhart, C.F. A Tangible Interface for Collaborative Urban Design for Energy Efficiency, Daylighting, and Walkability. In Proceedings of the 14th Conference of International Building Performance Simulation Association, Hyderabad, India, 7–9 December 2015.
38. Scofield, J.H. Efficacy of LEED-certification in reducing energy consumption and greenhouse gas emission for large New York City office buildings. *Energy Build.* **2013**, *67*, 517–524. [CrossRef]
39. Ma, J.; Cheng, J.C. Estimation of the building energy use intensity in the urban scale by integrating GIS and big data technology. *Appl. Energy* **2016**, *183*, 182–192. [CrossRef]
40. Olivo, Y.; Hamidi, A.; Ramamurthy, P. Spatiotemporal variability in building energy use in New York City. *Energy* **2017**, *141*, 1393–1401. [CrossRef]
41. Chan, A. Developing a modified typical meteorological year weather file for Hong Kong taking into account the urban heat island effect. *Build. Environ.* **2011**, *46*, 2434–2441. [CrossRef]
42. Bueno, B.; Norford, L.; Hidalgo, J.; Pigeon, G. The urban weather generator. *J. Build. Perform. Simul.* **2013**, *6*, 269–281. [CrossRef]
43. White Box Technologies. Weather Data for Energy Calculations. 2019. Available online: http://weather.whiteboxtechnologies.com/ (accessed on 1 August 2019).
44. US EIA. Residential Energy Consumption Survey (RECS). 2015. Available online: https://www.eia.gov/consumption/residential/ (accessed on 11 September 2018).
45. US EIA. Commercial Building Energy Consumption Survey (CBECS). 2012. Available online: https://www.eia.gov/consumption/commercial/ (accessed on 11 September 2018).
46. DOE. Residential Prototype Building Models. 2019. Available online: https://www.energycodes.gov/development/residential/iecc_models (accessed on 10 August 2019).
47. DOE. Commercial Reference Buildings. 2019. Available online: https://www.energy.gov/eere/buildings/commercial-reference-buildings (accessed on 1 August 2019).
48. National Renewable Energy Laboratory. U.S. Department of Energy Commericial Reference Building Models of the National Building Stock. Teachnic Report. Available online: https://www.nrel.gov/docs/fy11osti/46861.pdf (accessed on 10 August 2019).
49. The Engineering Toolbox. Available online: https://www.engineeringtoolbox.com/indoor-design-temperatures-d_109.html (accessed on 10 August 2019).
50. School Calendar from the Department of Education in the City of New York. Available online: https://www.schools.nyc.gov/calendar?school_years=1%7C2019-2020&mpp=12 (accessed on 10 August 2019).
51. Building Enery Models from PNNL. Available online: https://www.energycodes.gov/development/commercial/prototype_models (accessed on 10 August 2019).
52. IPCC. *Climate Change 2014: Synthesis Report. Contribution of Working Groups I, II and III to the Fifth Assessment Report of the Intergovernmental Panel on Climate Change*; Meyer, C.W., Ed.; IPCC: Geneva, Switzerland, 2014.
53. Solecki, W.; Rosenzweig, C.; Dhakal, S.; Roberts, D.; Barau, A.S.; Schultz, S.; Ürge-Vorsatz, D. City transformations in a 1.5 °C warmer world. *Nat. Clim. Chang.* **2018**, *8*, 177–181. [CrossRef]
54. Flörke, M.; Schneider, C.; McDonald, R.I. Water competition between cities and agriculture driven by climate change and urban growth. *Nat. Sustain.* **2018**, *1*, 51–58. [CrossRef]

 © 2020 by the author. Licensee MDPI, Basel, Switzerland. This article is an open access article distributed under the terms and conditions of the Creative Commons Attribution (CC BY) license (http://creativecommons.org/licenses/by/4.0/).

MDPI

St. Alban-Anlage 66

4052 Basel

Switzerland

Tel. +41 61 683 77 34

Fax +41 61 302 89 18

www.mdpi.com

Energies Editorial Office

E-mail: energies@mdpi.com

www.mdpi.com/journal/energies

CPSIA information can be obtained
at www.ICGtesting.com
Printed in the USA
BVHW091223120421
604734BV00013B/1241